Birth to five

Your complete guide to parenthood and the first five years of your child's life

Contents

About this book

No one needs a book to tell them what's good about being a parent. Parents turn to books when they need information, when they're anxious, when they've got questions or concerns, small or large. This is a book you can turn to.

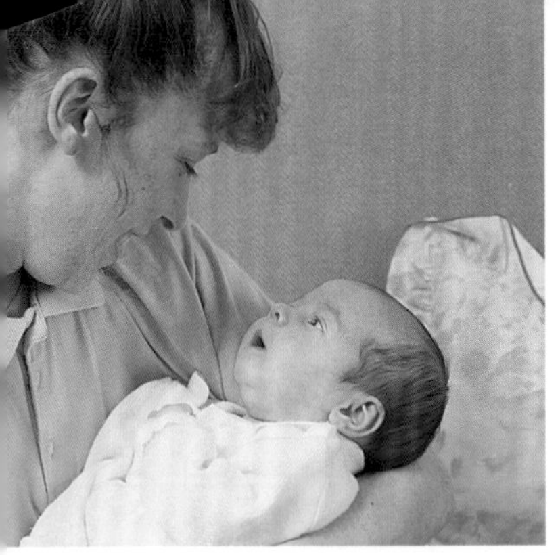

1 The first weeks

'I don't think I'll ever forget those first few days. Feeling so happy, though I don't know why. I couldn't sleep, I was sore, I couldn't move about very well, but I felt happier than I can ever begin to say.'

'There was none of this love at first sight. It was a long time before I came to love him. I can say that now, but at the time I couldn't tell anybody. I thought there was something wrong with me. There was all that work, and feeling rough myself, and because I didn't have this overwhelming feeling for him, none of it made much sense. But oh yes, after three or four months or so of all that, yes, it came right then.'

'I didn't think I'd feel the way I do about her. Sometimes I look at her when she's sleeping, you know, and I have to put my face down next to hers, just to check she's breathing.'

(A FATHER)

There's something very special and exciting about being alone for the first time with your new baby, but it can also be frightening. This is when you begin to realise that you can never go back. You're now responsible for a new human being. The responsibility may seem much too big. You may have a secret wish to run home to your own mother and ask her to take over. Or you may be the kind of person who just knows that you'll get through and that everything will turn out fine in the end.

In these early weeks you'll find there's a great deal to learn, and all of it at the same time. Today it might seem impossible, but in a matter of months you'll look back and wonder how it could have all seemed so hard. Think of these first few pages as a guide to the basic information you'll need to survive. Read Chapter 7 for more on how having a baby changes your life.

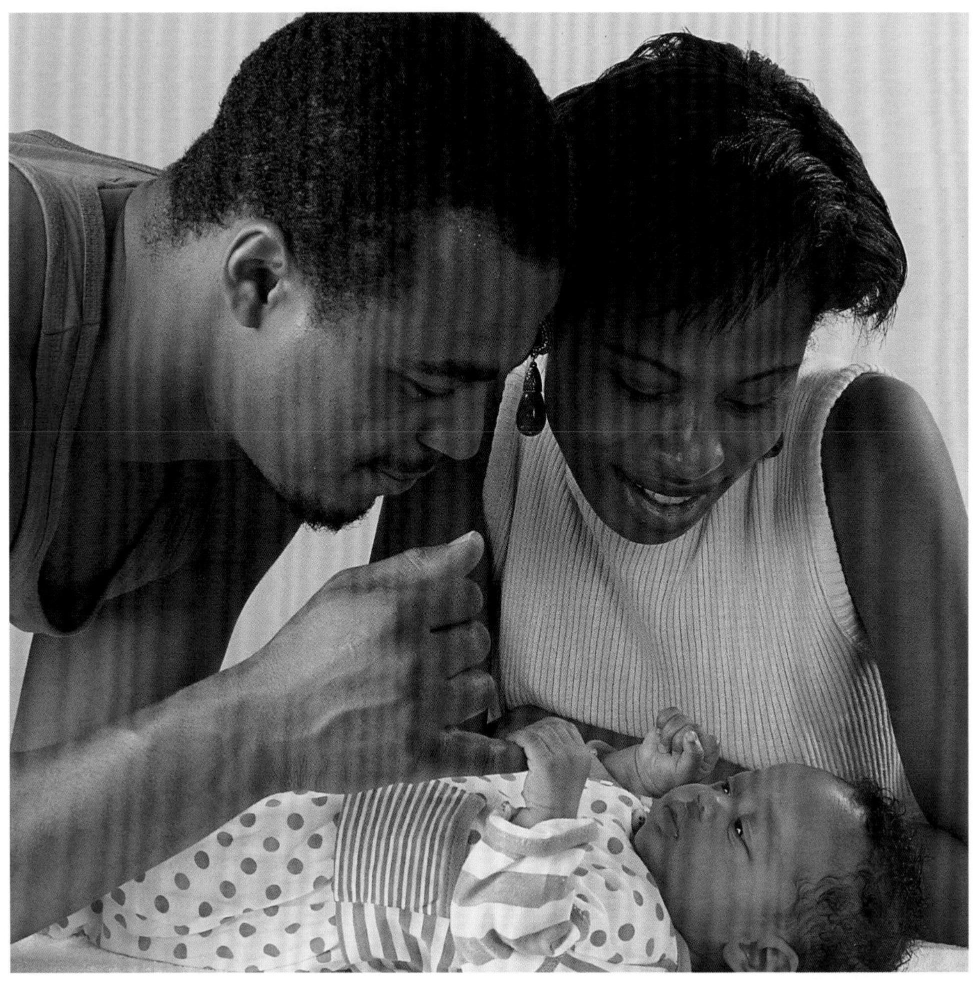

Is it an emergency?

As you get to know your baby you will gain more confidence as a parent and be able to spot when something is wrong more easily. But, in these early days when you are just getting to know your baby, you may not be able to tell what is simply a change in your baby's normal behaviour, or what is a real problem. For instance, is your baby crying because of hunger, or is he or she too hot or cold or ill? If you are worried, never be afraid to ask your midwife, health visitor or GP for help and advice – they are there to help you. See page 87 for how to know when your baby is ill.

Coping with the first few weeks

- Make your baby your first task and try not to worry about everything else.
- Ask for help from your partner, mother or friends. Sometimes people with small babies of their own can be the most help because they know what it's like. The health visitor and midwife will also help you to put things into perspective.
- Accept help and suggest to people what they can do: cook a meal and bring it round; do a stack of washing up; do bits of shopping when you run out; take the baby for a walk.
- Sleep whenever your baby allows you to.
- Practise relaxation techniques (see page 124).
- Keep a good supply of nutritious snacks, like fruit, milk and wholemeal bread, which you can eat without cooking.
- See friends when *you* want to and, if you're tired, tell your friends and suggest that they leave and come back later.
- Remember, this period is hard but it lasts for a relatively short time and it does get better.

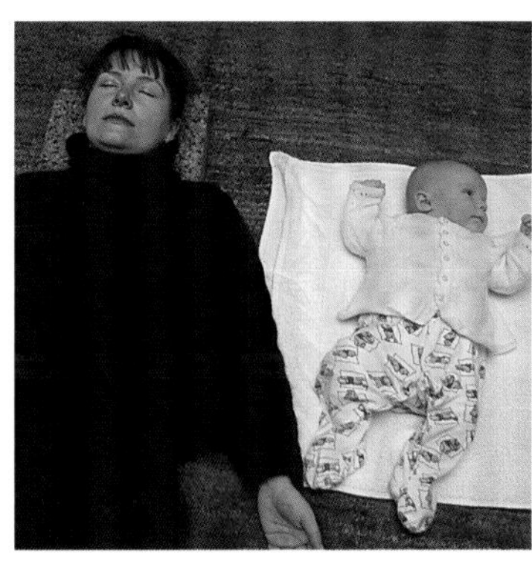

Is it the blues or postnatal depression?

*Two organisations that offer help are the **Association for Postnatal Illness** and the **Meet-a-Mum Association** (MAMA): their addresses are on page 147. Both organisations will put you in touch with other mothers who've been depressed themselves and know what it's like. Remember that what's called postnatal depression can happen a long time after the birth of a baby.*

'Friends kept telling me how well I was coping and I felt really proud. I wanted to be a coping person but underneath I felt I wasn't. And I couldn't admit it either. When I finally talked about it to friends, I found out that a lot of them felt the same way.'

The baby blues

During the first week after childbirth, most women get what is often called the 'baby blues'. Symptoms can include feeling emotional and irrational, bursting into tears for no apparent reason, feeling irritable or touchy or feeling depressed or anxious. All these symptoms are normal and usually only last for a few days. They are probably due to the sudden hormone and chemical changes which take place in your body after childbirth.

Puerperal psychosis

One or two mothers in a thousand will also develop an obvious severe psychiatric illness after the birth of their baby, which requires hospital treatment. Usually a complete recovery is made, although this may take a few weeks or months.

Postnatal depression

This lies between the baby blues and puerperal psychosis, and is an extremely distressing condition with many symptoms. Postnatal depression is thought to affect at least one in ten women, but many women suffer in silence or the condition may go unnoticed by health professionals.

Postnatal depression usually occurs two to eight weeks after delivery. In some cases the baby blues do not go away or the depression can appear up to six months or even a year after the birth of the baby. Some symptoms such as tiredness, irritability or poor appetite are normal if you have just had a baby, but usually these are mild and do not stop you leading a normal life. With postnatal depression you may feel increasingly depressed and despondent and looking after yourself or the baby may become too much. Some other signs of postnatal depression are:

- anxiety;
- panic attacks;
- sleeplessness;
- aches and pains or feeling unwell;
- memory loss or unable to concentrate;
- can't stop crying;
- feelings of hopelessness;
- loss of interest in the baby.

If you think that you are suffering from postnatal depression don't struggle on alone. It is not a sign that you are a 'bad mother' or are unable to cope. Postnatal depression is an illness, so ask for help just as you would if you had the flu or had broken your leg. Talk to someone you can trust, such as your partner or a friend, or ask your health visitor to call. It is also important to see your GP, and if you don't feel up to making an appointment, ask someone to do this for you, or arrange for the GP to call. You may also find it helpful to contact the Association for Postnatal Illness, Meet-a-Mum Association (MAMA) or the National Childbirth Trust (see page 147) (see also Feeling depressed, on page 125).

Feeding your baby

Breastfeeding

Breastfeeding is the healthiest start you can give your baby (see box below). Breastfeeding without other food or drink is recommended for the first six months (26 weeks) of an infant's life, as it provides all the nutrients a baby needs. After solids are introduced, ideally breastfeeding should continue until the end of the first year and beyond.

In the first few days both you and the baby will probably need help to learn about breastfeeding. Don't be afraid to ask for help. The next few pages help you to understand how your breasts produce milk and the correct position for successful breastfeeding.

Your milk supply

Your breasts produce milk in response to your baby feeding at your breast. The more your baby feeds, the more milk you produce. So, if you let your baby feed whenever he or she wants to feed, you're more likely to produce the amount of milk your baby needs. This is known as demand feeding and at first you may find that your baby will want to feed frequently.

Don't be tempted to give your baby a bottle at this stage. This reduces the time your baby spends suckling at your breast and therefore reduces the milk supply.

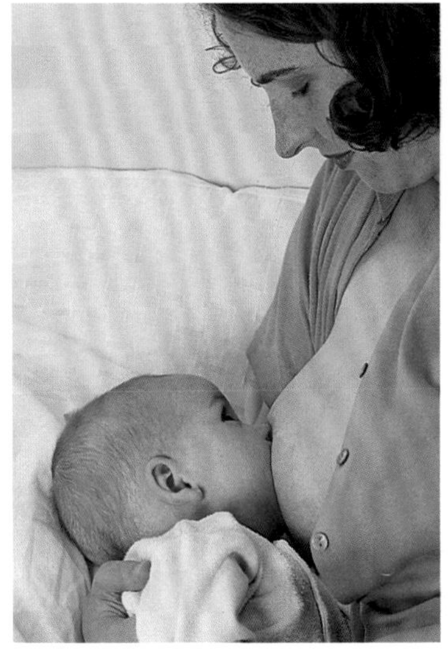

'There's nothing in the world more satisfying than to sit in a darkened silent room, in the middle of the night, with a warm baby in your arms, suckling contentedly.'

'I suppose I'd thought that I'd just put her to my breast and that would be it. I hadn't thought of it as something I might have to learn about and practise. So it came as a bit of a shock that the first few weeks were really quite tough. But I was determined I was going to do it, and yes, it's lovely now.'

Why breastfeeding is good for babies

- *Breast milk is the only food naturally designed for your baby. It contains all the nutrients your baby needs in the right amounts and in a form that is very easily digested. Its composition even changes as your baby grows.*
- *Breast milk contains growth factors and hormones to assist your baby's development.*
- *Your baby's immune system is not fully developed at birth. Antibodies in breast milk help protect your baby from infection.*
- *Because breastfed babies receive antibodies continuously while breastfeeding, they are much less likely to get ear, chest, urinary and gastric (vomiting and diarrhoea) infections.*
- *Breastfed babies are less likely to get tummy upsets or to be constipated.*
- *Breastfed babies are less likely to get allergies like eczema.*
- *Breastfeeding lowers the risk of juvenile diabetes in susceptible children.*
- *Children who are breastfed have better dental health.*
- *Breastfed infants are less likely to become obese in later childhood.*

Why breastfeeding is good for mums

- *Breastfeeding reduces the risk of breast and ovarian cancer.*
- *Breastfeeding helps reduce your risk of developing osteoporosis (bone thinning).*
- *Breastfeeding helps your womb return to its normal size more quickly, and because it uses up calories it will help you to lose some of the weight gained in pregnancy.*

Very occasionally a mother is advised not to breastfeed, e.g. if she is HIV positive, because of the risk of passing the virus on to the baby, or if she is taking some essential medication that may be harmful to the baby.

Hints for breastfeeding

- *Feed your baby as often and as long as he or she needs.*
- *Check your baby is well positioned and attached for feeding.*
- *Avoid using dummies or formula while breastfeeding as these can confuse your baby and reduce your milk supply.*
- *Keep your baby in the same room as you day and night.*
- *Eat and drink when you feel hungry or thirsty and try to eat a wide variety of foods (see page 10).*

Different kinds of breast milk
For the first few days after birth, your breasts produce a special food called 'colostrum', which looks like rich creamy milk and is sometimes quite yellow in colour. This contains all the food your baby needs. This also contains antibodies, which pass on to your baby your own resistance to infections.

The change from colostrum to milk begins on about the third day, and is known as 'transitional milk'. It becomes 'full' breast milk after two weeks. Don't worry if the milk looks very thin or appears blue-white in colour – this is normal. It still contains all the goodness your baby needs. The make-up of the milk also gradually changes throughout the course of the feed. The first milk which your baby takes flows quickly, is thirst-quenching and means your baby gets a drink at the start of every feed. As the flow slows down during a feed, the amount of fat in your milk increases.

How your baby feeds
If you hold and attach your baby correctly, it will feel comfortable and your baby will feed easily. Your baby needs to be able to squeeze the dark area around your nipple (the areola) to receive milk. See picture 5 opposite. The breasts are never empty, but the milk is 'let down' so that it can gather behind the nipple and areola. When a baby just sucks on the nipple, he or she doesn't get much milk and it feels painful.

Get comfortable and follow the step-by-step guide to breastfeeding below and opposite.

How to breastfeed

1 Holding your baby, turn your baby's body towards your tummy. Tuck your baby's bottom under your elbow. Hold your baby behind the neck and shoulders.

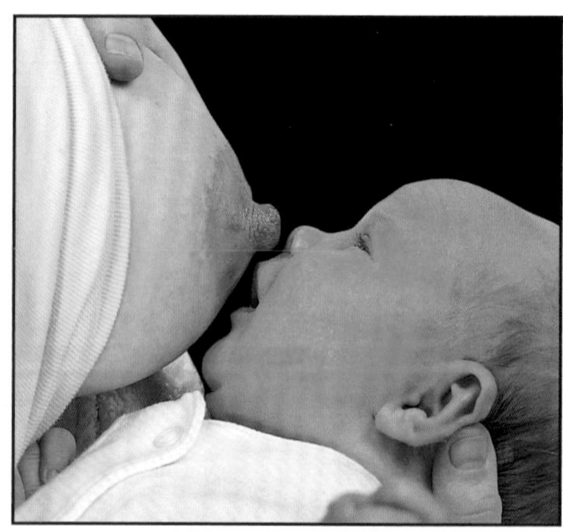

2 Be patient…
Start with your baby's nose opposite your nipple. Allow your baby's head to tilt back.

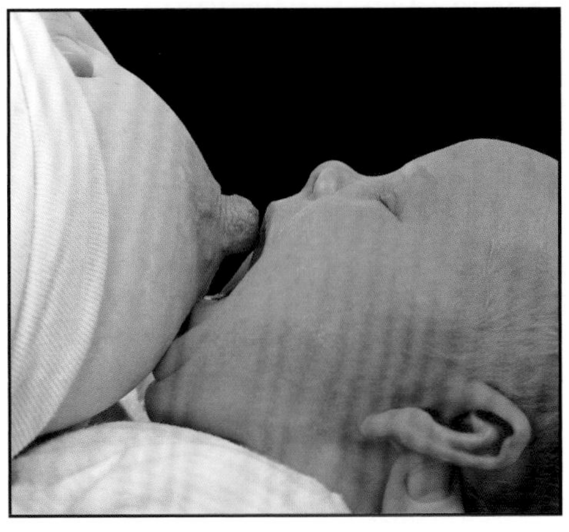

3 Move your baby's mouth gently across your nipple until your baby's mouth opens really wide.

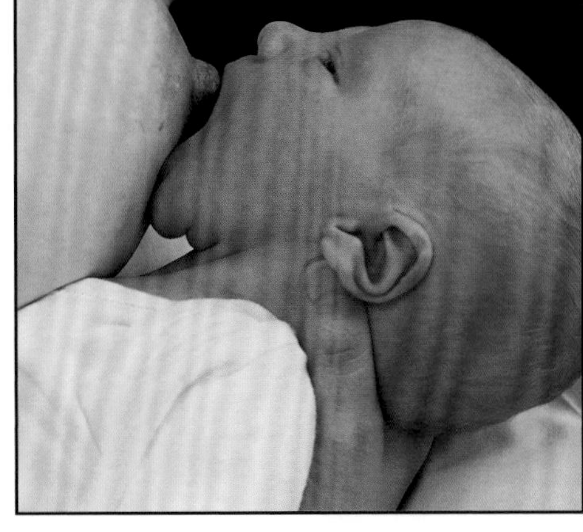

4 Speed…
Bring your baby towards your breast quickly. Your baby's bottom lip and chin should touch your breast first.

Signs that your baby is well attached

- *Baby's chin touching the breast*
- *Baby's mouth wide open*
- *Baby's cheeks full, not sucked in*
- *Baby's sucking changes from short sucks to longer deeper sucks with pauses*
- *If you can see your areola (darker area around nipple), more is visible above baby's lip*

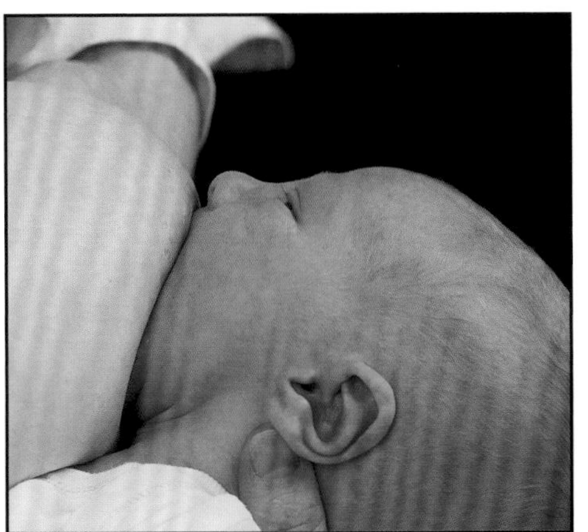

5 Your baby's chin is in close contact with your breast. Your baby is able to breathe easily. You can feel your baby has a big mouthful of breast.

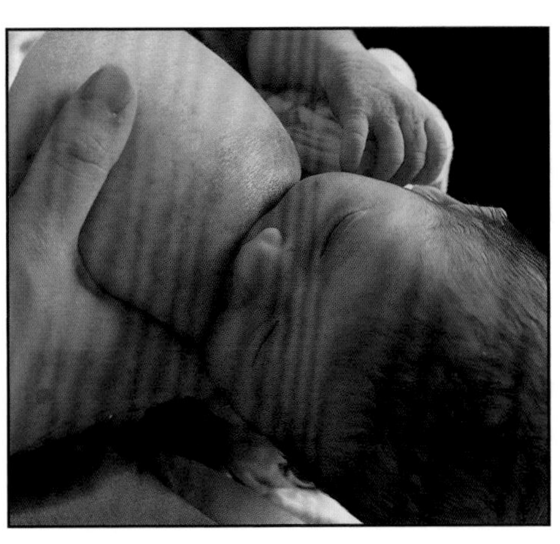

6 Breastfeeding…
You may need to support your breast.

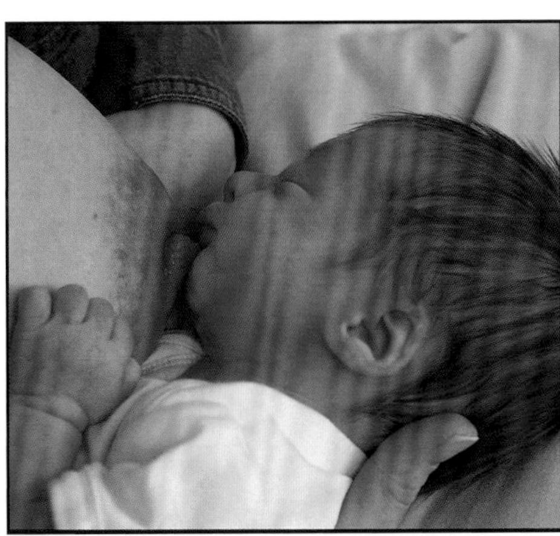

7 Babies love to breastfeed. They usually come off by themselves when they have had enough.

Breastfeeding feels comfortable. Your baby is relaxed. You can hear a soft swallowing. If it does not feel right … start again. Slide one of your fingers into your baby's mouth, gently break the suction and try again.

Further information on all aspects of breastfeeding is available on the Health Promotion Agency parents' website www.breastfedbabies.org

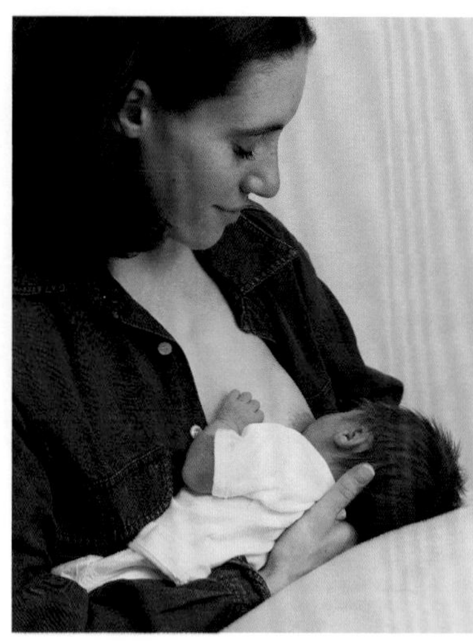

It is OK to ask for help

Any period of breastfeeding, however short, will benefit your baby but the maximum benefits are gained by feeding breastmilk and nothing else until around six months. If you stop breastfeeding it can be difficult to restart. If you need help with breastfeeding, ask your midwife or health visitor or contact a breastfeeding counsellor (see page 146) or your local breastfeeding support group. A list of local groups will be available from your health centre and online from www.breastfedbabies.org

Your diet

A healthy, well-balanced diet is important for you and your family's health. A healthy diet includes eating five portions of fruit and vegetables a day. Don't go for long periods without food or snatching a snack, as this can just leave you feeling tired.

There is no need to avoid eating any foods, but if you have an allergic reaction to certain foods, check with your health visitor before omitting any food from your diet.

Drinks containing caffeine and alcohol pass into breast milk. So keep your intake of tea, coffee, cola and alcohol low, as they may affect your baby's feeding, sleeping or digestion. Keep below the daily limit of two to three units for women, and avoid drinking alcohol before you feed your baby.

Some ideas for healthy foods

You could try:

- Milky drinks or unsweetened fruit juices.
- Baked beans on toast or baked potato.
- Fortified unsweetened breakfast cereals, muesli and other wholegrain cereals with milk.
- Fresh fruit.
- Sandwiches or pitta bread filled with salad vegetables, grated cheese, mashed salmon or sardine.
- Yogurts and fromage frais.
- Vegetable and bean soups.
- Ready-to-eat apricots, figs or prunes.

How often, how long?

Some babies settle into a pattern of feeding quite quickly. Others take longer. In the early weeks, you may find that your baby's feeds are sometimes long, sometimes short, sometimes close together, and sometimes further apart. Try to follow what your baby tells you. Feed when your baby asks to be fed, and for as long as your baby wants.

Once you've put your baby to your breast, let the feed go on until your baby wants to stop. Then, either straight away or after a pause, offer the other breast to see if your baby wants more. Always finish one breast before offering the other.

Allow your baby to decide when he or she has had enough. Both breasts might not always be wanted at each feed. Your baby will show that he or she has finished by either letting go of your breast or falling asleep. Start each feed on the breast that feels fullest.

If you feed as often and for as long as your baby wants, you'll produce plenty of milk and give your baby what he or she needs. At first, it may seem that you're doing nothing but feeding and changing nappies. Remember that this stage will not last very long. Young babies take longer to feed. As babies get older, the feeding time gets shorter. Growth spurts may also affect your baby's feeding patterns. Babies have growth spurts at approximately ten days, six weeks and three months. Your baby may feed more frequently at these times, until your milk supply increases to meet the bigger demand.

Twins, triplets or more

Breastfeeding twins, triplets or more multiples can be done. It may help to start feeding each of your babies separately until feeding is well established. You may need help putting your babies to the breast at the start, but once you have learned how to position and attach one baby at a time, you may wish to encourage twins to feed at the same time. If you breastfeed two babies together, you will not only save time, but also produce more milk, though you may have to wake one baby up to keep them feeding together. For more information about twins (or more), turn to page 29.

Hunger or thirst?

Breast milk is drink and food in one. If the weather is hot, your baby may want to feed more often. There's no need to give your baby drinks of water, even in a very hot climate.

How much is enough?

You may wonder whether your baby is getting enough. If you feed as frequently and for as long as your baby wants, you'll find that your baby will stop feeding when he or she is full-up. You can be sure your baby is getting enough milk if he or she:

- has plenty of wet nappies each day and is having nothing but breast milk;
- is growing and generally gaining weight; it is overall weight gain that is important – some babies gain weight steadily, other perfectly healthy babies gain little or no weight one week, then feed more often and make up for it over the next week or two (see pages 37–8);
- is awake and alert for some of the time.

If you notice that your baby isn't growing in length or generally gaining weight, and is very sleepy or lethargic with no alert times, then he or she may not be getting enough milk. Persistent green stools may also be an indication that your baby is not getting enough milk. Always make sure that your baby feeds fully on one breast before offering the other breast. If you are concerned, talk to your midwife or health visitor.

Night feeds are important. A small baby can receive as much milk at night as during the day, and night feeds encourage the body to make more of the hormone that produces breast milk. When your baby is small it's important for night feeds to continue.

If your baby seems unusually sleepy and is slow to start feeding, he or she may be ill, so contact your GP.

For information and advice about breastfeeding please ask your midwife, health visitor or GP. Other sources of advice are:

Association of Breastfeeding Mothers 020 7813 1481

Breastfeeding Network 0870 900 8787

La Lèche League 020 7242 1278
In Northern Ireland (028) 2564 7951

National Childbirth Trust 0870 444 8708
In Northern Ireland (028) 6862 1842

www.breastfeeding.nhs.uk

www.breastfedbabies.org

Feeding your baby *leaflet and* Off to a good start *booklet, published by the Health Promotion Agency.*

Frequently asked questions

'How soon can I start to put my baby to the breast?'
Providing you and your baby are both well, you will be able to hold him or her straight away. Skin-to-skin contact is a great way to get breastfeeding off to a good start. The midwife may ask if you would like to put your baby to your breast.

'I've heard that breastfeeding can hurt. How can I avoid this?'
If feeding hurts, your baby's position is probably wrong (see page 9) but if you can't get the position right yourself, ask for help. During the first week or two, some breastfeeding mothers feel some discomfort as their baby starts suckling at the beginning of a feed. As long as your baby is correctly positioned and attached, and the milk begins to flow, this discomfort stops.

'I've been feeding my baby for some time now, but my nipples are cracked and painful. What can I do?'
If your baby is in the right position at your breast, and attached correctly, feeding shouldn't hurt.

- Check that your baby is positioned and attached correctly (see page 9). Ask for help if you need it. Once your baby is positioned correctly, cracks should heal rapidly.

'Will anything else help to ease sore nipples?'
Yes. The following may help.

- Keep your nipples clean and dry, but avoid soap, which dries the skin too much.

- Change breast pads frequently. Avoid pads with plastic backing.

- Wear a cotton bra and let the air get to your nipples as much as possible.

- A few drops of milk rubbed into the nipple at the end of a feed may help.

'Could sore nipples be caused by anything else?'
Thrush in your baby's mouth can sometimes cause sore nipples. Thrush is an infection that results in small white patches in the baby's mouth, which don't wipe away. If you think your baby has thrush, both you and your baby will need medical treatment, so see your GP.

'My baby stops and starts and cries and just doesn't seem to settle down.'
If your baby is restless at your breast and doesn't seem satisfied by feeds, he or she may be suckling on the nipple alone and not getting enough milk. Check your baby is in the right position and attached properly to your breast. Ask for help if you need to. Colic may also be a problem (see page 23).

'My baby sicks up a lot of milk after her feed.'
Some babies sick up more milk than others during or just after a feed. This is called 'possetting', 'regurgitation' or 'gastric reflux'. If your baby is gaining weight and is generally healthy, this is nothing to worry about. But if this happens often, or if your baby is frequently or violently sick, appears to be in pain, or you're worried for any other reason, see your health visitor or GP. If your baby brings back a lot of milk, she may be hungry again quite quickly. But never force your baby to take more than she wants.

'My friend complained her breasts became very swollen and hard and painful when she started breastfeeding. How can I prevent this happening to me?'
This is called breast engorgement. It is important to distinguish this from the normal breast fullness or heaviness that occurs when you start to produce milk after three or four days, which does not cause swelling or pain. Engorgement can happen if there has been a delay in starting breastfeeding, or you limit the amount of time, or the frequency, of feeding your baby. It rarely happens if you feed on demand. Making sure your baby is correctly attached to the breast and letting him or her feed early and frequently can help to prevent engorgement.

If feeding is difficult for some reason, ask for help. To ease the swelling, try a hot bath or bathe your breasts with some warm water. Smooth out some milk with your fingers, stroking gently downwards towards the nipple. Or try holding a face cloth wrung out in very cold water against your breast. Check your bra's not too tight.

'I have a hard, painful lump in my breast. What is it?'
It's probably milk which has built up because a duct is blocked and isn't being emptied properly. Check that your bra isn't too tight and that nothing is pressing into your breast as you feed.

A good feed on the blocked breast will help. As you feed, massage the lump towards the nipple. If left untreated, blocked ducts can lead to mastitis.

'There is a red, hot, painful patch on my breast and I feel quite unwell. Why?'
You may have mastitis. Don't stop feeding as you need to keep your milk flowing. Try different positions to empty different parts of your breast. Try the suggestions for relieving engorged breasts and blocked ducts, get lots of rest, and try not to wear a bra, especially at night. A health visitor or breastfeeding counsellor can offer information, help and support (see page 11).

If you have an infection you may need to take antibiotics. Your doctor can prescribe one that is safe to take while breastfeeding.

Expressing milk

It is useful to learn how to express your milk for the following reasons:

- your baby may be in Special Care;
- to help your baby latch on to a full breast;
- your breasts feel full;
- so someone else can give the expressed milk to your baby.

You can express milk by hand, using a hand pump or an electric pump.

Hospitals often keep machines for people who need to express milk and you can be shown how to use one.

Alternatively, the Association of Breastfeeding Mothers, La Lèche League and the National Childbirth Trust all have breast pumps for hire (see page 146).

If you've plenty of milk you'll probably find expressing quite easy, particularly if you do it in the morning. Your midwife or health visitor will show you how to express milk by using either an electric or hand pump or by hand.

You must express your milk into a sterilised bottle, which you can then cap and keep in the fridge. Keep it for no longer than 24 hours. You can also freeze breast milk for one week in the freezer compartment of the fridge or up to three months in the freezer. Freeze it as soon as possible after expressing, and certainly within a couple of hours (there are specially designed breast milk freezer bags).

Thaw frozen breast milk in a fridge and when it is thawed use it within 24 hours. Or you can put the container into luke warm water to thaw. When it is warmed to room temperature, use at once or throw away. **Never refreeze.**

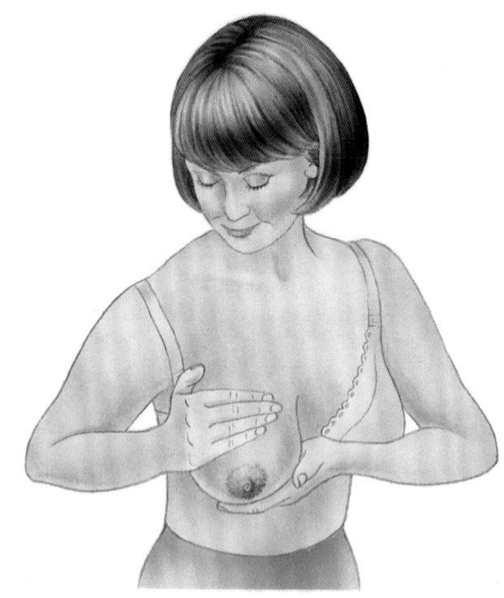

Gently massage your breast towards the nipple to stimulate the let-down reflex.

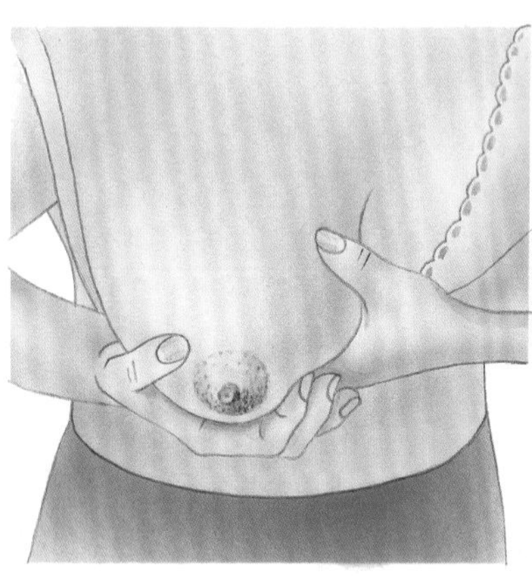

Milk will begin to gather behind the areola (area of dark skin around the nipple).

Bottle feeding expressed milk

If you are planning to go back to work, or if you want someone else to feed your baby expressed breast milk once in a while, it is a good idea to get your baby used to a bottle and teat.

It is best to get breastfeeding right for you and your baby before you introduce a bottle. Babies squeeze the breast to obtain milk, but suck on a teat like drinking from a straw. So once breastfeeding is well established, feels comfortable and your baby is content, you can start expressing milk and giving it in a bottle.

Shake the breast milk that has been kept in the frige before use.

Breast milk separates very quickly into fat and whey.

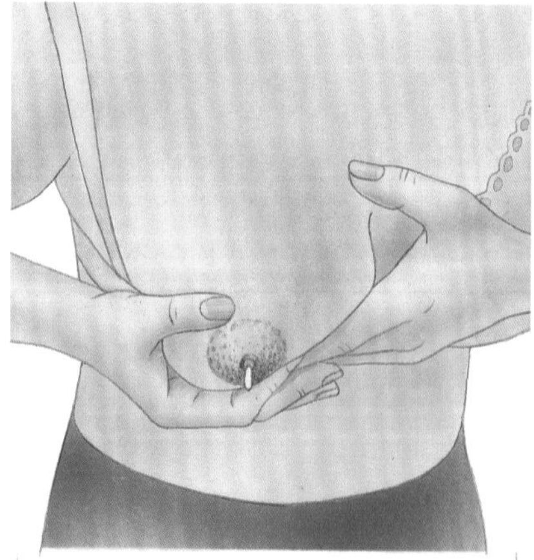

Gently squeeze the breast between the first finger and thumb. Keep pressing and releasing. The milk will start to flow.

Combining breast and bottle

Once breastfeeding is well established, you may want to introduce infant formula milk (if, for example, you are returning to work, or simply want someone else involved in feeding). Mothers returning to work often breastfeed in the morning and/or evening and their babies have a bottle of infant formula during the day (see pages 16–18). Introducing infant formula milk will affect the amount of breast milk you produce.

Changing from breast to bottle

Don't stop breastfeeding suddenly as this can cause your breasts to become hard, swollen and uncomfortable. Give yourself time for the changeover and cut out one feed at a time, starting well before your return to work. It's probably best not to give the first bottle feed at times when your baby is tired and it may help if someone other than you gives the first feeds. Your baby is not then near your breast, smelling your breast milk. You may experience difficulties at first, but most babies get used to the new arrangements in time. Keep on trying and offering infant formula milk. If you are concerned that your baby is not getting enough milk, speak to your health visitor. See also **How much is enough?** on page 11. Changing from breast to bottle feeding can be an emotional time for you. It's best to do it gradually to give yourself time to adapt.

Bottle feeding

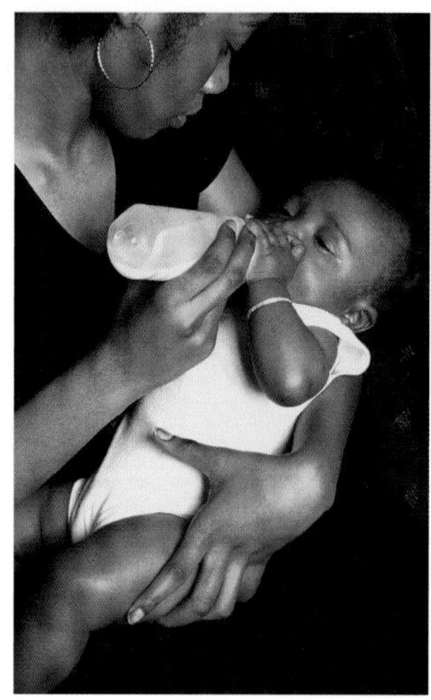

What you'll need

- You'll need at least **six bottles and teats**. Ask your midwife or other mothers about the type of bottle and teats to buy. If you are offered second-hand bottles make sure that they are not scratched as you will not be able to sterilise them properly.
- You'll also need **a supply of baby milk** (also called infant formula). Discuss the different brands with your midwife or health visitor and then make your own choice. If you are on benefits, check whether you can claim free or reduced-price milk for your baby (see page 145).

Sterilising

All the equipment used for feeding your baby needs to be sterilised. By sterilising your feeding equipment, you will reduce the chance of your baby getting sickness and diarrhoea.

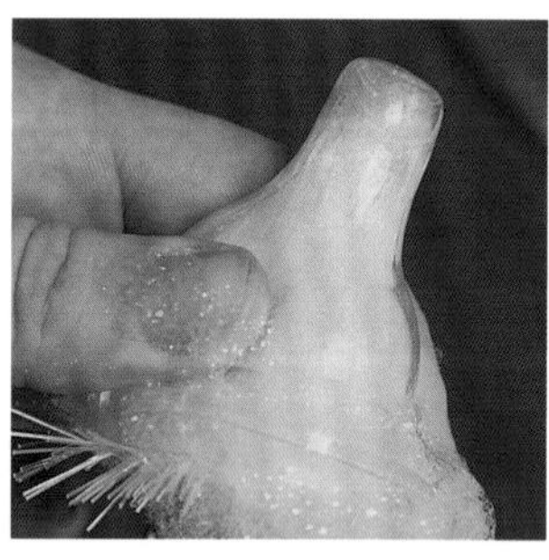

How to sterilise
Clean the bottle and teat in hot soapy water as soon as possible after a feed, using a clean bottle brush. Squirting water through the teat helps remove every trace of milk.

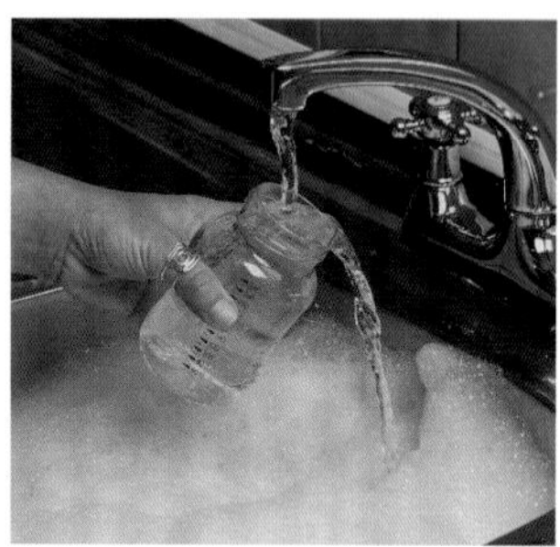

Rinse all your equipment before sterilising.

Cold water sterilising

Follow the manufacturer's instructions.
Change the sterilising solution every 24 hours.
Leave feeding equipment in the sterilising solution for at least 30 minutes.
Make sure there is no air trapped in the bottles or teats when putting them in the sterilising solution.
Keep all the equipment under the solution with a floating cover.

Steam sterilising

Follow the manufacturer's instructions.
Make sure the openings of the bottles and teats are facing down in the steriliser.
Any equipment not used straight away should be re-sterilised before use.

Making up a feed

Before making up a feed, clean the surface you are going to use. It's really important that you WASH YOUR HANDS.

If you are using a cold water steriliser, shake off any excess solution from the bottle and the teat or rinse the bottle with cooled boiled water from the kettle.

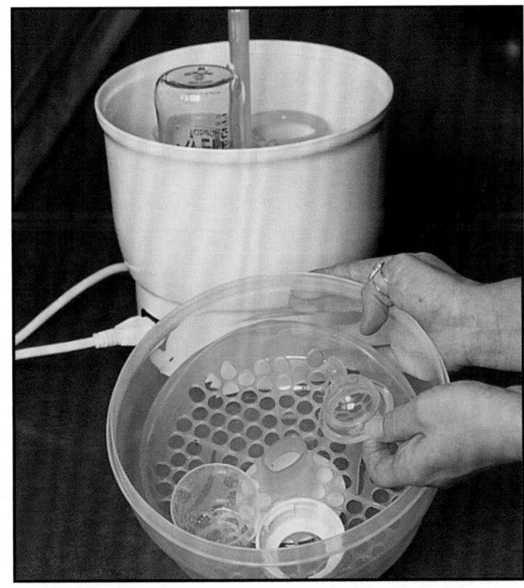

Stand the bottle on a clean surface. Keep the teat and cap on the upturned lid of the steriliser. Avoid putting them on the work surface.

When making up infant formula milk use fresh tap water to fill the kettle. After it has boiled let the water cool. Always put the cooled boiled water in the bottle first. Always check the water level is correct. Follow the manufacturer's instructions.

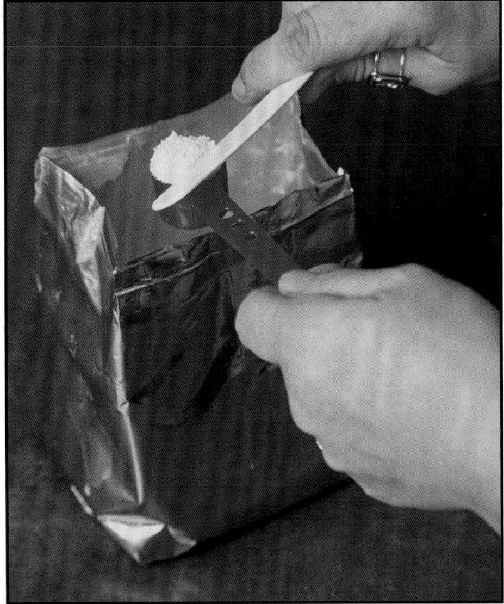

Loosely fill the scoop with milk powder and level it off without compacting it. Only use one scoop of powder to 30 ml or 1 oz water.

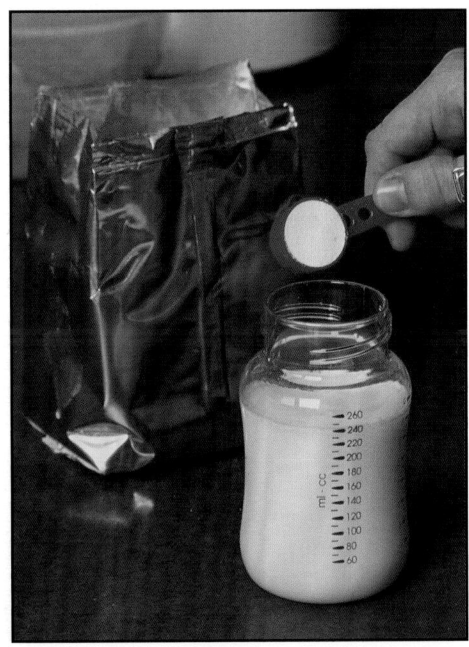

Add the milk powder to the water. Making up a feed with too much powder can give your baby constipation.

If there is a strong history of ***allergies*** *in your family, such as eczema, asthma or food allergies, and you do not want to breastfeed, seek advice as early as possible from your GP or health visitor. Infant formula based on cow's milk is the better option, but if your baby has an allergic reaction to milk formula, it may be necessary to use non-dairy alternatives, such as hydrolysed protein formulae. Soya-based formulae should only be used or advised in exceptional circumstances, for example, for babies of vegan parents. Remember that breast milk is the best form of nutrition for babies. Don't change to non-dairy baby milks without talking to your doctor or health visitor first. Unmodified goat's milk or sheep's milk are not nutritionally suitable for babies under one year of age.*

Bottle feeding help and advice

If you want help or advice on bottle feeding, talk to your midwife or health visitor, or to other mothers with experience of bottle feeding.

Holding the edge of the teat, put it on the bottle. Screw the retaining ring into the bottle. Cover the teat with a cap. Shake the bottle until the powder is dissolved.

Store made-up bottles in the coldest part of the fridge (5°C). Do not keep for more than 24 hours. When feeding your baby, keep the teat full of milk, otherwise your baby will take in air. If the teat flattens while you are feeding, pull gently on the bottle to release the vacuum. If the teat blocks, start again with another sterile teat. Never prop up a bottle and leave your baby to feed alone – he or she may choke.

THROW AWAY ANY LEFT-OVER MILK.

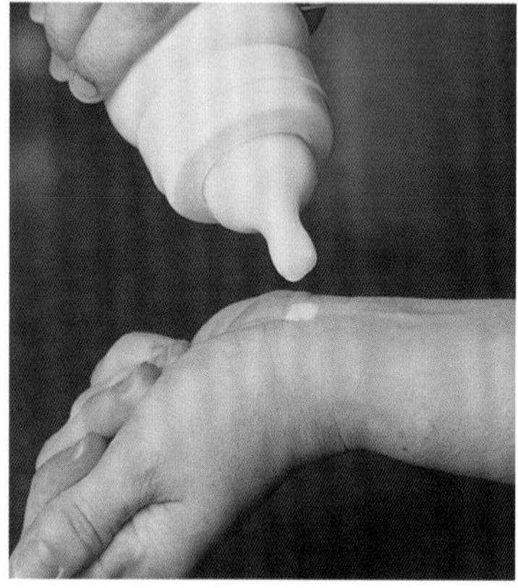

Don't leave your baby alone with a bottle as a way of getting him or her off to sleep. There's a danger of choking.

Feeding your baby

If you want to warm your baby's milk, stand the bottle in hot water. Heating the milk in a microwave oven is dangerous as the milk continues to heat up after it has been taken out. Test the temperature of the feed by dropping a little onto the inside of your wrist.

If you are making up more than one feed at a time, use individual bottles. Do not use a jug.

Problems with bottle feeding

'Early on, if the feeds weren't going well, I'd think, well, perhaps I'd better try a different kind of milk, or a different bottle, or a different teat, or whatever. But it's the same as doing anything the first time. It's a while before you know what you're doing, and then you settle down and start to enjoy it.'

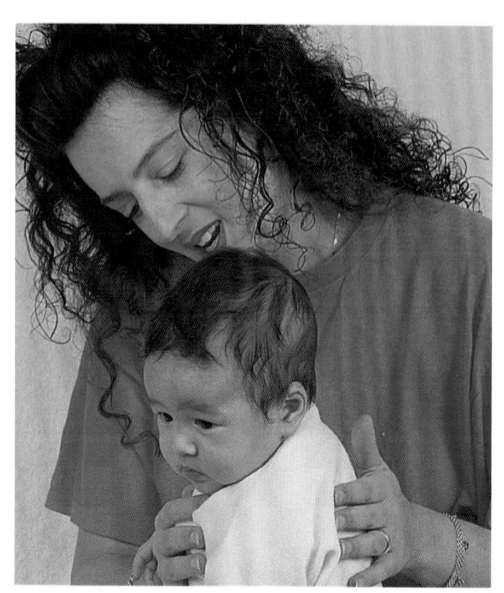

If your baby swallows a lot of air while bottle feeding and is then put down to sleep, the trapped wind may cause discomfort and your baby may cry. After a feed, it may help to hold your baby upright against your shoulder or propped forward on your lap. Then gently rub your baby's back so that any trapped air can find its way up and out quite easily. Some babies are never troubled by wind, others seem to suffer discomfort after every feed. For information about colic, see pages 23–4.

Sickness vomiting
Some babies sick up more milk than others during or just after a feed. (This is called 'possetting', 'regurgitation' or 'gastric reflux'.) It's not unusual for a baby to sick up quite a lot, but many mothers get upset or worried about this. If your baby is gaining weight there is usually nothing to worry about. But if this happens often or if your baby is frequently or violently sick, appears to be in pain, or you're worried for any other reason, see your health visitor or GP.

Cover your baby with a thick bib when feeding and have a cloth or paper towels handy to mop up any mess. (If you sprinkle a damp cloth with bicarbonate of soda, this will remove the worst of the smell.) Check too that the hole in your baby's teat is not too big. Sitting your baby upright in a baby chair after a feed can help, and the problem usually stops after six months when your baby is starting on solid foods and drinking less milk. If your baby brings back a lot of milk, remember he or she is likely to be hungry again quite quickly. Do not force your baby to take on more than they want.

Constipation
Always add the recommended amount of infant formula milk powder to the water. Milk feeds that contain too much infant formula milk powder can make your baby constipated. Babies fed on infant formulae milk can get thirsty, so offer your baby cool boiled tap water if he or she is unsettled between feeds.

Sleeping

Some babies sleep much more than others. Some sleep in long patches, some in short. Some soon sleep right through the night, some don't for a long time. Your baby will have his or her own pattern of waking and sleeping, and it's unlikely to be the same as other babies you know.

In the early weeks your baby's sleeping pattern is very unlikely to fit in with your need for sleep. Try to follow your baby's needs. You'll gradually get to know when sleep is needed. Don't catch up on housework while your baby sleeps. Snatch sleep and rest whenever you can.

A baby who wants to sleep isn't likely to be disturbed by household noise, so there's no need to keep the house silent while your baby sleeps. In fact, it will help you if your child gets used to sleeping through a certain amount of noise.

Most parents want their children to learn to sleep for the longest period at night – when they are sleeping – and it helps if you encourage night-time sleeping right from the start by teaching your baby that the night-time is different from the daytime. During night feeds:

- keep the lights down low;
- keep your voice low and don't talk much;
- put your baby down as soon as you have fed and changed him or her;
- don't change your baby if a change is not needed.

If your baby always falls asleep in your arms, at your breast, in your partner's arms, or with someone by the cot, he or she might not easily take to settling alone. This might not matter to you and may be unavoidable in the early weeks, particularly with a breastfed baby, but, if you want your baby to get used to going off to sleep alone, it's wise to start putting the baby down before he or she falls asleep right from the beginning, whenever this is possible. However, you may need to wait until the baby is alert for longer or more frequent periods. Remember though, the longer you leave it, the more difficult it will become.

'It wasn't that she wouldn't sleep when she needed to. She just didn't need it. Or at least, she needed a whole lot less than we did. It's not getting your baby to sleep that's the problem; it's getting enough sleep yourself.'

'I would just get one of them off to sleep when the other one woke for a feed. I was desperately tired but gradually they got into a pattern and at last I could get some sleep myself.'

Disturbed nights can be very hard to bear. If you're bottle feeding, encourage your partner to share the feeds. Many fathers find this a valuable time for getting to know their babies. If you're breastfeeding, your partner may be happy to take over the early morning changing and dressing so that you can go back to sleep, or once breastfeeding is established he could occasionally give a bottle of expressed breast milk. If you're on your own, you could ask a friend or relative to stay for a few days so that you can sleep.

Don't give your baby a pillow or duvet (quilt) until he or she is one year old.

Once you've established a pattern, you may want to try and shift things around a bit. For example, you may wake your baby for a feed just before you go to bed in the hope that you'll get a good long stretch of sleep before he or she wakes again. See pages 55–6 for more information about sleeping problems in older babies and children. CRY-SIS, the organisation for parents of crying babies, can also offer help with sleeping problems (address on page 146).

Safe sleeping

Reducing the risk of cot death

Sadly, we don't yet know why some babies die suddenly and for no apparent reason from what is called cot death or Sudden Infant Death Syndrome (SIDS). But we do know that placing a baby to sleep on his or her back from the very beginning reduces the risk, and that exposing a baby to cigarette smoke or overheating a baby increases the risk.

All the advice we now have for reducing the risk of cot death and other dangers, such as suffocation, is listed below.

- **Always put your baby to sleep on his or her back.**
- **Don't sleep with your baby in certain situations (see right).**
- **Cut out smoking in pregnancy and after baby is born (this applies to fathers too!).**
- **Don't let anyone smoke in the same room as your baby.**
- **Don't let your baby get too hot and don't overheat the room (see** The right temperature, **right).**
- **Keep your baby's head uncovered in bed – place your baby in the 'feet to foot' position (see picture).**
- **Don't sleep on a sofa with your baby.**
- **If your baby seems unwell, seek advice promptly.**

The 'feet to foot' position means that the baby's feet are right at the end of the cot to prevent the baby wriggling under the covers.

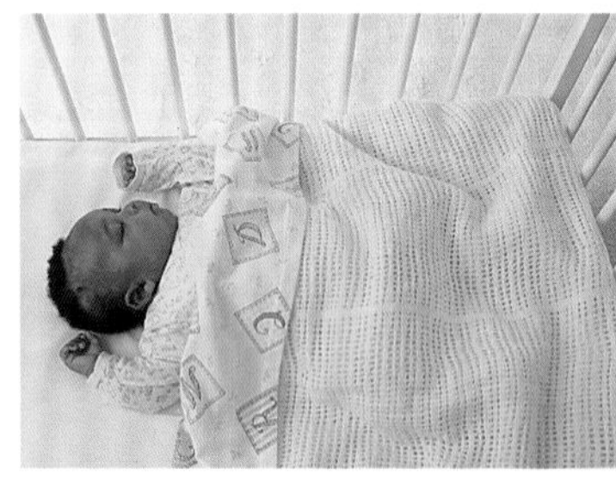

The safest place for your baby to sleep is in a cot in your room for the first six months. While it's lovely to have your baby with you for a cuddle or a feed, it's safest to put your baby back in the cot before you go to sleep. It is dangerous to share a bed with your baby if you or your partner:

- are smokers (no matter where or when you smoke);
- have been drinking alcohol;
- use drugs, take medication that makes you drowsy;
- are very tired.

There is also a risk that you might roll over in your sleep and suffocate your baby, that your baby could get caught between the wall and the bed, or could roll out of an adult bed and be injured. Never sleep with a baby on a sofa or armchair.

Keep your baby's head uncovered. Babies whose heads are covered accidentally with bedding are at an increased risk of cot death.

Sleep your baby on a mattress that is firm, flat, well fitting and clean. The outside of the mattress should be waterproof, like PVC. Cover the mattress with a single sheet. Use sheets and lightweight blankets but not duvets, quilts, baby nests, wedges, bedding rolls or pillows.

To prevent your baby wriggling down under the covers, place your baby's feet at the foot of the cot or pram. Make the covers up so that they reach no higher than the shoulders. Covers should be securely tucked in so they cannot slip over the baby's head.

The right temperature

Small babies aren't very good at controlling their own temperature. It's just as important to prevent them getting too hot as it is to avoid them getting chilled. Overheating can increase the risk of cot death. Babies can overheat because of too much bedding or clothing, or because the room is too hot.

- When you check your baby, if he or she is sweating or their tummy feels hot to the touch, take off some of the bedding. Don't worry if baby's hands or feet feel cool - this is normal.
- It is easier to adjust for the temperature with changes of lightweight blankets. Remember, a folded blanket counts as two blankets. In summer, if it is very warm, your baby may not need any bedclothes other than a sheet.
- Babies do not need hot rooms; all night heating is rarely necessary. Keep the room at a temperature that is comfortable for you. About 18° C (65° F) is comfortable.
- Even in winter, most babies who are unwell or feverish need fewer clothes.
- Babies lose excess heat from their heads, so make sure their head cannot be covered with bedclothes.
- Babies should never sleep with a hot water bottle or electric blanket, next to a radiator, heater or fire, or in direct sunshine.
- Remove hats and extra clothing as soon as you come indoors or enter a warm car, bus or train, even if it means waking your baby.

Clean air

Babies shouldn't be exposed to tobacco smoke either before birth or afterwards. If you, or anyone else who looks after your baby, smoke, then don't smoke anywhere near the baby. It would be even better if everyone could make an effort to give up completely.

Smoke is present in the air that is breathed out for a considerable time after smoking has taken place. Babies and young children who breathe in cigarette smoke are more likely to get coughs, asthma attacks, and chest and ear infections. For more on quitting smoking see page 123.

Babies enjoy a variety of movements when awake, and it is good for them and their development to experience different positions and to play on their front when awake.

If your baby seems at all unwell, seek medical advice early and quickly (see page 87). Do remember that cot death is rare. Don't let worrying about cot death spoil the first precious months you have with your baby.

Babies with jaundice

Many babies get jaundiced – which means they have yellow skin and eyes – for up to two weeks following birth. This is not a reason to stop breastfeeding, but it is important to ensure that all is well. If your baby is still jaundiced **after** two weeks, see your GP. This is particularly important if your baby's stools are pale or the urine is dark orange. Your GP will arrange any tests that might be needed.

Vitamin K

We all need vitamin K to make our blood clot properly so that we won't bleed too easily. Some newborn babies have too little vitamin K. Although this is rare, it can cause them to bleed dangerously into the brain. This is called 'haemorrhagic disease of the newborn' or vitamin K deficiency bleeding (VKDB). To reduce the risk, you should be offered vitamin K, which will be given to your baby either by mouth or by injection. Your doctor or midwife will be able to explain these options.

Crying

A lot of people seem to think that babies shouldn't cry. They think that if babies do cry there must be a reason and you, the parent, should be able to do something about it. But all babies cry, and some cry a lot. Sometimes you'll know the reason. Often you'll try everything to stop it – change nappies, feed, rock, play – and yet nothing seems to work. Here are some things you can try.

- **Let your baby suckle at your breast.**
- **Hold your baby close,** rocking, swaying, talking, singing. Or put your baby in a sling, held close against you. Move about gently, sway and dance.
- **Rock your baby** backwards and forwards in the pram, or go out for a walk or a drive. Quite a lot of babies sleep in cars, and even if your baby wakes up again the minute you stop, you've at least had a break.
- **Find things to look at or listen to** – music on the radio or a tape, a rattle, a mobile above the cot.
- **If your baby is bottle fed you can give him or her a dummy,** sterilised for small babies, never sweetened. Some babies find their thumb instead. Later, some will use a bit of cloth as a comforter; you can wash this as often as you need.
- **Stroke your baby** firmly and rhythmically, holding him or her against you or lying face downwards on your lap. Or undress your baby and massage with baby oil, gently and firmly. Talk soothingly as you do it. Make sure the room is warm enough. Some clinics run courses to teach mothers baby massage – ask your midwife or health visitor about this.
- **Give your baby a warm bath.** This calms some babies instantly, but makes others cry even more. Like everything else, it might be worth a try.
- **Quietly put your baby down after a feed and leave the room for a few minutes.** Sometimes all the rocking and singing succeeds only in keeping your baby awake.

Remember

- **This difficult time won't last forever.** Your baby will gradually start to take more interest in the things around him or her and the miserable, frustrated crying will almost certainly stop.
- **Never shake your baby. Shaking makes a baby's or infant's head move violently. It causes bleeding and can damage the brain.** Sometimes you will feel very tired and even desperate. You might feel that you are losing control and have an urge to shake your baby. But don't, this is dangerous. Put your baby down safely in the cot or pram and calm yourself; don't be angry with your baby.

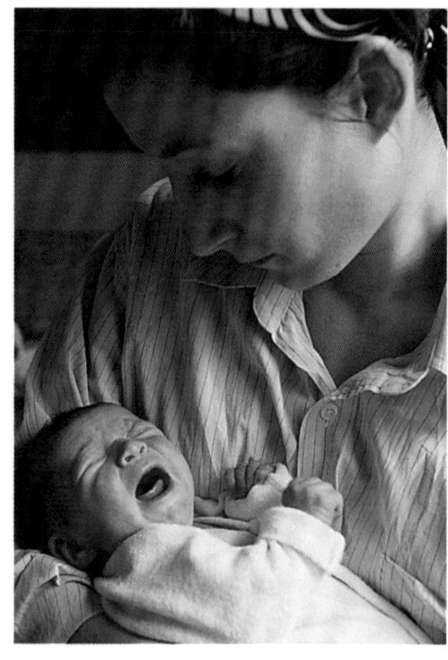

A warning cry

Although all babies cry sometimes, there are times when crying may be a sign of illness. Watch out for a sudden change in the pattern or sound of your baby's crying. Often there may be a simple explanation: if you've been socialising more than usual, your baby might simply be overtired and fretful. But if you feel that something is wrong, follow your instincts and contact your GP. *See page 87 for more on what to do if you think your baby is ill.*

'At first it really upset me. I felt I ought to be able to comfort him, I ought to be able to make him happy, and he wasn't happy, and I couldn't comfort him, no matter what I did. And then it went on so long, it felt like forever, and I was still upset, but I got sort of worn out by it, almost angry, because I was so disappointed that things weren't like I wanted them to be. I wanted to enjoy him, and I wanted him to be like other babies, smiling, gurgling, all of that, and he was just dreadful with the crying.'

If you're finding it hard to cope you may need some help or support. Look on pages 123–4 for suggestions. You could also ask for help from a friend, your health visitor or doctor. Or contact CRY-SIS (see page 146) who will put you in touch with other parents who've been in the same situation.

Colic

Many babies have particular times in the day when they cry and cry and are difficult to comfort. Early evening is the usual bad patch. This is hard on you since it's probably the time when you are most tired and least able to cope.

Crying like this can be due to colic. Everybody agrees that colic exists, but there's disagreement about what causes it or even if there is always a cause. Some doctors say that it's a kind of stomach cramp, and it does seem to cause the kind of crying that might go with waves of stomach pain – very miserable and distressed, stopping for a moment or two, then starting up again.

The crying can go on for some hours, and there may be little you can do except try to comfort your baby and wait for the crying to pass.

If you are concerned about your baby's crying, you may want to ask your GP or health visitor about it. Make a list of the questions you want to ask them so you won't forget anything. It can help if you keep a record of how often and when your baby cries, for example, after every feed or during the evening. This may help you to identify the times when you need extra support or to see if a change of routine could help. For example, if your baby cries more in the afternoon and you go out in the morning, taking him or her out in the afternoon may be better. Such information may help the GP or health visitor to diagnose the problem. You might want to ask:

- Is my baby poorly?
- Is there any medication that could help?
- Is there anything I can do to help ease my baby's pain?

'It was every evening. We'd be there, rocking her and walking up and down. We got so exhausted we were desperate. And then it stopped, gradually. You don't think you can bear it, but you do bear it, because there's nothing else for it. And in the end, it stops.'

'At some points I just didn't want to be involved at all. The first few months it was so much of a shock … I think that first bit – the sleepless broken nights and constant crying – I just couldn't handle it. I could quite easily have left it all to her, but then gradually I got used to it and you start to bond with the baby.'

(A father)

Coping with a colicky baby is extremely stressful. It may be best to tell yourself that there's nothing very much you can do. You just need to hang on as best you can until this part of your baby's life is over, which will certainly be only a few weeks. Just knowing that you're not causing the crying, and you can't do much to prevent it, may make it easier for you to bear. Try to take some time out for yourself whenever you can – maybe just handing over to someone else so that you can have a long, hot soak in the bath in the evening. Make sure that you get a decent meal every day to keep up your energy. If a crying baby occupies all your evening, then make lunch your main meal.

If the strain gets too much

- There may well be times when you're so tired you feel desperate, angry and can't take any more. Don't be ashamed to ask for help.

- **Try to share the crying times.** Think about handing your baby over to someone else for an hour. Nobody can cope alone with a constantly crying baby. You need someone who'll give you a break, at least occasionally, to calm down and get some rest.

- **Think about putting your baby down in the cot or pram and going away for a while.** Make sure your baby is safe, close the door, go into another room, and do what you can to calm yourself down. Set a time limit – say, ten minutes – then go back.

- **Ask your health visitor if there is any local support for parents of crying babies.** Some areas run a telephone helpline. An organisation called CRY-SIS has branches in many areas and offers support through mothers who have had crying babies themselves. See page 146 for details of this and other support organisations.

Other remedies

- Some parents find giving their baby colic drops or gripe water helps. Others find these remedies are ineffective.

- Try massaging your baby's tummy in a clockwise direction with one drop of pure lavender oil to 10 ml of oil, such as baby or olive oil.

- A drop of lavender oil placed on a cotton wool ball on a warm radiator or in a vaporiser may also soothe your baby.

NAPPIES

WHAT'S IN A NAPPY?

What should my baby's stools look like?

Your baby's stools will be sticky and greenish/black at first (called 'meconium'). They will then change to a yellow or mustard colour, and do not smell in a breastfed baby. Stools of a bottle-fed baby are darker brown and more smelly. Some infant formulas can also make the motions dark green. Breastfed babies have quite runny stools. Bottle-fed babies' stools are firmer. If you change from breast to bottle feeding, you will find the stools become darker and more paste-like.

How often should my baby's bowels be opened?

Some babies fill their nappies at or around every feed. Some, especially breastfed babies, can go for several days, even a week, without a bowel movement. Both are quite normal.

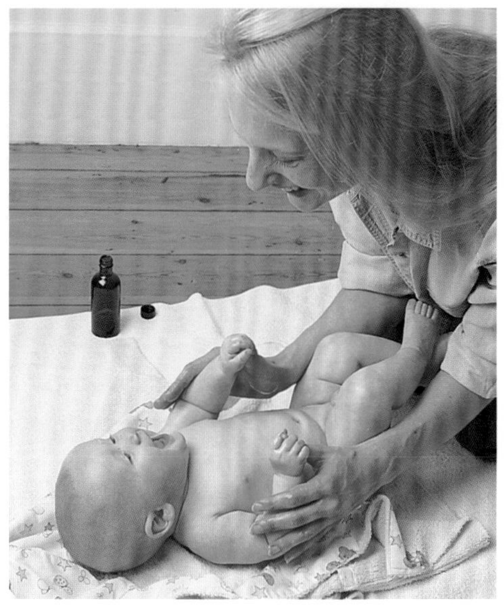

Nappy rash

Most babies get nappy rash at some time in the first 18 months. This is most commonly caused by the skin being in prolonged contact with ammonia from urine or bacteria from stools burning or irritating the skin, which may then break open. Other causes include:

- *a sensitive skin;*
- *rubbing or chaffing;*
- *strong soap, detergent or bubble bath;*
- *baby wipes containing alcohol;*
- *diarrhoea or illnesses;*
- *changes in diet such as weaning or changing from breast milk to formula.*

In its early stages the rash may appear as red patches on your baby's bottom or there may be general redness. The skin may look sore and be hot to touch and there may be spots, pimples or blisters.

It is usual for babies to strain or even cry when passing a stool. Your baby is not constipated if the stools are soft when passed, even if the bowels have not been opened for a few days.

Is it normal for my baby's stools to change?
From day to day or week to week your baby's stools will probably vary a bit. But if you notice a marked change of any kind, such as the stools becoming very smelly, very watery, very pale (see page 21 for information on jaundice), or becoming hard, particularly if there's blood in them, you should talk to your doctor or health visitor.

Nappy changing

Some babies have very delicate skin and need changing the minute they wet themselves if they're not to get sore and red. Others seem to be tougher and get along fine with a change before or after every feed. All babies need to be changed when they're dirty to prevent nappy rash and because they can smell awful!

Getting organised

- Get everything you need for changing in one place before you start. The best place to change a nappy is on a changing mat or towel on the floor, particularly if you've more than one baby. If you sit down you won't hurt your back and, as your baby gets bigger, he or she can't wriggle off and hurt him or herself. If you're using a changing table, keep one hand on your baby at all times.

- Make sure you've a supply of nappies. If you're using washable cloth nappies, ask your midwife to show you how to fold and pin them (although most now come with Velcro or popper fastening and waterproof wraps).

- You'll need a supply of cotton wool and a bowl of warm water or baby lotion, or baby wipes.

- Make sure you've a spare set of clothes. In the early weeks you often need to change everything.

To protect your baby against nappy rash

- *Change the nappy as soon as you can when it becomes wet or soiled. You may find your young baby needs changing 10 to 12 times a day, and older children at least 6 to 8 times.*

- *Clean the whole nappy area thoroughly, wiping from front to back. Use a mild baby soap with plain water, or specially formulated baby lotion or gentle baby wipes. If using soap and water, rinse off the soap and pat dry gently.*

- *Lie your baby on a towel and leave the nappy off for as long and as often as you can to let fresh air get to the skin.*

To treat nappy rash

*Follow the steps outlined in **To protect your baby against nappy rash** on page 25 and also:*

- *Apply a nappy rash cream to help healing – ask your health visitor or pharmacist to recommend one.*
- *If the rash does not go away after treatment or there is a persistent bright-red moist rash with white or red pimples which also affects the folds of the skin, this may be due to a thrush infection. In this case, a special anti-fungal cream available from your pharmacist or on prescription from your doctor will be needed.*

Nappy Services

If you use disposable nappies, it is worth enquiring whether any shop in your area provides a free delivery service. Or, if you use washable cloth nappies, you may be able to use a nappy laundering service (see page 150).

Getting started

- If your baby is dirty, use the nappy to clean off most of it. Then, using the cotton wool, a mild baby soap and warm water, baby lotion or gentle baby wipes, clean girls from front to back to avoid getting germs into the vagina. Boys should be cleaned around the penis and testicles (balls). Don't pull back the foreskin when cleaning the penis. It's just as important to clean carefully when you're changing a wet nappy.
- You can use a barrier cream, which helps to protect against nappy rash, but it's usually enough just to leave your baby's skin clean and dry. Some babies are sensitive to these creams and some thick creams may clog nappies or affect the ability of disposable nappies to absorb wetness.
- Avoid using baby powder because it can make your baby choke.
- If you're using a washable cloth nappy, fold it, put in a nappy liner if you wish, pin it with a proper nappy pin that won't spring open; or you could use a nappy with velcro fasteners. Then put on or tie on plastic pants.
- If you're using disposable nappies, take care not to get water or cream on the sticky tabs as they won't stick. You can now buy extra tabs to stick disposable nappies (or sticky tape will do).

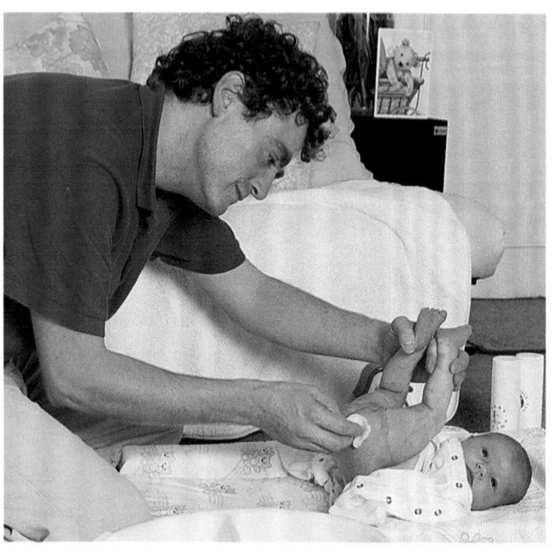

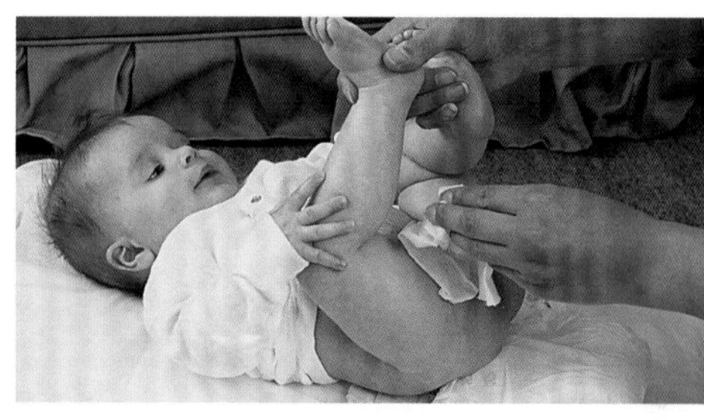

Nappy hygiene

Put as much of the contents as you can down the toilet. If you're using nappies with disposable liners, the liner can be flushed away, but don't ever flush a nappy down the toilet because you'll block it.

Disposable nappies can be rolled up and resealed with the tabs. Put them in a plastic bag kept only for nappies, then tie it up and place it in an outside bin.

Washable cloth nappies. These are easily laundered in a normal 60°C wash. There may be a nappy laundering service near where you live who deliver a pile of freshly laundered nappies to your home and take away the soiled ones to be washed every week. They supply everything you need: wraps, liners and storage bin. For more information see page.150.

Remember to wash your hands after changing a nappy and before doing anything else in order to avoid infection. It's worth remembering that the polio virus is passed in a baby's stools for a month after each polio immunisation. Tell your childminder or babysitter, or anyone else who is likely to change nappies during this time, to be extra careful about washing their hands after changing the nappy and disposing of its contents as there is a very small risk of the virus causing polio in an unimmunised person. They may wish to have a polio booster themselves.

Washing and Bathing

Washing

Wash your baby's face, neck, hands and bottom carefully every day. This is often called 'topping and tailing'. Choose a time when your baby is awake and contented and make sure the room is warm. Organise everything you need in advance – a bowl of warm water, a towel, cotton wool, a fresh nappy and, if necessary, clean clothes.

- Hold your baby on your knee, or lie your baby on a changing mat, and take off all your baby's clothes except for a vest and nappy. Then wrap your baby in the towel.
- Dip the cotton wool in the water (not too much) and wipe gently around your baby's eyes from the nose outward, using a fresh piece of cotton wool for each eye.
- Using a fresh piece of cotton wool, clean around your baby's ears, but don't clean inside them.
- Wash the rest of your baby's face, neck and hands in the same way and dry them gently with the towel.
- Now change your baby's nappy as described on page 25.

Bathing

Bathing two or three times a week is quite enough, but you can do it daily if your baby enjoys it. Don't bath your baby straight after a feed or when your baby is hungry or tired. Make sure the room is warm. Have everything you need at hand – a baby bath or washing-up bowl filled with warm water, two towels (in case of accidents!), baby bath liquid (but avoid this if your baby has particularly dry skin) or baby soap, a clean nappy, clean clothes and cotton wool.

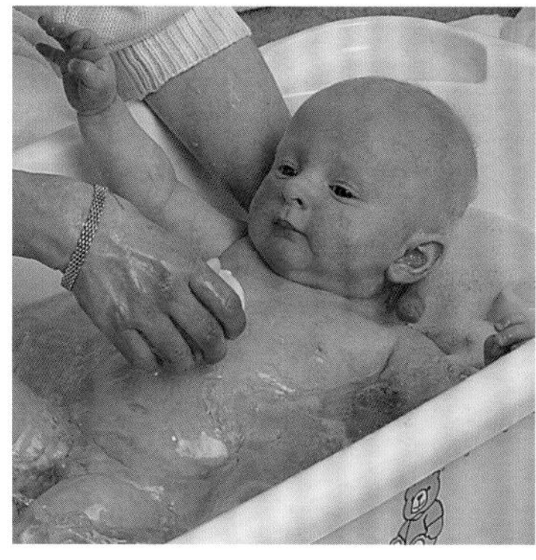

- Make sure the water is warm, *not* hot; check it with your wrist or elbow.
- Hold your baby on your knee and follow the instructions given above for cleaning his or her face.
- Wash your baby's hair with baby soap or liquid, then rinse carefully, supporting your baby over the bowl. Dry gently.
- Now remove your baby's nappy, wiping away any mess. If you're using baby soap, soap your baby all over (avoiding his or her face) while still on your knee, keeping a firm grip while you do so.
- Lower your baby gently into the bowl using one hand to hold your baby's upper arm and support his or her head and shoulders; keep your baby's head clear of the water. Use the other hand to gently swish the water over your baby without splashing. ***Never* leave your baby alone in the bath;** not even for a second.
- Lift your baby out and pat dry, paying special attention to the creases. You may want to use this time to massage oil into your baby's skin. Many babies love this and it may help your baby relax and sleep. Lay your baby on a towel on the floor as both the baby and your hands might be a bit slippery.

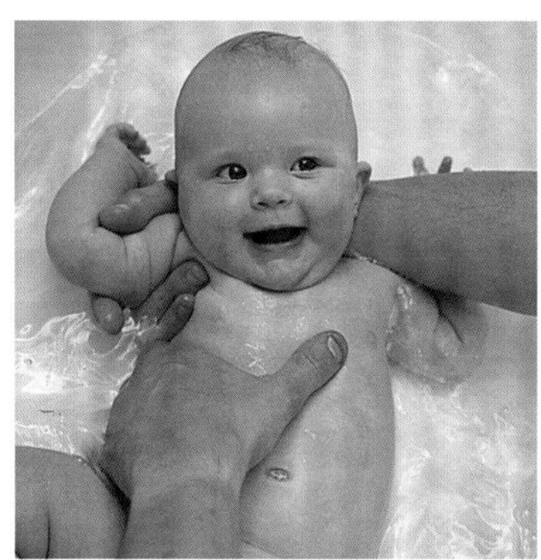

If your baby seems frightened of bathing and cries, you could try bathing together, but make sure the water is not too hot. It's easier if someone else holds your baby while you get in and out.

Taking your baby out

When you carry your baby in either a car or baby seat, try not to hold it with just one hand as this can put a strain on your muscles and joints and lead to backache. Instead hold the seat close to you with both hands.

Your baby is ready to go out as soon as you feel fit enough to go yourself.

Walking

Walking is good for both of you. It may be easiest to take a tiny baby in a sling. If you use a buggy, make sure your baby can lie down with his or her back flat.

In a car

It's illegal for anyone to hold a baby while sitting in the front or back seat of a car. The only safe way for your baby to travel in a car is in a properly secured, backward-facing, baby seat, or in a carrycot (not a Moses basket) with the cover on and secured with special straps.

If you have a car with air bags in the front your baby should **not** travel in the front seat (even facing backwards) because of the danger of suffocation if the bag inflates.

Some areas have special loan schemes to enable you to borrow a suitable baby seat when you and your baby first return from hospital. Ask your midwife or health visitor.

In cold weather

Make sure your baby is wrapped up warm in cold weather because babies chill very easily. **Take the extra clothing off when you get into a warm place** so that your baby doesn't then overheat, even if he or she is asleep.

In hot weather

Children are particularly vulnerable to the effects of the sun, as their skin is thinner and they may not be able to produce enough of the pigment called melanin to protect them from sunburn. Children with fair or red hair, blue eyes and freckles are especially at risk, as the paler the skin, the less melanin is produced, and the more likely the child is to get burnt in the sun. Keep babies under six months out of the sun altogether. Older children should always be protected, either by covering them up or with a high protection sunscreen (sun protection factor 15+). Babies' and children's skin burns easily, even in sun which wouldn't affect your own skin. See page 111 for further tips on protecting your child from the sun.

Twins (or more)

Parents with only one child often think that having two together is much the same sort of experience, but doubled. If you have twins, you'll know differently. Caring for twins, or more, is very different from caring for two of different ages. There's certainly a lot more work, and often you need to find different ways of doing things.

You need as much support as you can get. If you've more than two babies you may be able to get a home help from your local council or in Northern Ireland from your local Health and Social Services Trust. Find out what their policy is. A few hours of help with housework a week could make a big difference. If your council doesn't provide home helps, ask your health visitor for any suggestions. The Multiple Births Foundation also offers professional support and a range of direct services to families of twins and other multiple births (the address is on page 151).

You may get a lot of help from family and friends, but it also helps to be in contact with other parents of twins. The Twins and Multiple Births Association (TAMBA) offers a lot of helpful information, including information about local Twins Clubs. Through these clubs you can meet other parents whose experiences are like yours, and get support and practical advice. Often you can get secondhand equipment too, such as twin prams and buggies.

2 How your child will grow

Your baby may walk at 11 months. Your neighbour's baby may still be crawling at 16 months. Both are quite normal. One child may be talking in sentences at two years old, another may have just started to put two words together. Both are normal. Each child is different because each is an individual. This chapter looks at the way children grow.

How children develop

'When he does something new that he's never done before, that's magic. It's like no other baby in the world has ever done it.'

(A FATHER)

'My mum said, "Isn't she walking yet?" And as it happened, the little boy next door who's about the same age was up and walking and Annie was just sitting there not doing a thing. My mum said I was walking at that age. She kept going on about it.'

'I want to know that she's all right and, you know, keeping up.'

(A FATHER)

Children aren't just born different, they also have different lives and they'll learn different things. A child who plays a lot with toys will be learning to use his or her hands and eyes together. A child who goes out to the park every day will soon learn the names of ducks and trees. A child who is often talked to will learn more words. A child who's given love and praise for learning new things will want to learn more.

Some children have difficulty learning, perhaps because of physical problems with, for example, hearing or seeing. You may already know that your child's development is likely to be slower than normal or you may be worried about your child's progress. Your child may be offered regular development reviews (see page 36) but you don't have to wait for a check-up. If you're concerned, talk to your health visitor or GP. If something's holding your child back, the sooner you find out, the sooner you can do something to help. For more on this see page 40. For more about play and learning see pages 41–7.

A guide to development

This guide gives an idea of the age range within which most children gain certain skills. The ages given are averages. Lots of perfectly normal children gain one skill earlier, another later than average. You can tick off each thing as your child achieves a new skill and keep it as a record for development reviews *(see page 36)*

YEARS: 2, 3, 4, 5
MONTHS: 1, 2, 3, 4, 5, 6, 7, 8, 9, 10, 11, 12, 13, 14, 15, 16, 17, 18, 24, 36, 48, 60

Movement

- Lift their heads, while lying on their fronts.
- Sit without support. If your baby is not sitting unsupported by nine months, talk to your health visitor or GP.
- Start trying to crawl. Some babies crawl backwards before they crawl forwards. Some learn to walk without ever crawling. Others are bottom shufflers.
- Pull themselves upright and stand, holding on to the furniture.
- Walk alone. If your child is not walking by 18 months, talk to your health visitor or GP.
- Learn to kick or throw a ball. Throwing sometimes takes longer than kicking.

Handling things

- Reach out for objects.
- Can hold an object and will lift it up to suck it. At first, babies can hold objects, but are unable to let go.
- Learn to pass things from hand to hand.
- Learn to let go of things, for example, to drop something or give it to you.
- Feed themselves 'finger foods'.
- Begin to feed themselves very messily, with a spoon and to take off easily removed clothes (like loose, short socks).
- Begin to build with bricks. Large bricks are easiest to start with.
- Enjoy scribbling with a crayon.
- Can draw what you see is a person (with a face and maybe arms and legs). Like much else, this depends a lot on how much practice and encouragement they get.
- Can use a knife and fork.

Hearing and talking

- Startled by sudden, loud noises.
- By 4 months: Make cooing noises and enjoy making more and more different sounds.
- By 6 months: Make repetitive noises and enjoy making more and more different sounds.
- By 7 months: Turn to your voice across the room, or to very quiet noises on either side if not distracted by something else.
- By 12 months: Respond to their own name, say something like 'mama' and 'dada' to parents.
- By 18 months: Can say between 6 and 20 recognisable words, but understand many more. They also start to use language in play, for example, when feeding a teddy or doll, or talking on a toy telephone.
- By 2 years: Can put at least two words together and can point to parts of their body.
- By 3–3½ years: Can talk well in sentences, chant rhymes and songs, and talk clearly enough to be understood by strangers. A few 3-year-olds may be difficult to understand. It's normal for a 2-year-old to pronounce words incorrectly. If your 3-year-old is hard to understand mention this to your health visitor.

Seeing

- In the first few weeks: especially like looking at faces. Babies will focus on a face close in front of them and follow it.
- By 2 weeks: Begin to recognise their parents.
- By 4–6 weeks: May start to smile.
- By 6 weeks: Can follow a brightly coloured moving toy held about 20 cm (8 in) away.
- By 6 months: Can see across a room.

Feet – and first shoes

Babies' and small children's feet grow very fast and it's important that the bones grow straight.

- The bones in a baby's toes are soft at birth. If they're cramped by tight bootees, socks, stretch suits or pram shoes, the toes can't straighten out and grow properly. So keep your baby's feet as free as possible. Make sure bootees and socks leave room for the toes, both in length and width. If the feet of a stretch suit become too small, cut them off and use socks instead.

- Don't put your child into proper shoes until he or she can walk alone, and keep them only for walking outside at first.

- When you buy shoes, always have your child's feet measured by a qualified fitter. Shoes should be about 1 cm (a bit less than ½ in) beyond the longest toe and wide enough for all the toes to lie flat.

- Shoes with a lace, buckle or velcro fastening hold the heel in place and stop the foot slipping forward and damaging the toes. If the heel of a shoe slips off when your child stands on tiptoe, it doesn't fit.

- Buy footwear made of natural materials, i.e. leather, cotton or canvas, as these materials 'breathe'. Plastic shoes make feet perspire and may cause fungal infections and abrasions.

- Have your child's feet measured for each new pair of shoes. Children under four years old should have their feet measured every 6–8 weeks. Those over four should have their feet measured every 10–12 weeks.

- Check that socks are the right size and discard any outgrown or misshapen socks. Cotton ones are best.

- Don't keep shoes for 'best' as your child may outgrow these without having proper wear.

Common foot problems

When children first start walking, it is normal for them to walk with their feet apart and to 'waddle'. It is also common for young children to appear to be 'bow-legged', 'knock-kneed' or walk with their toes turned in or out. Most minor foot problems in children correct themselves. But if you are worried about your child's feet or how he or she walks in any way, talk to your doctor or health visitor. If necessary, your child can be referred to a chiropodist, orthopaedic surgeon or paediatric physiotherapist.

- ***Bow legs*** *– a small gap between the knees and ankles when the child is standing up is normally seen until the child is two. If the gap is pronounced or it does not correct itself, check with your doctor or health visitor. Rarely, this could be a sign of rickets – a bone deformity.*

- ***Knock knees*** *– this is when a child stands with his or her knees together and the ankles are at least 2.5 cm (1 in) apart. Between the ages of two and four, a gap of 6–7 cm (2–2¾ in) is considered normal. Knock knees usually improve and correct themselves by the age of six.*

- ***In-toeing*** *(pigeon-toed) – here the child's feet turn in. The condition usually corrects itself by the age of eight or nine and treatment is not usually needed.*

- ***Out-toeing*** *(feet point outwards) – again this condition usually corrects itself and treatment is not needed in most cases.*

- ***Flat feet*** *– if when your child stands on tiptoe the arch forms normally, no treatment is needed.*

- ***Tiptoe walking*** *– if your child walks on tiptoe, talk to your doctor or health visitor.*

- Walk out of any shop that asks you the size of your child's feet and does not measure them.
- Never rely on the question 'do they feel comfortable?' Because children's bones are soft, distortion and cramping can be present without your child feeling it.
- Never buy secondhand shoes or hand shoes down as these take on the shape of the previous owner and will rub and not support vital areas.
- After washing your child's feet, dry well between the toes, and cut toenails straight across – they can become ingrown if cut shaped.

Teeth

The time when babies get their first primary teeth (milk teeth) varies. A few are born with a tooth already through. Others have no teeth at one year old. Most get their first tooth at around six months, usually in front and at the bottom. Most have all their primary teeth by about two and a half. The first permanent 'second' teeth come through at the back at around the age of six.

There are 20 primary teeth in all, 10 at the top and 10 at the bottom.

Teething

Some teeth come through with no pain or trouble at all. At other times you may notice that the gum is sore and red where the tooth is coming, or that one cheek is flushed. Your baby may dribble, gnaw and chew a lot, or just be fretful, but it's often

hard to tell whether this is really due to teething.

It can help to give your baby something hard to chew on, such as a teething ring, or a crust of bread or breadstick, or a peeled carrot **(stay nearby in case of choking)**. Avoid rusks because almost all contain some sugar. Constant chewing and sucking on sugary things can cause tooth decay even if your baby has only one or two teeth.

For babies over four months old, you can try sugar-free teething gel rubbed on the gum. You can get this from the pharmacist. For younger babies you should talk to your GP or health visitor. You may also want to give sugar-free baby paracetamol. Follow the instructions on the bottle for your child's age, or check with your pharmacist, GP or health visitor.

People put all sorts of things down to teething – rashes, crying, bad temper, runny noses, extra dirty nappies – but be careful not to explain away what might be the signs of illness by saying it's 'just teething'.

Fluoride

Fluoride is a natural element found in our diet, mostly in fish and tea, which can help prevent tooth decay. It is also present in many water supplies, but usually at a level too low to be beneficial. In the UK, Birmingham and Newcastle have fluoride added to the water supply at the ideal level, as do most cities in the USA.

In areas with little or no fluoride in the water, some children may benefit by taking fluoride drops (for babies) or tablets as dietary supplements. They should ***not*** *be used in areas with fluoride naturally present or artificially added to the water, as an excessive fluoride intake is undesirable. Therefore, advice from your dentist is essential before giving them. Fluoride in toothpaste is very effective – for babies use a tiny smear and for children only use a small pea-sized amount on the brush.*

Looking for sugars on the label

- *The following are sugars that can cause dental decay – sucrose, glucose, dextrose, maltose, fructose, hydrolysed starch.*
- *Invert sugar or syrup, honey, raw sugar, brown sugar, cane sugar, muscavado and concentrated fruit juices all contain sugars.*
- *Fruit juices too contain sugars, which can cause decay. Always dilute these.*
- *Maltodextrin is not a sugar, but may cause decay.*

Caring for your child's teeth

- Keep down the number of times each day that your child eats or drinks something sugary.
- Brush your child's teeth thoroughly twice each day, using a small pea-sized amount of fluoride toothpaste or a tiny smear for babies; help an older child. Let your child see you brushing your teeth too.

Cutting down on sugar
Sugar causes tooth decay. It's not just the amount of sugar in sweet food and drinks that matters but, perhaps more importantly, how often there are sugary things in the mouth. This is why sweet drinks in a bottle and lollipops are so bad. The teeth are bathed in sugar for quite a long time.

- **From the time you start your baby on foods and drinks other than milk, avoid giving sweet things.** Try to encourage savoury tastes. Watch for the sugar in baby foods in tins and packets (even the savoury varieties), rusks and in baby drinks, especially fizzy drinks, squash and syrups.
- **If you give your child sweet foods and fruit juice try to limit these to mealtimes** to avoid tooth decay. Well-diluted fruit juice containing vitamin C and given in a cup with a meal can also help iron to be absorbed. Between meals, it is better to give milk or water as a drink.
- **Try to find treats other than biscuits or sweets,** and ask relatives and friends to do the same. Use things like stickers, badges, hair slides, crayons, small books, notebooks and colouring books, soap and bubble baths. These may be more expensive than one small sweet, but they all last longer.
- **If children are given sweets or chocolate, it's less harmful for their teeth if they eat them all at once and after a meal** than if they eat, say, a little every hour or so.
- Children who eat sweets every day have nearly double the decay compared with children who eat sweets less often.
- **Be aware of the amount of sugar the whole family's eating.** Look for ways of cutting down. See page 81 for some suggestions.
- **Avoid giving baby juices or sugar-sweetened drinks at bedtime** or in a bottle, and keep drinking times short. Only milk or water should be given as a drink during the night (unless your baby is still young enough to need a night feed).
- **Ask your pharmacist and doctor for sugar-free medicine for your child.**
- **Try to avoid giving drinks containing artificial sweeteners, such as saccharin or aspartame. If you do, dilute with at least 10 parts water to 1 part concentrate.**

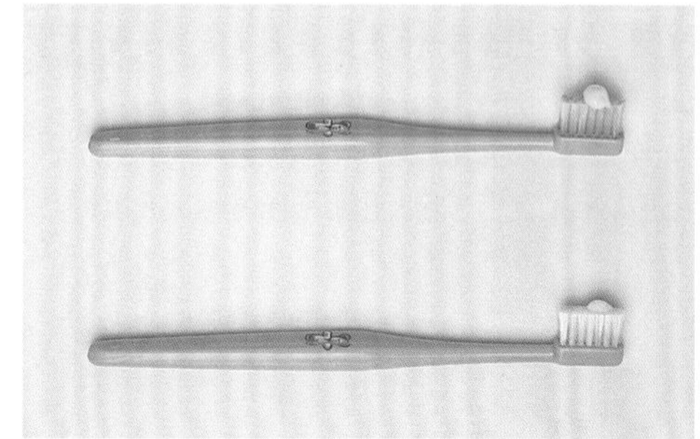

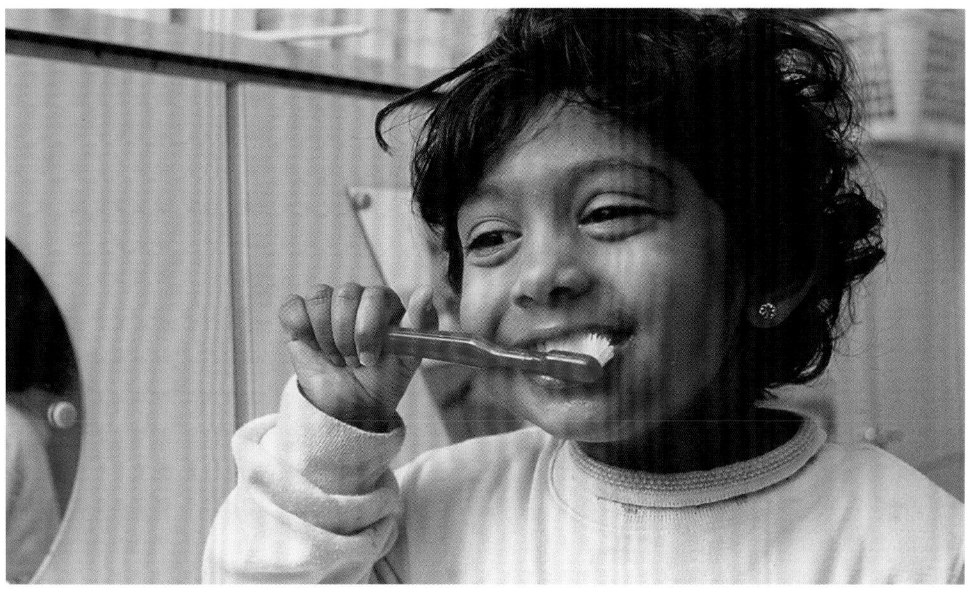

Brushing your child's teeth

- **Start early, as soon as your baby's teeth start to come through.** Buy a baby toothbrush and use it with a tiny smear of fluoride toothpaste. Check with your dentist whether baby toothpaste has enough fluoride for your baby's needs. Don't worry if you don't manage to brush much at first. The important thing at the start is to get teeth brushing accepted as part of the everyday routine. That's why it's important you do it too.

- **Gradually start to brush your child's teeth more thoroughly, brushing all the surfaces of the teeth.** Do it twice a day - just before bed, and whatever other time in the day fits in best. Not all children like having their teeth brushed, so you may have to work at it a bit. Try not to let it become a battle. If it becomes difficult, try games, or try brushing your own teeth at the same time and then helping your child to 'finish off'.

- **Go on helping your child to brush until you're sure he or she is brushing well enough – at least until the age of seven.**

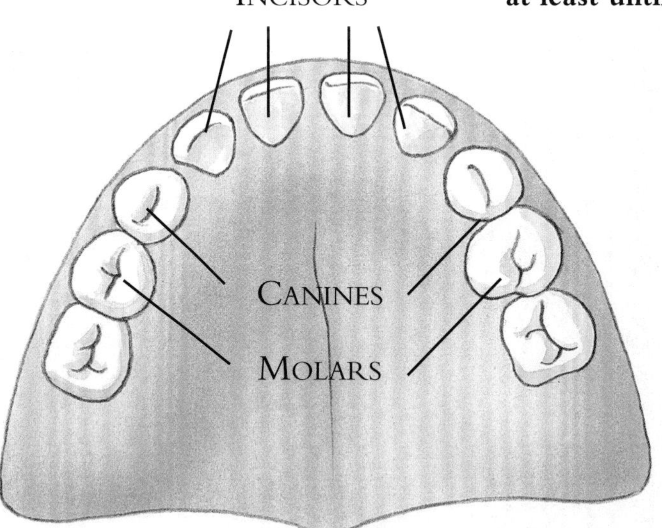

How to brush

The best way to brush a baby's teeth is to sit him or her on your knee with the head resting against your chest. Stand behind an older child and tilt his or her head upwards. Brush the teeth in small circles covering all the surfaces and let your child spit the toothpaste out afterwards. Rinsing with water has been found to reduce the benefit of fluoride. You can also clean your baby's teeth by wrapping a piece of damp gauze with a tiny amount of fluoride toothpaste on it over your finger.

Taking your child to the dentist

You can take your child to be registered with a dentist under the NHS as soon as your child has been born – even before any teeth come through. Your dentist can give advice on your child's oral health. NHS dental treatment for children is free.

Take your child with you when you go to the dentist, so that going to the dentist becomes a normal event. If you need to find a dentist, you can ask at your local clinic or contact your local health authority, or in Northern Ireland your Health and Social Services Trust – the address and telephone number will be in the phone book.

Keeping an eye on your baby's growth and development

Parent-held records

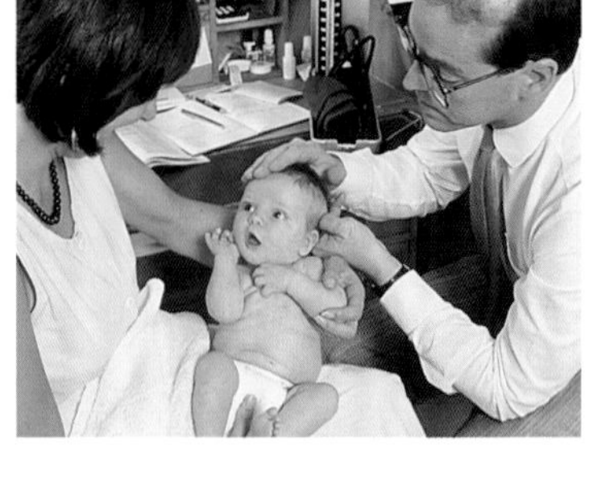

After your baby's birth you'll usually be given a personal child health record or parent-held record for your baby. This is a way of keeping track of your child's progress. It makes sure that, wherever you are and whatever happens to your child, you'll have a copy of the records for your own information and for health professionals when and where you may need it.

To start with you'll want to use the records mainly to record your child's height and weight. Then you can add information about immunisations (see pages 102–7), childhood illness and accidents.

You may find that when your child is reviewed, the doctor or health visitor will not formally 'test' your child but will ask you questions about what he or she can or can't do. It is therefore helpful if you record these details in your child's personal child health record and complete the questionnaires in the book before your child has a review. Don't forget to take the book with you when you take your child for a review!

Development reviews

Your GP and health visitor will offer you regular development reviews. The review gives you, the parents, an opportunity to say what you've noticed about your child. You can also discuss anything at all that may concern you about your child's health and general behaviour. Not just the big things, but the kinds of worries and niggles that every parent has but feels unsure about taking to a doctor or nurse.

The review programme

Development reviews will usually be carried out by your health visitor, a doctor, or both. They may be carried out at a regular clinic session or in your own home. The aim is to spot any problems as early as possible so that, if necessary, some action can be taken. So, even if you think your child is doing fine, it's worth having the review. Your health visitor will tell you when it's due, but, if you're concerned about something at any other time, don't wait. Ask to see someone.

You can usually expect to be invited to a development review when your child is:

- 6–8 weeks old;
- 6–9 months old;
- 18–24 months old;
- 3–3½ years old;
- 4½–5½ years old (before or just after your child starts school).

In some parts of the country, the age that your child is reviewed may vary slightly from those given above, especially after the age of three.

Height and weight

Your child's height and weight are a very useful guide to general progress and development. You can have your baby regularly weighed at your child health clinic or doctor's baby clinic. Older children should be weighed and measured as part of other health checks. Babies vary in how fast they put on weight, but usually weight gain is quickest in the first six to nine months, and then it slows down.

- Most babies double their birthweight by four to five months.
- Most babies treble their birthweight by one year.

Some weeks your baby will gain weight; some weeks he or she will not gain weight. This doesn't matter. What's looked for is a general weight gain over a period of weeks.

Understanding your child's height and weight chart

Your child's growth will be recorded on 'centile' charts so that his or her progress can be easily followed. Boys and girls have different charts because boys are on average heavier and taller and their growth pattern is slightly different. This page shows an example of a boy's height, weight and head size centile lines for babies up to one year old; page 38 shows a girl's height and weight centile lines for children from one to five.

Boys | 0 to 1 year

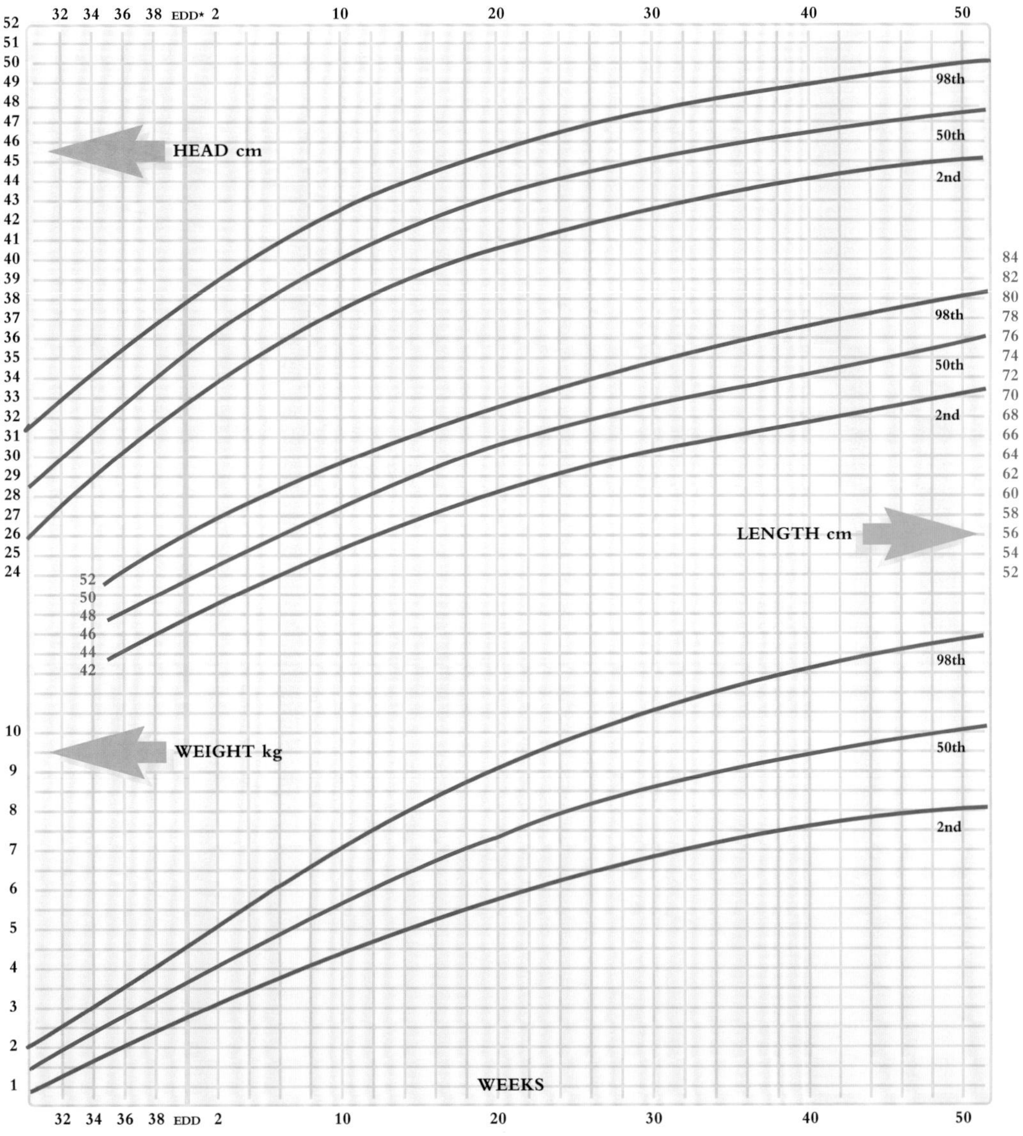

HEAD cm

LENGTH cm

WEIGHT kg

98th

50th

2nd

WEEKS

32 34 36 38 EDD* 2 10 20 30 40 50

*EDD is the expected date of delivery

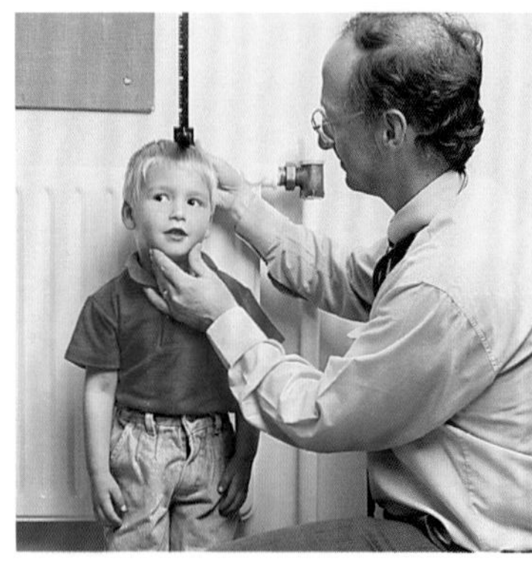

Remember that, even if your child's development is satisfactory at one review, development is a continuous process. It is therefore important that you continue to observe your child's development, attend all the reviews and talk to your health visitor or GP if you have any concerns about your child between these reviews.

The centile lines printed on the charts show roughly the kind of growth expected in weight and in length. On each of the charts the middle line (shown as a red line in this book) represents the national average for white British babies. For example, if 100 babies are weighed and measured, 50 will weigh and measure more than the amount indicated by the red line, and 50 will weigh and measure less.

Most babies' and children's weight and height will fall between the two centile lines coloured blue in this book. Only four out of every 100 babies and children will have weights and heights that fall outside these centiles.

As these data are based on the average heights and weights of white children, it's worth bearing in mind that if you're of Asian origin, your baby will on average be lighter and shorter. If you're of African-Caribbean origin your baby will on average be heavier and longer.

Your child's height and weight (and head size if under a year) will be plotted as a curved line on one of these charts. This makes it easy to see how your child is developing.

Whatever weight and length your baby is at birth, he or she should have a fairly steady growth, resulting in a line curving in roughly the same way, and usually inside, the centile lines on the chart. **During the first two years of life it is quite usual for a baby's line to cross the centiles on the chart from time to time, but if at any time your baby's weight line suddenly goes up or drops (and it may drop, for example, because of illness), talk to your health visitor or GP about it.**

Girls | 1 to 5 years

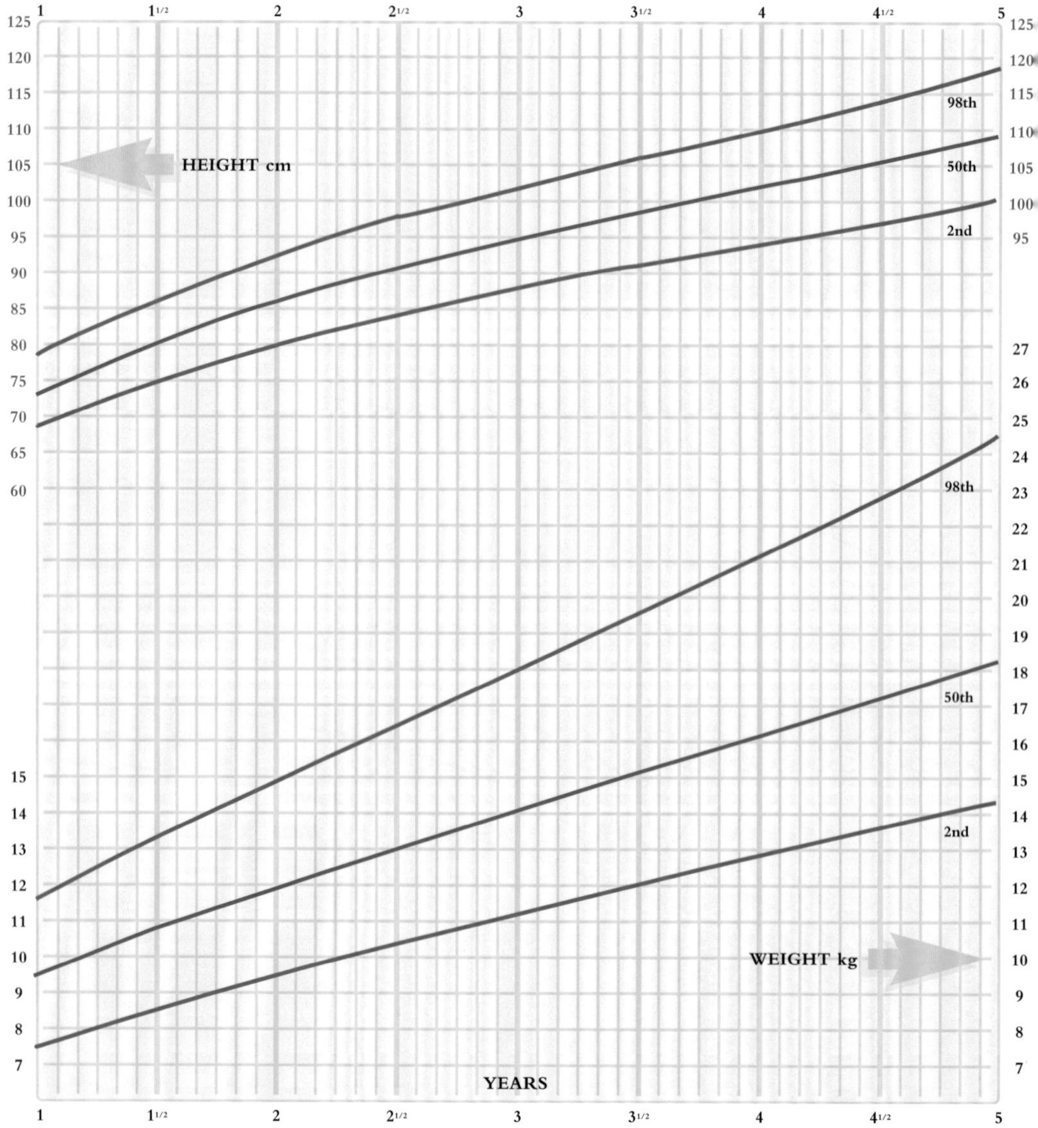

HEIGHT cm

98th

50th

2nd

WEIGHT kg

YEARS

1 1½ 2 2½ 3 3½ 4 4½ 5

If you don't speak English

If your first language is not English, or your child's first language is not English, you can have help from an interpreter, linkworker or health advocate who can speak your language. Ask your health visitor about this help if you need it.

You should also talk to your health visitor or GP if, after the age of two, your baby's height curve does not follow a centile line or starts to veer upwards or downwards from it.

General development

Some health visitors may ask your child to do little tasks, such as building with blocks or identifying pictures. Others may simply watch your child playing or perhaps drawing, and get an idea from this observation, and your comments, of how your child is doing. If you look at the development chart on page 31, you'll have an idea of the kind of physical and verbal skills they're looking for.

If your child seems slow in one particular area of development, you'll have the opportunity to discuss what the reason may be, and to see whether there's anything useful that needs to be done to speed things up.

Eyesight

A baby should be able to see from birth. Eyesight develops gradually over the next six months.

By the first review, you'll have noticed whether or not your baby can follow a colourful object held about 20 cm (8 in) away with his or her eyes. If this isn't happening you should mention it.

At birth a baby's eyes may roll away from each other occasionally. If a baby is squinting all, or much, of the time, tell your health visitor and your GP. If your baby is squinting, you'll need to be referred to an orthoptist or ophthalmologist who specialises in understanding children's eyes.

It is important that any vision problems are identified as soon as possible, particularly if your child has any other disability (cerebral palsy or Down's syndrome) as visual impairment can cause serious educational and social difficulties. Children themselves may not know that their vision is impaired. Eye examinations are available free of charge to all children under 16 years of age, and they do not have to be able to read to have one.

Hearing and talking

Hearing and talking are linked. If your child can't hear properly, he or she will have great difficulty learning to talk and may need to be taught other ways of communicating. So the sooner hearing problems are discovered the greater the chance that something can be done.

It isn't only hearing that is important though. Babies don't learn to talk unless they're talked to, even if, at first, the conversation is limited to making noises at each other. By learning to take it in turns to make babbling noises, your baby is learning what a conversation feels like. Most parents quite naturally join in babbling sessions with their babies and so they're very often the first people to notice if there's a problem.

If you're ever worried about your child's language development, talk to your GP or health visitor. Your child may be helped by referral to a speech and language therapist.

Your baby's hearing may be tested at birth in the hospital. No baby is 'too young' for a hearing assessment.

You should expect a hearing assessment at six to nine months. If there's no apparent problem, but you're still worried, ask for another appointment. If a problem is found, your baby will need to have a follow-up assessment because hearing loss may be temporary, being due to a cold or a passing infection.

If your child doesn't seem to hear properly at the second appointment, or you are still worried, ask for a referral to a specialist.

Tips for helping your child learn to talk

- *Start talking to your child right from birth – say what you are doing about the house, e.g. when unpacking shopping.*
- *Start looking at books with your baby from an early age.*
- *Point things out when going for a walk, e.g. 'There's a bus, the bus is red.'*
- *Have fun singing nursery rhymes and songs, especially those with actions.*
- *Encourage your child to listen to different sounds.*
- *Gain your child's attention when you want to talk together.*
- *Increase vocabulary by giving choices, e.g. 'Do you want an apple or a banana?'*
- *Give your child opportunities to talk.*
- *Don't have the television on as a background noise.*
- *If your child says something incorrectly, say it back the right way. Do not make your child repeat it.*

Bilingual children

Many children grow up in a family in which more than one language is spoken. It can give children a good head start and they don't usually have problems. The important thing is to talk to your child in whatever language feels comfortable to you. This may mean one parent using one language and the other using another. Children usually adapt to this very well.

Children with special needs

Some questions you may like to ask

You may find it helpful to write these down.

- *Is there a name for my child's problem? If so, what is it?*
- *Are more tests needed to get a clear diagnosis or confirm what's been found out?*
- *Is it likely to get better or likely to get worse, or will it stay roughly the same?*
- *Where is the best place to go for medical help?*
- *Where is the best place to go for practical help?*
- *How can I get in touch with other parents who have children with a similar problem?*
- *How can I find out how best to help my child?*

Coping with your feelings

At whatever stage in your child's life you receive a diagnosis of disability or illness, you'll have difficult feelings to cope with and some hard decisions and adjustments to make. Your GP, health visitor, social worker or counsellors of various kinds may all be able to help. So may other parents who've been through similar experiences. But, even with help, all parents say it takes time. Throughout that time, and afterwards, it's right to think about your own life and needs as well as your child's.

For some families, everything is not 'all right'. Sometimes what begins as a worry does turn out to be a more serious problem or disability.

If this happens to you, your first need will be for information about the problem and what it's likely to mean for your child and for you. You'll have a lot of questions (see box). Put them all to your GP, your health visitor and specialists to whom you are referred. You may find it easier to make a list.

Be determined and persist if you need to. Not all health professionals talk easily or well to parents. And you yourself may find it's difficult to hear and take in all that's said to you first, or even second, time round. Rather than live with unanswered questions, go back and ask again for the information or opinion you feel you need. Or you could take along a tape recorder. If, in the end, the honest answer is 'I don't know' or 'We're not sure', that's better than no answer at all.

Help for children with special needs

Child development centres
In some areas, teams of professionals (doctors, therapists, health visitors, social workers), usually working from what is known as a child development centre, are available to help support children with special needs and their families. You can be referred to such a team through your GP or health visitor.

Voluntary organisations
You can also get information, advice and support from organisations dealing with particular disabilities, illnesses and other problems. Through them, you can often contact other parents in situations like your own. See pages 146–51 for the names and addresses of some organisations that might be able to help.

Specialist help
There are many services available to help children who have special needs to learn and develop, for example, physiotherapy, speech and language therapy, occupational therapy, home learning schemes, playgroups, opportunity groups, nurseries and nursery schools and classes. To find out what's available in your area, ask your health visitor, GP, social services department or the educational adviser for special needs at your local education department. See pages 131–3 for more information about the services, including information about regional variations.

Special needs assessment
Local education authorities who think a child over two years old may have special educational needs *must* make an assessment of his or her needs. For a child under two an assessment must be made if a parent *asks* for it. This assessment is a way of getting advice about your child's educational needs. You can take part in the assessment yourself. The Advisory Centre for Education (see page 146) offers advice on education and produces a handbook on the subject.

Benefits advice
If you've a child with disabilities you may be able to get a Disability Living Allowance, which you can claim on form DLA1. To get this form ring the Benefit Enquiry line for people with disabilities: Freephone 0800 882200 (in Northern Ireland 0800 220674).

3 Learning and playing

What we call playing is really the way children learn. With toys and their imaginations they practise all the skills they'll need as they grow up. The more they play, the more they learn, and the best thing about it is that they love it.

Playing with you

Young children find it hard to play alone. They need attention from someone who can play with them. Gradually they'll learn to entertain themselves for some of the time, but first they need to learn how to do that.

In the meantime, you can't spend all your time playing. You've other things to do and other people to attend to. Fortunately, children learn from everything that's going on around them, and everything they do. When you're washing up, your toddler can stand next to you on a chair and wash the saucepan lids; when you cook, make sure your baby can see and talk to you as you work.

The times when they're not learning much are the times when they're bored. That's as true for babies as of older children. So what really matters?

- Find a lot of different things for your child to look at, think about and do (see **Ideas for play** on pages 43–4).
- Make what you're doing fun and interesting for your child, so you can get it done.
- Make some time to give all your attention to what your child wants to do.

Toy safety

- *It is best to buy toys that carry the British Standard kitemark or the Lion mark, or CE mark, as these conform to safety standards.*
- *Take care if you buy toys from car boot sales or market stalls or secondhand toys as these may not conform to safety standards and could be dangerous.*
- *Take safety measures such as 'Not suitable for a child under 36 months' seriously (0–3 sign). This sign warns that a toy is unsuitable for a child under three because of small parts.*

- *Check that the toy has no sharp edges that could hurt your child, or small parts that your child could put in his or her mouth and choke on.*

'I'd play with them all day if I could. I tell you, it's much more fun than doing the housework.'

'There are things I've got to do. She's forever asking me to play and I'm forever saying "In a minute, in a minute."'

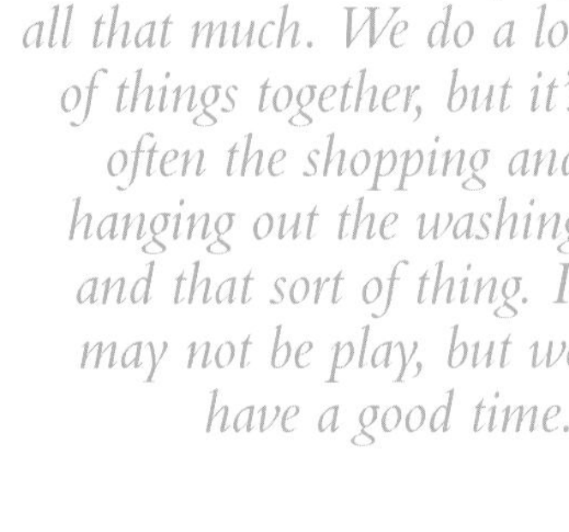

'I don't know that we play all that much. We do a lot of things together, but it's often the shopping and hanging out the washing and that sort of thing. It may not be play, but we have a good time.'

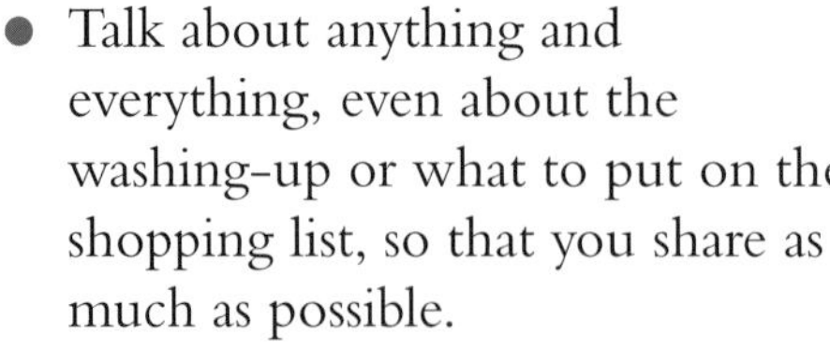

- Talk about anything and everything, even about the washing-up or what to put on the shopping list, so that you share as much as possible.
- Find a place and time when your child can learn how to use his or her body by running, jumping and climbing. This is especially important if you don't have much room at home.
- Find other people who can spend time with your child at those times when you really do need to attend to something else.

Toys for children with special needs

Toys for children with special needs should match their mental age and ability. They should be brightly coloured and offer sound and action. If a toy made for a younger child is used by an older child, the strength of the toy should be taken into account.

Children who have a visual impairment will need toys with different textures to explore with their hands and mouth. A child who has a hearing impairment will need toys to stimulate language.

Making time

Some things do have to happen at certain times, and your child does slowly have to learn about that. But when you're with your child try not to work to a strict timetable. Your child is unlikely to fit in with it and then you'll both get frustrated. A lot of things can be pushed around to suit the mood of you and your child. There's no rule that says the washing-up has to be done before you go to the playground, especially if the sun's shining and your child's bursting with energy.

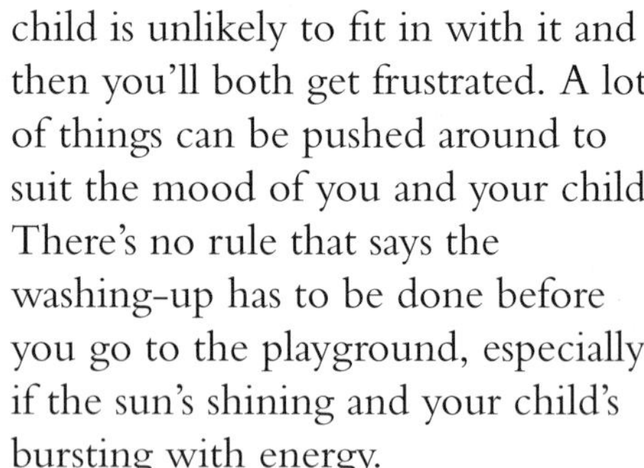

Keep your child fit

Children want to use their bodies to crawl, walk, run, jump and climb. The more opportunity you can give them, the happier they'll be, and you'll probably find that they sleep better and are more cheerful and easy going when they've had the opportunity to run off some energy. At the same time you'll be helping their muscle development and general fitness, and if they start to see outdoor activities and sports as a part of their lives, you'll be laying down the habits that will keep them fitter as adults. Make time for your children to exercise.

- Allow your baby to lie and kick his or her legs.
- Make your floor a safe place for a crawler to move around.
- Make time for your toddler to walk with you rather than using the buggy.
- Take toddlers and young children to the park to try climbing and swinging or just so that they have a safe space to run.
- Find out what's on for parents and babies at the local leisure centre.
- Take your baby swimming. There is no need to wait until your child has had his or her immunisations.

Ideas for play

Rattles (from 4 months). Use washed-out plastic screw-top bottles with lentils or dried beans inside. Glue the top securely so it won't come off. Some dried beans are poisonous and small objects can be dangerous for young children.

Play dough (from about 18 months). Put 1 cup of water, 1 cup of plain flour, 2 tbsp of cream of tartar, ½ cup of salt, 1 tbsp of cooking oil, and some food colouring or powder paint in a pan. Stir over a medium heat until this makes a dough. Cool. Store in a plastic box in the fridge.

Junk modelling (30 months). Collect all sorts of cardboard boxes, cartons, yoghurt pots, milk bottle tops – anything – and some children's glue, strong enough to glue cardboard, but not to mark clothes. The sort with a brush is easiest to use.

Pretend cooking (from 18 months). Use a bowl and spoons for measuring out and mixing small quantities of 'real' ingredients (flour, lentils, rice, sugar, custard powder) and put out in egg cups or bowls. Use water to mix.

Television gives your child a lot of entertainment, and you a bit of peace. It gives you more peace if it's not on all the time. Make sure you know what your child's watching. And watch with your child when you can so you can talk about what you see.

Playing with water is fun for all ages – in the bath, sink, a plastic bowl, paddling pool. Use plastic bottles for pouring and squirting, plastic tubing, sponge, colander, straws, funnel, spoons - anything unbreakable. Remember, **never** leave a young child alone with water.

Dressing up (from 18 months). Collect old hats, bags, gloves, scarves, nighties, lengths of material, tea towels, old curtains. Ask friends and relatives, or try jumble sales. Take care that clothes for young children do not contain loose cords, strings or ribbons that could wrap around your child's neck and cause strangulation or cause a fall. Paper plates or cut-up cereal packets make good masks – cut slits for the eyes and tie on with string.

Reading. Even quite small babies like looking at picture books. Local libraries usually have a good range of children's books and sometimes run story sessions for young children.

Drawing and painting (from 18 months). Use crayons, felt tips, powder paint. Add washing-up liquid and water to powder paint for a thicker paint. You can use old envelopes slit open and the inside of cereal packets for paper.

Walking. Encourage your child to walk with you (using reins for safety) as soon as he or she is able. It may be slower, but children need exercise, and so do you!

How to make sure your child learns what you want him or her to learn

When children play they're learning what they want. Often these will also be the things you want them to learn, but for some things they may need extra encouragement, like using the potty (see page 52), washing or dressing themselves, learning what not to touch and where it's not safe to run. It's worth thinking about how you do it.

- **Wait until you think your child is ready.** Forcing something too soon usually ends in failure. You get cross and upset, your child gets cross and upset, and the whole thing becomes impossible. If it doesn't work out, leave it for a few weeks and try again.
- **Try not to make it seem too important.** Your child may learn to eat with a spoon because it's fun but still want to be fed when he or she is tired, or may enjoy the first few times on the potty because you're so pleased and then get bored with the idea. In time he or she will see that it is worthwhile learning to be more grown-up and independent.
- **Keep it safe.** If your child is under three years old, he or she can't really understand why not to touch your stereo or pull leaves off your pot plants, so keep things you don't want touched well out of the way and you'll both be less frustrated. Time enough to learn about not touching when your child can understand why.
- **Be encouraging.** Your happiness is your child's best reward for good behaviour. If you give your child a big smile, a cuddle or praise when he or she does something right, your child is much more likely to try doing it again. Giving your child attention and praise for doing something right works much better than telling him or her off for doing something wrong.
- **Don't ask for perfection** or for instant success. It's safest to expect everything to take much longer than you'd hoped.
- **Set an example.** Whatever it may look like, your child does want to be like you and do what you do. So seeing you wash in the bath, brush your teeth or use the toilet does help.
- **Avoid fuss and confrontation.** Once something gets blown up, it can take longer and be much more difficult for everybody to calm down.
- **Be firm.** Children need you to decide some things for them, and need you to stick to your decisions. They need some firm guidelines. So try not to waver. You might start something like potty training, decide your child isn't ready, and give up for a while. That's fine. But a child who is in nappies one day, out the next and back in them the next is bound to get confused.
- **Be consistent.** For the same reason, it's important that everybody involved in looking after your child is teaching more or less the same things in more or less the same way. If you and your partner, or you and your

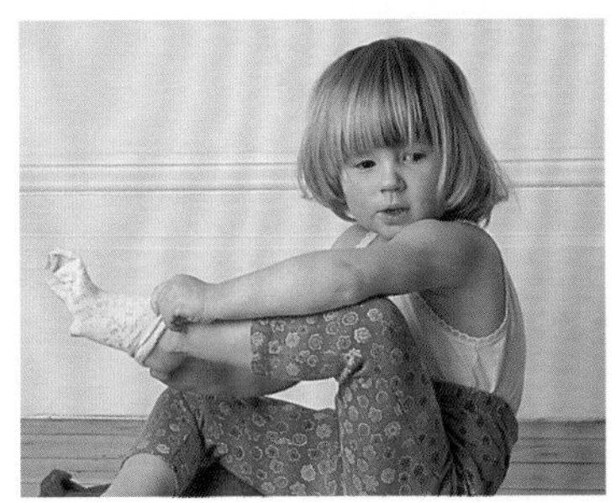

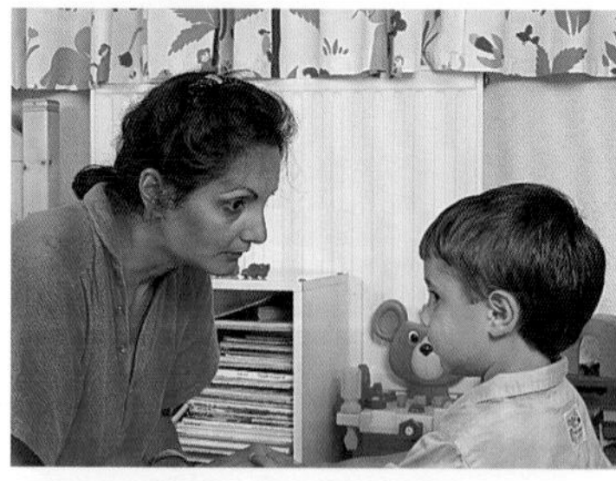

'At playgroup he could run about and make a mess. At home there was just no room. He was happier and I was happier.'

'I would worry about mine being looked after by someone else in case they didn't want to know me.'

childminder, do things very differently, your child won't learn so easily and may well play you off against each other.

- **Do what's right for your child, for you and for the way you live.** It doesn't matter what the child next door can or can't do. Don't compete and don't ask your child to compete.

No parent is perfect, and some children seem to find these lessons particularly difficult to learn. See pages 58–64 for dealing with difficult behaviour.

Making friends

Learning how to make friends is one of the most important things your child will do. If your child learns early how to get on well with others, he or she will get off to a better start at school, and a happy child learns better than a child who's anxious and afraid of others.

It's never too soon to start, especially if yours is an only child. Even babies and small children like other children's company, although at first they play alongside each other rather than with each other. Ask your health visitor if there's a new parents group meeting in your area. Getting together with other parents can be good for you too (see **Loneliness** on page 129).

As your child starts to crawl and walk, you could try a parent and toddler group or a 'one o'clock club'. These can be great for energetic children from 18 months to three years old, and give you a bit of relaxation and company.

Ask other mothers or your health visitor about groups in your area. Or look on the clinic notice board, or in the newsagent's or toy shop windows. Your local library may also have information, and may itself run story sessions for pre-school children.

To begin with, your baby or toddler will want you, or another trusted adult, nearby for safety. By the time your child is three, he or she will be ready to spend time without a parent or childminder to run to.

Playgroups, nursery schools or nursery classes all have a lot to offer – more organised play of different kinds, the chance to be with other children and make friends, probably space to run around in.

Find out what's available in your area well in advance as there may be waiting lists. It may be worth putting your child's name down on several lists.

Playgroups

Playgroups can be found in most areas. They vary in what they offer and how they're run. Some are free, others charge a small fee, though the amount varies. Sometimes you'll be able to leave your child for, say, a couple of hours once or twice a week, so you can begin to get your child used to being away from you. Sometimes you'll be asked, or might want, to stay and help. Playgroups are often run by parents themselves. To find out about local playgroups or pre-schools:

- Ask your local Children's Information Service (CIS).
- Contact the Pre-School Learning Alliance (address on page 146).

Nursery classes and nursery schools

A nursery class is part of an infant school. A nursery school is a separate school. In most areas they only provide sessions of about 2½ hours a day. Since April 2004, all children are entitled to a free part-time nursery place at the start of the school term following their third birthday. To find out what is available ask your local Children's Information Service or your local education department.

During this time your child will follow the Foundation stage of the National Curriculum for 3–5 year-olds. Learning activities are carefully planned with the emphasis on learning through play.

Primary school (reception class)

In Northern Ireland children who have reached the age of four on or before 1 July must commence primary school at the beginning of the September following. Many primary schools have reception classes and groups that admit children who have reached their fourth birthday but are below compulsory school age. However, as the standard of quality across the sector is uneven, one of the objectives of the Pre-School Education Expansion Programme was the replacement of reception places, where possible, with alternative pre-school provision which meets the standard of the programme. A significant number of reception places have now been replaced by new statutory and voluntary/private sector funded places. Each Education and Library Board's Primary Schools Admissions Criteria booklets detail those schools which continue to offer reception provision.

When you can't be there

Choosing childcare while you work

If you're returning to work, you'll need to consider how your baby or child will be looked after when you're not there – not just the need for adults, but also for other children as companions.

Although playgroups and nursery classes rarely keep children for long enough to be useful to a working parent, they can still be used alongside other care from childminders or nannies, so they're worth keeping in mind as you consider your options.

All childminders and daycare providers (with the exception of nannies who work in your home) should be registered with Ofsted. Your local Children's Information Service (CIS) will be able to give you information about available care options.

Childminders

Childminders look after small numbers of children in their own homes. Anybody paid to look after children under eight in this way for more than two hours a day has, by law, to apply to register as a childminder with Ofsted. This doesn't apply to close relatives, but does apply to friends or neighbours. Childminders are registered to care for up to three children under five, including any of their own. Registered childminders are visited by Ofsted inspectors to check that their homes are suitable and that the level of care they provide meets the National Standards for childcare. So, if you go to a childminder you don't know, ask to see the registration certificate.

You should be able to get the names of childminders with vacancies from your local CIS. Other working parents will also be able to tell you about childminders. If you don't already know parents who use childminders, ask your health visitor to put you in touch.

Home Child Carers

Childminders can now apply to be registered as Home Child Carers. This allows them to look after your

Whatever registered childcare provision you choose for your 0–3 year-old the childcare provider will probably be following the principles and practice set out in Birth to three matters. *This is a set of resources for childcare workers guiding them to think about*

- *your child;*
- *your child's needs;*
- *the things your child enjoys doing;*
- *ensuring that your child's time is spent in a happy and productive way.*

In Northern Ireland at present, all funded pre-school settings follow the curriculum set out in the 1997 document Curricular guidance for pre-school education *published by the Council for the Curriculum, Examinations and Assessment (CCEA). As part of its review of the curriculum, CCEA is developing a new* ***foundation stage*** *curriculum for children in their pre-school year and in Years 1 and 2. This proposes a less formal and more play-based approach than the current Key Stage 1 curriculum, to link the early years of primary school with the pre-school year, thus easing the transition from pre-school to primary school.* Curricular guidance for pre-school education *will be revised on the basis of this change.*

'I wanted him to go to a childminder because I felt if I had to work that was a much more natural setting for him to grow up in … I don't know, though; maybe a nursery school would have been better where he could have learned to co-operate with people more.'

Before a final agreement is made to place your child with a childminder, ask for a written agreement or contract which safeguards both you and the childminder. It avoids forgetting important things like retainers for holiday periods, extra money for extra time and under what circumstances, payment for any extra expenses, etc. It is easier and makes for a happier relationship if you have a framework.

children in your own home with the safeguards which registration with Ofsted gives. Contact your local CIS to help you find the details of Home Child Carers in your area.

Nannies, mother's helps and au-pairs

Nannies, mother's helps and au-pairs don't have to be registered by Ofsted, which means you don't have the safeguards which the registration of childminders provides. You can contact them through agencies, which will charge you a fee, or through advertisements in your local paper or national magazines. You could try advertising locally yourself.

If you employ a nanny you're responsible for paying her tax and national insurance as well as her wages. You may find that there's another working parent nearby who'd like to share the cost and services of your nanny. Working Families (see page 146) can provide you with more information on employing a nanny.

Au-pairs are young women or men who come from another country on a one-year basis to learn English. If you invite an au-pair to live in your house, he or she should not do more than 35 hours work a week. You provide bed and board and pocket money and access to English lessons in return for help in the home.

Day nurseries

Day nurseries run by local authorities are quite rare. They often have long waiting lists, and only a limited number of places for very young children. Priority is usually given to parents who, for one reason or another, are under a lot of stress and are unable to cope, to parents of children with special needs, and sometimes to working single parents. To get a place at a council nursery, apply to your local CIS. Your need will then be assessed by a social worker.

To contact your social services department, look in your phone book under the name of your local authority. (In Northern Ireland contact your local Health and Social Services Trust.)

There may be nurseries in your area run privately or by a voluntary organisation. These nurseries must be registered with Ofsted, and you can find out about them by calling your local CIS (see page 146).

You may be lucky enough to have a nursery or crèche where you work. If one doesn't exist, but there are a number of parents wanting and needing one, it's worth discussing the possibility with your employer.

Sharing/group care

Sharing/group care means getting together with other parents with needs like your own and organising your own childcare. This can work well if at least some of you work part-time. Your health visitor may be able to put you in touch with other parents who work or want to work and need childcare. The Daycare Trust (address on page 146) supplies information about setting up group care. If the group runs for more than two hours a day, or for more than five days a year, it will need to be registered with Ofsted.

The cost of childcare

The costs of childcare vary and can be very high. You'll have to ask. The cost of a nursery place may depend on your income and you may be entitled to assistance with childcare under the Working Tax Credit (see page 141), or if you are a student aged 16–19, the Care to Learn Scheme.

It is up to you to agree pay with a childminder, but the National Childminding Association (see page 146) can give advice.

Making childcare work

- **First consider your child's needs and what is available.** There are few nursery places for babies and you may prefer leaving a small baby in the care of a single person who you can get to know. A toddler or pre-school child may be happier in a group atmosphere, making friends and learning new skills, although a very shy child might prefer, for example, a childminder, but would like to go to a playgroup or one o'clock club to meet other children.

- **Your needs are important too.** Will the childcare cover your working hours or will you be looking for someone else to cover the extra time? If the arrangements are too complicated, your child may feel anxious and you'll feel very stressed.

- **Before you decide on childcare, visit the childminder or nursery,** talk and ask all the questions on your mind (see the box on page 50 for ideas). Talk about hours, fees, what the fees cover, and what happens during holidays, when there's illness, or an emergency. Write questions down as it's easy to forget things.

- **Consider transport arrangements.** How easily can you get there from work and from home?

- **It helps if children can settle in gradually.** If you can, start by leaving your child for a short time and build up. This might mean starting to leave your child before you actually go back to work.

- **Tell your childminder or nursery all about your child,** his or her routine, likes and dislikes, feeding information (particularly if you're still breastfeeding), and so on. When you leave or collect your child, try to make time to talk and find out how things are going.

- **There may be special worries you want to talk about.** If your child has asthma, for example, you'll need to be sure that your childminder doesn't keep pets. You'll also want to know whether the childminder, or any other people in the house, smoke. Or you may need to explain to a white childminder how to do a black child's hair. Perhaps you worry about your child being given certain things to eat. If this is important to you, it's right to talk about it.

- **Make sure that you and your childminder or nursery workers can agree about such issues** as discipline, potty training, and so on.

- **Support and reassure your child in every way you can.** The early weeks are likely to be difficult for both of you. A regular routine and a handover that's as smooth as possible both help. Expect crying when you leave, maybe for longer than just the early weeks, but remember the crying usually stops once you've gone. You can ask how long it has gone on. It's best neither to linger long nor to leave and then go back. Try to keep promises about

'The first day was really terrible. I remember hoping that Andrew's salary would have doubled overnight and that I wouldn't have to go back. But I have to say, now I've got to know the childminder, I enjoy it. And even on the bad days when he's really crying I call the childminder and she says he's settled 10 minutes after I've left.'

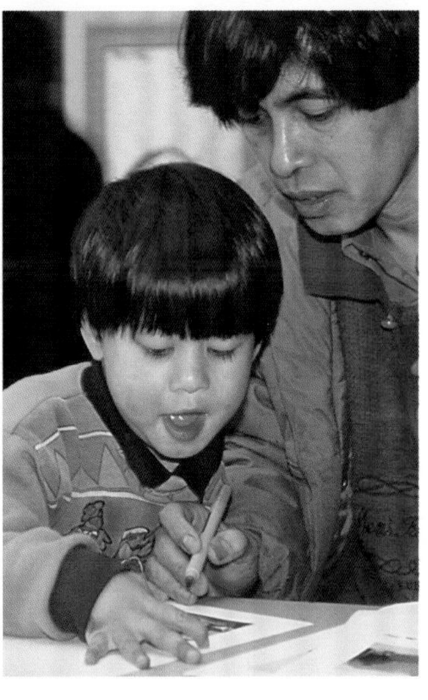

Questions you might want to ask

- *How many children are there in a group/school/class, and how many staff?*
- *How many of the staff are permanent and what are their qualifications?*
- *What would my child's day be like?*
- *What sort of discipline is used?*
- *What facilities are there, such as equipment, space to play outside, space to run around inside when the weather is bad?*
- *Are trips and visits organised?*
- *What teaching is there about different races, cultures and religions?*
- *Are parents expected to help on a regular or occasional basis, perhaps with cooking or outings?*
- *What meals and snacks are provided and is there a nutrition policy?*
- *Can I be reassured that my baby's particular dietary needs will be met, such as Kosher, vegetarian or no nut products? If not, can I bring in food and will it be kept separate.*

when you'll return and explain to older children when that will be.

- **Chat with older children about the daily routine,** about the person or people caring for them, about what they've done while away from you. Try to show it's a part of normal life and something to look forward to.
- **It will help you to get into a routine,** and you need to make time with your child part of that routine. A lot of other things will have to go, especially the housework, but not sleep or meals. Share out the work at home with your partner if you can.
- **Children do well in high-quality daycare.** So you've no need to feel guilty about not always being there, but if you're worried about the quality of care, then it's important to do something about it. Contact the Ofsted early years helpline for help and advice on how to make a complaint (0845 601 4772).

Finding a playgroup, nursery or infant school

Go to see the group or school
See a few if you have a choice. Talk to the people in charge, look at what's going on, ask questions (see box).

Trust your feelings
If you like the feel of a place and the children seem happy and busy, that's a good sign. You know best the kind of place that will suit your child.

Talk to other parents whose children are at the group or school
Your health visitor may also be able to tell you about other parents' views and experiences.

Talk about ways of settling your child in happily
Staff may suggest ways of helping with this. At a playgroup or nursery school you might, for example, stay with your child at first and then go away for longer and longer periods. Some children are helped by this sort of gentle start; for others a clean break seems to work best. Some take to change and separation quite easily; others find it hard. Be prepared to give support and reassurance for quite some time if needed.

In some situations, more support and reassurance may be needed. For example, it may be that your child will be one of very few black children at a mainly white school, or one of very few white children. In this situation, talk to the school beforehand about the kind of difficulties that a different colour, culture or language might bring. Find out how the school will handle these, make suggestions yourself if you want to, and explain your child's needs. Talk with your child too in whatever way seems best.

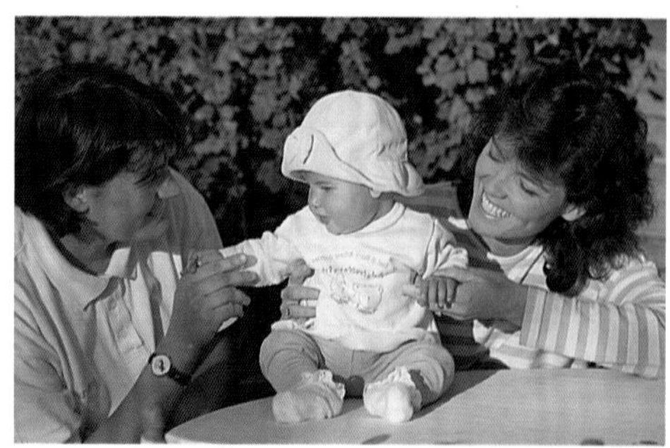

4 Habits and behaviour

There are some things that our children need to learn just so that we all get along together. The big issues for most parents are that our children should learn to:

- **use a toilet;**
- **sleep through the night;**
- **behave reasonably well in public and private.**

Sometimes we feel so anxious about these goals that we actually make it harder for our children to achieve them. This chapter helps you to step back a bit and see how you are managing.

Potties and toilets

What to expect

Daytime
Children get bladder and bowel control when they're physically ready for it and want to be dry and clean. The time varies, so it's best not to compare your child with others.

- Most children can control their bowels before their bladders.
- By the age of two, one in two children are dry during the day.
- By the age of three, nine out of ten children are dry most days. Even then all children have the odd accident, especially when they're excited or upset or absorbed in doing something.

Night-time
Learning to stay dry throughout the night usually takes a child a little longer than staying dry during the day. He or she has to respond to the sensation of having a full bladder while asleep either by waking up and going to the toilet, or holding on until morning. Although most children do learn this between the ages of three and five, it is estimated that:

- a quarter of three-year-olds wet the bed;
- one in six five-year-olds wet the bed.

'It's hard not to push them. You see these other children, you know, younger than yours, and they're all using the potty or the toilet, and there's yours, still in nappies. But they all learn in the end and, looking back, it wasn't that important. At the time I thought it was dreadful because Al was the only child in nappies. But it was only me that minded. Al certainly didn't care, so what does it matter?'

Learning to use a potty

'My mother-in-law kept telling me that all her three were potty trained by a year. At the time, I didn't know whether to believe her or not. I mean, it didn't really seem possible, but I wasn't sure. Looking back now, I suppose she must have spent a lot of time just putting her children on the potty. They didn't really know what they were doing, but if there was something in the potty, she counted that as potty trained. Well, for a start, I haven't got the time or patience for that. And anyway, it doesn't seem worth it. Just catching what comes isn't the same as potty training.'

When to start

It helps to remember that you can't and shouldn't try to force your child to use a potty. In time he or she will want to use it. Your child will not want to go to school in nappies any more than you would want him or her to. In the meantime, the best thing you can do is to encourage the behaviour you want.

Many parents seem to think about starting potty training around 18–24 months, but there's no particular time when success is guaranteed. It's probably easier to start in the summer, when washing dries better and there are fewer clothes to take off.

Try to work out when your child is ready. Most children go through three stages in developing bladder control.

- They become aware of having a wet or dirty nappy.
- They get to know when they are peeing, and may tell you they're doing it!
- They know when they need to pee, and may say so in advance.

You'll probably find that potty training is fastest if your child is at the last stage before you start. If you start earlier, be prepared for a lot of accidents as your child learns.

What to do

- **Leave the potty around where your child can see it and get to know what it's for.** If there are older children around, he or she may see them using it and their example will be a great help. Let your child see you using the toilet and explain what you're doing.
- **If your child regularly opens his or her bowels at the same time each day, take off the nappy and suggest that he or she tries going in the potty.** If your child is the slightest bit upset by the idea, just put the nappy back on and leave it a few more weeks before trying again.
- **As soon as you see that your child knows when he or she is going to pee, try the same thing.** If your child slips up, just mop it up and wait for next time. It usually takes a while for your child to get the hang of it, and the worst thing you can do is to make your child feel worried about the whole thing.
- **Your child will be delighted when he or she succeeds, and a little praise from you will make it better still,** but don't make a big deal of it and don't use sweets as a reward. You may end up causing more problems than you solve.

When the time's right, your child will *want* to use the potty.

Problems with toilet training

Wet children in the day

- **If your child shows no interest in using the potty, don't worry.** Remind yourself that, in the end, your child will want to be dry for him or herself. If your child starts to see the whole business as a battle of wills with you, it'll be much harder.

- **Take the pressure off.** This might mean giving up the potty and going back to nappies for a while, or just living a wet life and not letting it get you or your child down. It might help to talk to someone about the best action. What you don't want to do is to confuse your child by stopping and starting too often.

- **Show your child that you're pleased, and help your child to be pleased, when he or she uses the potty or toilet or manages to stay dry, even for a short time.** Be gentle about accidents. You need to explain that it's not what's wanted. But do your best not to show irritation or to nag. Once a child becomes worried, the problem often gets worse.

- **If your child has been dry for a while (night or day) and then starts wetting again, there may be an emotional reason, such as a new baby or new house.** Be understanding and sympathetic. Your child will almost certainly be upset about the lapse and will not be doing it 'on purpose'.

- **By the time your child starts school, he or she is likely to be just as upset by wetting as you are, so do all you can not to be angry.** Your child needs to know you're on his or her side and will help to solve what is now your child's problem more than yours. You can also obtain helpful information from the Enuresis Resource and Information Centre (ERIC) (see page 146 for address).

Bedwetting

Bedwetting up to the age of five is considered normal, and treatment is not usually given. You may, however, find the following measures helpful if your four- or five-year-old wets the bed.

- Try not to get angry or irritated with your child.

- Protect the mattress with a good plastic protective cover.

- Check whether your child is afraid to get up at night – would a night light or potty in the room help?

- **Don't** cut back on fluids as the bladder tends to adjust and holds less. It is better for your child to drink around six or seven cups of fluid during the day so that his or her bladder learns to hold a larger capacity. However, avoid giving fizzy drinks, citrus juices and drinks with caffeine, such as tea, cola and chocolate, before your child goes to bed as these can stimulate the kidneys to produce more fluid.

- If your child is constipated, this can also irritate the bladder at night.

Constipation and soiling

Your baby or child is constipated if he or she doesn't empty the bowel properly (some stool stays inside) when going to the toilet. The stool is usually, but not always, hard and difficult to pass. The stools may also look like little pellets.

Most children simply grow out of wetting. If this does not seem to be happening when your child is ready for school, talk to your GP or health visitor about it. You may be referred to a clinic for expert help – not for your sake, but for your child's sake.

If a child who has been dry starts to wet the bed again, this may be due to threadworms. See page 99 for more information.

If your child continues to be constipated, talk to your health visitor or GP. If it's not sorted out, in the end it'll become more of a problem for your child than for you, and he or she may need your help in solving it.

If your child has sleep problems, both parents or carers should agree a sleep management plan and stick to it.

Another sign of constipation can be if pants are soiled with diarrhoea or very soft stools. This may happen because there is not enough fibre in your child's diet to keep things moving, or it can be something that starts as an emotional problem. Drinking too much milk can also cause constipation.

Even if passing a stool isn't painful, once a child is really constipated they lose the sensation of wanting to go to the toilet, at which point they need professional help.

- If your child becomes constipated, it can become painful to pass stools. The pain means that your child will then hold back even more, become more constipated, have more pain, and so on. It's important to stop this spiral. Ask your health visitor or GP to recommend a suitable laxative. If it doesn't solve the problem quickly, talk to your GP.

- Once the initial problem has been sorted out, it's important to stop it coming back. Make sure your child eats plenty of fibre. Fruit and vegetables, wholemeal bread or chapattis, wholegrain breakfast cereals, baked beans, frozen peas and sweetcorn are good sources of fibre, and children often like them. Also give lots to drink – clear drinks rather than milk. All this will help to prevent constipation.

- If dietary changes aren't helping, consider whether something could be upsetting your child. A young child may be afraid of using the potty. Be reassuring. Let your child be with you when you go to the toilet. And try to be as relaxed as you can be about it.

Sleeping

In some families, children simply go to bed when they're ready, or at the same time as their parents. Some parents are happy to cuddle their children off to sleep every night, but others want bedtime to be more organised and early enough to give their children a long sleep and some child-free time for themselves.

How much sleep is needed?
Like adults, the sleep patterns of babies and children vary. From birth, some babies need more or less sleep than others, but below are the average amounts needed in 24 hours, including naps in the day.

- **Newborns to three months.** A newborn baby spends roughly the same amount of time asleep as awake, but may spend as many as 16–18 hours out of 24 asleep, or as little as 8. Inevitably, sleep will be disturbed by the need for night feeds. Such problems as being too hot or too cold may also disturb your baby's sleep.

- **Three to six months.** As your baby grows, the need for night feeds becomes less frequent and periods of sleep get longer. Some babies will sleep for around eight hours or even longer at night, and, by four months, may spend on average twice as long asleep at night as they do during the day.

- **Six to twelve months.** At this age, night feeds are no longer necessary, and some babies may even sleep for up to 12 hours at a stretch at night. However, teething discomfort or hunger may cause some babies to wake during the night.

- **By twelve months**, babies sleep for about 12–15 hours altogether.
- **A two-year-old** may sleep for about 11–12 hours at night, with one or two naps in the day.
- **Most three–four-year-olds** need about 12 hours sleep, but some may need only 8 or 10 hours, and others 14. Some may need a nap in the day.

Regular bedtimes

Some future sleep problems may be avoided if you can establish a simple and soothing bedtime routine early. This can include a bath, changing into night clothes, feeding, cuddling, then putting to bed.

Put your baby down awake rather than getting him or her to sleep by rocking or cuddling in your arms, otherwise your baby may not learn to fall asleep in the cot, and may need nursing back to sleep if he or she wakes up again.

As your child gets older, keeping to a similar bedtime routine is also important. This should include a 'winding down' period and the avoidance of excitement and over-stimulation before bedtime. An example of a routine could be:

- bathtime, and put in night clothes;
- a milky drink or supper;
- brushing of teeth;
- a bedtime story;
- making sure your child's comforter, such as a dummy, cuddly toy or security blanket, is nearby;
- a good night kiss and cuddle;
- leaving a dim light on if necessary.

Sleep problems

Difficulties in settling down to sleep and night waking are common in young children aged 1–5 years. These can be persistent, but what is a sleep problem for one family may not be one for another. If you are happy for your baby to go to bed at the same time as you, or for your child to sleep in your bed, that's fine. If, however, you or your child are suffering from lack of sleep because your child will not go to bed or wakes during the night, you may like to try some of the suggestions below. Research has shown that changing habits in ways like these is more effective than drugs in treating sleep problems.

Refusing to go to bed

- Decide what time you want your child to go to bed.
- Close to the time that your child falls asleep, start a 20-minute 'winding down' bedtime routine. Bring this forward by 5–10 minutes a week until the right bedtime is reached.
- If a very late bedtime has been established, gradually reduce this by 15–30 minutes each night until you reach the time the child is to go to bed.
- Put your child to bed and set limits on the amount of time spent with him or her. For example, read one story only, then tuck your child in and say good night.
- Make sure your child has a dummy, if used, favourite toy, or comforter before settling into bed.
- Leave a crying child for 5–10 minutes before going back in. Resettle your child down again.

Getting help for sleep problems

Most sleep problems can usually be solved by using simple techniques. But patience, consistency and commitment are usually needed if these have gone on for some time. It is important that both parents should agree on a sleep plan and stick to it.

If you've tried the suggestions on these pages and your child's sleeping is still a problem, talk to your GP or health visitor. They may suggest other solutions or suggest that you make an appointment at a sleep clinic if there is one in your area. Sleep clinics are usually run by health visitors who are specially trained in the management of sleep problems and who can give you the help and support you need. Your GP may also prescribe a drug for very short-term use but it is far better to tackle the long-term issue. In the meantime, if you're desperate, try to find someone else to take over for the odd night, or even have your child to stay. You'll cope better if you can catch up on some sleep yourself.

Make sure your baby over six months is not waking from hunger. If you gave the last solid food around 5–6 pm, try offering some more food such as bread or a breakfast cereal around 7–8 pm, as well as a milk drink.

Other sleep problems

Nightmares
Most children have nightmares at some stage. They often begin between the ages of 18 months and 3 years. Nightmares are not usually a sign of emotional disturbance but may occur if your child is anxious about something or has been frightened by a television programme or story.

After a nightmare your child will need comforting and reassuring. If your child has a lot of nightmares and you cannot find the cause, talk to your GP or health visitor.

Night terrors
These can begin under the age of one, but are most common in three–four-year-olds. They usually start with the child giving a scream or thrashing about while still asleep. He or she may sit up and talk or look terrified while still sleeping.
Night terrors normally have no importance, and your child will eventually grow out of them. Don't wake your child during a terror, but, if they happen at the same time each night, try to break the pattern by gently waking your child up about 15 minutes beforehand. Keep your child awake for a few minutes before letting him or her go back to sleep. He or she will not remember anything in the morning.

Don't pick him or her up or take him downstairs again. Put a child who gets up back to bed again.

- Leave a drink of water within reach and a dim light on if necessary.
- Don't keep checking to see if your child is asleep.
- **Be prepared to repeat this routine for several nights. The important thing is to be firm and not to give in.**

Waking during the night

By the time your child is six months old, it is reasonable to expect him or her to sleep through most nights. However, up to half of all children under five go through periods of night waking. Some will just go back to sleep on their own, others will cry or want company. If this happens, try to think why your child is waking up and decide what you want to do about it.

For example:

- Is it hunger? A later feed or some cereal last thing at night might help your baby to sleep through the night.
- If your child seems afraid of the dark, a nightlight should be given.
- Is your child waking from fears or bad dreams? If so, try to find the reason.
- Is your child too hot or too cold? If so the bedclothes or heat should be adjusted.

If no cause is found, and your child continues to wake and cry, or wants company, here are some suggestions for coping.

Scheduled waking
If your child wakes up at the same time every night, try waking him or her 15-60 minutes before this time and then resettling them to sleep. For some children this can help to reduce night waking.

Let your child sleep in the same room as a brother or sister
If you think your child is lonely, and the brother or sister does not object, putting children in the same room can often result in them both sleeping through the night.

Teach your child to fall back to sleep alone
- Check everything is all right and settle your child down with the minimum of talking.
- Do not give anything to eat, and only water to drink if necessary.
- Do not take your child downstairs or into the parental bed.
- Leave your child and let him or her cry for a short period.
- Repeat the above routine, gradually extending the time period before checking.
- Continue the routine each night until your child sleeps.
- Be prepared for this routine to take several nights or even a week or two before it is effective.

A NEW BABY IN THE FAMILY

Coping with two children is very different from coping with one, and it can be tough at first, especially if your first child isn't very old. So far as the baby goes, you've got more experience and probably more confidence, which helps, but the work more than doubles, and dividing your time and attention can be a strain.

It's not unusual for the birth of a second baby to alter your feelings towards your first child. It would be strange if it didn't. At first you may feel that you're somehow not loving your first one as much or enough.

Some parents say they feel very protective towards the baby and 'go off' the older one for a while. It simply takes time to adjust to being a bigger family and loving more than one child.

Your older child, no matter what his or her age, has to adjust too. You can probably help with this, and that will help you.

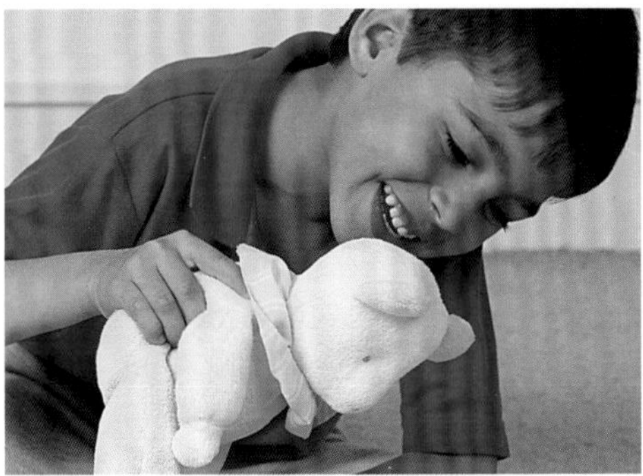

- **Try to keep as many of the old routines and activities as you can,** like going to playgroup, going to visit friends, telling a bedtime story. This may not be easy in the early weeks, but it gives reassurance.

- **Don't expect your older child to be pleased with the baby or to feel the way you do.** It's lovely if the pleasure is shared, but it's best not to expect it.

- **Do expect an older child to be more demanding and to want more and need more of you.** Someone like a grandparent can often help by giving the older one time. But try to give some special attention yourself, and have some time alone together, so your older child doesn't feel pushed out.

- **Older children don't always find babies very lovable, but they often find them interesting.** You may be able to encourage this. There's a lot you can say and explain about babies, and children like to be given facts. Talk about what your older one was like and did as a baby. Get out the old toys and photos. And try to make looking after and playing with the baby a good game, without expecting too much.

- **Feeds are often difficult.** An older child may well feel left out and jealous. Find something for him or her to do, or make feeds a time for a story or a chat.

- **Be prepared for your older child to go back to baby behaviour for a time** – wanting a bottle, wetting pants, wanting to be carried. It's hard, but don't always refuse requests, and try not to get angry.

- **There'll be jealousy and resentment,** shown one way or another, sooner or later. You can only do so much. If you and your partner, or you and a grandparent or friend, can sometimes give each other time alone with each child, you won't feel so constantly pulled in different directions.

'When you've got the one, you don't know how easy it is. Once you've got the two of them, it's much more than twice the work. At the beginning when the second's only a baby still, that's the most difficult time of all.'

'When I only had one, if he had a tantrum, I found I could ignore it and stay fairly calm. Now, with the two of them, if I try to ignore anything, it turns into a full-scale war.'

'I feel split in two. They pull me in different directions the whole time and it's almost impossible to do right by both of them. What's right for the baby is wrong for my older one, and the same the other way round. I love them both, but there doesn't seem any way of showing them that, or of being fair.'

Dealing with difficult behaviour

'You get a lot of advice about how to handle your children and I think, because a lot of the time you feel very unsure of yourself, you get to think there's a "right" way. When you read something, or get a bit of advice, or see somebody handling their child a certain way, you forget to stop and think, you know, "Is that me?" '

'The thing is that what you have to ask of them isn't always what you'd want to ask. It's how things are. My husband works nights and he has to sleep mornings. There's no way round that. If the children are noisy, he can't sleep.'

People have very different ideas about good and bad behaviour. What's bad behaviour to you may be accepted as normal by other parents, and vice versa. Sometimes it's a matter of a particular family's rules. Sometimes it's more to do with circumstances. It's much harder to put up with mess if you haven't got much space, or with noise if the walls are thin.

People react to their children's behaviour very differently. Some are tougher than others, some are more patient than others, and so on. It's not just a matter of how you decide to be. It's also how you *are* as a person.

It's best to set your own rules to fit the way you live and the way you are. And it's best to deal with your child's behaviour your way. But for all parents there will be times when your child's behaviour gets you down or really worries you. There are times when nothing you do seems to work. What do you do then?

Understanding difficult behaviour

Try to step back and do some thinking.

Is it really a problem?
In other words, is your child's behaviour a problem that you feel you must do something about? Or might it be better just to live with it for a while? Sometimes it's trying to do something about a certain sort of behaviour that changes it from something that's irritating for you into a real problem for your child. But if a problem is causing you and your child distress, or upsetting family life, then you do need to do something about it.

It's also worth asking yourself whether your child's behaviour is a problem in your eyes, or only in other people's. Sometimes some kind of behaviour that you can happily ignore, or at any rate aren't worried about, is turned into a problem by other people's comments.

Is there a reason for your child's difficult behaviour?
There usually is, and it's worth trying to work out what it is before you do anything. Here are just some of the possible reasons for difficult behaviour.

- Any change in a child's life, like the birth of a new baby, moving house, a change of childminder, starting playgroup, or even a much smaller change, can be a big event. Sometimes children show how they're feeling by being difficult.

- If you're upset or there are problems in your family, your children are likely to pick that up. They may then become difficult at just the time when you feel least able to cope. If a problem is more yours than your children's, don't blame yourself for that, but try not to blame your children either.

- You'll know your child's character and may be able to see that a certain sort of behaviour fits that character. For example, some children react to stress by being loud and noisy and wanting extra attention, others by withdrawing and hiding away.

- Sometimes your child may be reacting in a particular way because of the way you've handled a problem in the past. For example, you may have given your child sweets to keep him or her quiet at the shops, so now your child screams for sweets every time you go there.

- Could you accidentally be encouraging the behaviour you most dislike? If a tantrum brings attention (even angry attention) or night-time waking means company and a cuddle, then maybe your child has a good reason for behaving that way. You may need to try to give more attention at other times, and less attention to the problem.

- Think about the times when the bad behaviour happens. Is it, for example, when your child is tired, hungry, over-excited, frustrated or bored?

Changing your child's behaviour

Do what feels right
For your child, for you and for the family. If you do anything you don't believe in or anything you feel isn't right, it's far less likely to work. Children usually know when you don't really mean something.

Don't give up too quickly
Once you've decided to do something, give it a fair trial. Very few solutions work overnight. It's easier to stick at something if you've someone to support you. Get help from your partner, a friend, another parent, your health visitor or GP. At the very least, it's good to have someone to talk to about progress or lack of it.

Try to be consistent
Children need to know where they stand. If you react to your child's behaviour in one way one day and a different way the next, it's confusing. It's also important that everyone close to your child deals with the problem in the same way.

Try not to over-react
This is very hard. When your child does something annoying, not just once, but time after time, your own feelings of anger or frustration are bound to build up. But if you become very tense and wound up over a problem, you can end up taking out your feelings on your child. The whole situation can get out of control. You don't have to hide the way you feel. It would be inhuman not to show irritation and anger sometimes, but, hard as it is, try to keep a sense of proportion. Once you've said what needs to be said and let your feelings out, try to leave it at that. Move on to other things that you can both enjoy or feel good about. And look for other ways of coping with your feelings (see page 60).

Talk
Children don't have to be able to talk back to understand. And understanding might help. So explain why, for example, you want your child to hold your hand while crossing the road, or get into the buggy when it's time to go home.

'Your children's behaviour takes over your life. I just felt that I changed totally when I had a second child. I felt my patience had gone completely. If I saw parents shouting in the street, I used to think that was a terrible thing. When I had one, I could reason with her and we'd sort it out. When I had two, one only had to do something the slightest bit wrong and I would fly off the handle.'

'You think, if I handle this right, they'll learn, it'll get better. But you know sometimes it's just that you have to let time go by. Everything I wanted to happen happened in the end. Sometimes you can try too hard with them.'

If you can think about your child's behaviour a bit and begin to understand it, you're more likely to find a right answer. And even if you can't find an answer, you'll probably cope better.

'Sometimes I will smack her because she's done something really bad or really dangerous. But other times I know I want to smack her just because of the way I'm feeling, and after, I'll feel bad about it. When it's like that, I just walk away. If John's at home, I'll ask him to take over. And if I'm on my own, I just go into another room and count to ten.'

'It drives me mad. He's plenty old enough to use the toilet, but he won't have anything but the potty, and I'm running around all day emptying it. I had to leave him for a morning with my sister. So I took the potty and told her, you know, I'm sorry, but he won't use the toilet. And when I got back, it turned out he'd gone to the toilet every time, no fuss, nothing said or anything.'

'I think what's so wearing is that it all depends on mood. Not their mood, but mine too. And you have to hide your feelings away so much, and they just let theirs out. If they want to lie down and cry because their favourite T-shirt's in the wash or you won't buy them something at the shops, they just do it. And when they do it in front of other people, that's awful.'

REMEMBER

It's all right not to be a 'perfect' parent.

Be positive about the good things
When a child is being really difficult, it can come to dominate everything. That doesn't help anybody. What can help is to say (or show) when you feel good about something. Make a habit of often letting your child know when he or she is making you happy. You can do that just by giving attention, a smile or a hug. There doesn't have to be a 'good' reason. Let your child know that you love him or her just for being themselves.

Rewards
Rewards can put pressure on a child, when maybe what's needed is to take the pressure off. If you promise a treat in advance, and your child doesn't manage to 'earn' it, it can cause a lot of disappointment and difficulty. Giving a reward after something has been achieved, rather than promising it beforehand, is less risky. After all, a hug is a reward.

Smacking
Smacking may stop a child at that moment from doing whatever he or she is doing, but it is unlikely to have a lasting effect. Children learn most by example. If you hit your child, you're telling the child that hitting is reasonable behaviour. Children who are treated aggressively by their parents are more likely to be aggressive themselves and to take out their angry feelings on others who are smaller and weaker than they are. Parents do sometimes smack their children, but it is better to teach by example that hitting people is wrong.

When every day is a bad day

No parent 'does it well' all of the time. All parents have bad days, and most go through times when one bad day seems to follow another. Since you can't hand in your notice, or take a week off, you have to find some way of making life work.

When you're tired or in a bad mood, or when your child is tired or in a bad mood, it can be hard to get on together and get through the day. You can end up arguing non-stop. Even the smallest thing can make you angry. If you go out to work, it's especially disappointing if the short time you've got to spend with your child is spoilt by arguments.

Most children also go through patches of being difficult or awkward over certain things – dressing, eating, or going to bed at night.

Knowing that it makes you cross or upset probably makes them still more difficult. And you become more and more tense, and less and less able to cope.

Stop! and start again

When you're in a bad patch, a change in routine or a change in the way in which you're dealing with a problem can be all that's needed to stop an endless cycle of difficult behaviour. Here are some ideas.

- **Do things at different times.** An argument that always happens at one time of day may not happen at another. Do the difficult things when your child is least tired or most co-operative. For example, try dressing your child after breakfast rather than before; have lunch earlier, or later, and so on.

- **Find things to do (however ordinary) that your child enjoys, and do them together.** Let your child know that you're happy when he or she is happy. Every time he or she does something that pleases you, make sure you say so. We all prefer praise to blame, and, if you give your child lots of opportunities to see you smile, the chances are that he or she will learn that a happy mother is more fun than a cross one.

- **Ask yourself whether the thing you're going to tell your child off about really matters.** Sometimes it does, sometimes it doesn't. Having arguments about certain things can get to be a habit.
- **When you lose your temper because you're tired or upset, say you're sorry.** It'll help you both feel better.
- **Don't expect too much.** You may think that sitting still and being quiet is good behaviour. Some children can manage this for a while. Others find it torture because they want to be learning and exploring every waking minute. If your child never keeps still and is 'into' everything, you'll be happier giving him or her as much opportunity as possible to run off steam and explore safely.
- **Don't expect a child under the age of three to understand and remember what they are allowed to do.** Even after the age of three it's hard for a child to remember instructions.
- **Don't expect perfect behaviour.** If you don't expect perfect behaviour, then you won't feel so disappointed and angry if you don't get it. After all, if it's all right for you to be a less than perfect parent, then it's all right for your child to be less than perfect too. It's just hard to live with sometimes.

Talk about it

It does help to talk and be with other people, especially other parents. It's often true that 'only parents understand'. A lot look very calm and capable from the outside (and you may too), but alone at home most get frustrated and angry at times.

If you don't already know other parents living nearby, look on page 133 for how to find out about local groups. Groups don't suit everybody, but at the very least they're a way of making friends. And a group that is run by parents can often give more than friends who haven't got children the same age. If one doesn't seem right for you it's worth trying a different one.

Sometimes it isn't your child whose mood is a problem, it's you. If you're miserable, trying to be happy for your child's sake may seem impossible. Read Chapter 7 for more about this.

'I've just stopped asking myself to be perfect. I've stopped trying so hard. You don't have to be perfect, and, if you were, I don't think it would be that good for your child. People have to take me as they find me. That goes for the children, and it goes for people who drop in and find yesterday's washing-up in the sink and a heap of dirty washing on the floor.'

When you can't cope

If every day is a bad day, and you feel that things are getting out of control, *get help*. Talk to your health visitor and/or phone a helpline (see box). Talking to someone who understands what you're going through may be the first – and biggest – step towards making things better.

Look on pages 146–51 for organisations that provide help and support to new mothers.

You can talk in confidence to:

- *Parentline Plus*
  0808 800 2222 (or see your local phone book)
  www.parentlineplus.org.uk
- *NSPCC Help Line*
  0808 800 5000
  www.nspcc.org.uk

  Northern Ireland
  028 9035 1135
- *NSPCC Cymru Wales*
  0808 2026 7000
  email helplinecymru@nspcc.org.uk
- *Parents Advice Centre (Northern Ireland)*
  028 9023 8800
  www.pachelp.org

'When it gets too much, I drop everything and get out. I go and see people, find somebody to talk to. I'm a different person when I'm with other people.'

Tempers and tantrums

Help for difficult behaviour

You can get help for especially difficult behaviour, so don't feel you have to go on coping alone. Talk to your health visitor or GP, or contact your local child guidance clinic (you can sometimes go without a referral). Sometimes all you need is encouraging support to help you hold on until the problem is over.

Your child can also be referred to a specialist for help. If you've got a special problem, it's right to get special help.

Having a difficult child is an enormous strain. You need help too. See page 61 for more on this.

Tantrums may start around 18 months, are common around two years, and are much less common at four. One in five two-year-olds has a temper tantrum at least twice a day. One reason is that around this age children often want to express themselves more than they are able. They feel frustrated and the frustration comes out as a tantrum. Once a child can talk more, tantrums often lessen.

- **Tantrums tend to happen when children are tired or hungry.** Sleep or food might be the answer.

- **If sleep or food isn't the answer, try to work out the reason and tackle that.** It may be frustration. It may be something like jealousy. More time and attention and being extra loving, even when your child is not so lovable, can help.

- **Even if you can't be sure why your child has a temper tantrum, try to understand and accept the anger your child is feeling.** You probably feel the same way yourself very often. If you think about that, you may be better able to accept your child's feelings.

- **When a tantrum is starting, try to find an instant distraction.** Find something to look at, out of the window for example. Make yourself sound really surprised and interested in it.

- **If your child has a tantrum, try sitting it out.** Don't lose your temper or shout back. Ignore the looks you get from people around you. Stay as calm as you can and try not to get involved, but don't give in. If you've said 'no', don't change your mind and say 'yes' just to end the tantrum. If you do change your mind, your child will think that tantrums pay. For the same reason, don't buy your way out with sweets or treats. If you're at home, you could try walking away into another room.

- **Tantrums often seem to happen in shops.** This can be really embarrassing, and embarrassment makes it extra hard to cope and stay calm. Keep shopping trips short. You could start by going out to buy one or two things only, and then build up from there. Once you've managed one quick trip without trouble, you're beginning to make progress.

- **Some parents find it helps to hold their child, quite firmly, until the tantrum passes, although a struggling child can be hard to contain.** This usually only works when your child is more upset than angry, and when you yourself are feeling calm and able to talk gently and reassuringly.

HITTING, BITING, KICKING, FIGHTING

A child who is aggressive can cause parents a lot of anxiety, but most young children will occasionally bite or hit someone or push another child. So, if your child is sometimes aggressive, this does not mean he or she is going to grow up like this. Toddlers are also curious and may not understand that biting or pulling hair hurts. However, if your child is being aggressive, he or she needs to understand that this is not acceptable. Here are some suggestions for dealing with it.

- **Don't hit, bite or kick back.** It makes behaving like that seem all right. You can still make it clear that it hurts and you won't allow it.

- **If you're with other children, say you'll leave,** or ask others to leave, if the behaviour continues – and do it!

- **If the behaviour is directed at you at home and your warning is ignored,** place your child in another room, where it is safe for them to be, for a short period.

- **Talk.** Children often go through patches of insecurity or upset and let their feelings out by being aggressive – at playgroup, for example. If by talking you can find out what's worrying your child, you may be able to help.

- **Try to show your child how much you love him or her, even though you don't love the way he or she is behaving.** Children who are being aggressive aren't so easy to love. But extra love may be what's needed.

- **Help your child let his or her feelings out some other way.** Find a big space, like a park, and encourage your child to run and to shout to get rid of the angry feelings inside. Just letting your child know that you recognise the feelings will make it easier for him or her to express them without hurting anyone else.

- **If you are seriously concerned about your child's behaviour, talk to your health visitor or doctor.**

OVERACTIVE CHILDREN

There is no doubt that a substantial proportion of children are overactive, and some may be described as suffering from 'attention deficit hyperactivity disorder', as this condition is now called. But quite a lot of children who are difficult to manage, and who have problems concentrating, are not necessarily overactive too. Alternatively, some children may suffer from a mild form of hyperactivity only. So, the difficulty for parents, and sometimes for health professionals, is deciding what are 'normal' behaviour problems in a child and what are symptoms of attention deficit hyperactivity disorder which require early treatment and management.

Below are some tips on managing an active child. If these, or the other information in this chapter on dealing with difficult behaviour, do not help, then talk to your health visitor or GP. You can also obtain information from the Hyperactive Children's Support Group (see page 146).

- **Keep to a daily routine as much as you can.** Routine can be important if your child is restless or difficult. Routine may also help you stay calmer and stand up better to the strain.

- **Make giving your child time and attention a part of the routine.** In different ways, your child may be demanding your attention most of the day, if not most of the night as well. A lot of the time you'll have to say 'no'. This is easier to say, and may be easier for your child to accept, if there are certain times each day when you do give all your attention to your child.

- **Avoid difficult situations as much as you can** – for example, by keeping shopping trips short. It's often no good even expecting an overactive difficult child to sit still at meals or behave well in a supermarket. And try lowering your expectations. Start by asking your child to be still, or controlled, or to concentrate, for a very short time, then gradually build up.

- **Try to get out every day to a place where your child can run around and really let go.** Go to a park, or a playground, or whatever safe, open space there is. Find ways of helping your child burn off energy.

- **Try cutting out cola drinks, tea and coffee**. These drinks all contain caffeine. Some children are sensitive to this and it can make them 'jumpy'. So you could try cutting them out and see if it helps.

5 Feeding your child

Food is one of life's greatest pleasures and yet it's also a source of worry for most parents. What should children eat? Can I afford to give it to them? Will they eat it? The next few pages will give you some basic guidelines on how to get your baby through the stage of weaning and on to family foods.

Starting solid food

When to start

Breast milk or infant formula milk provides all the nourishment your baby needs for the first six months.

Experts recommend that babies should start solid foods from the age of six months. At this stage he or she needs more iron and nutrients than milk alone can provide. You should aim to gradually increase the variety and amount of solid foods so that by 12 months they have become the main part of the diet, with breast or formula milk to drink alongside.

It is recommended that you do not wean before six months. At this age weaning will be easier and your baby will be able to progress more quickly to finger foods, etc. Before six months most babies' digestive systems and kidneys are not fully developed. Weaning too soon may cause problems, such as food allergies. If you choose not to follow this advice, you should never wean before four months (make sure you follow the separate weaning advice on page 68).

If your baby was born prematurely, ask your paediatrician for advice about what is best for your baby.

'With your first baby, you worry about what you give them, and how much, and whether they'll like it. But with your second, it's much more like they have to fit in with the rest of the family, and you don't think about it so much. They take what's going and they do it for themselves really.'

'I think there's a lot of pressure on you to stop breastfeeding and, you know, get on to something a bit more substantial. People are always sort of pushing you on to the next stage. It's hard to know what's best when people are saying to you "Isn't she weaned yet?" and "Have you tried this, have you tried that?".

How will I know my baby is ready?

Babies are usually ready to start on solid food at six months. You will notice that at six months your baby:

- *shows interest in what you or your family are eating – picking up food and putting it in his or her mouth;*
- *can sit up – even though he or she may need some support;*
- *is still hungry after finishing a milk feed;*
- *after sleeping through the night, starts waking again to be fed.*

Go on breastfeeding, alongside giving 'solid' food, for as long as you and your baby want.

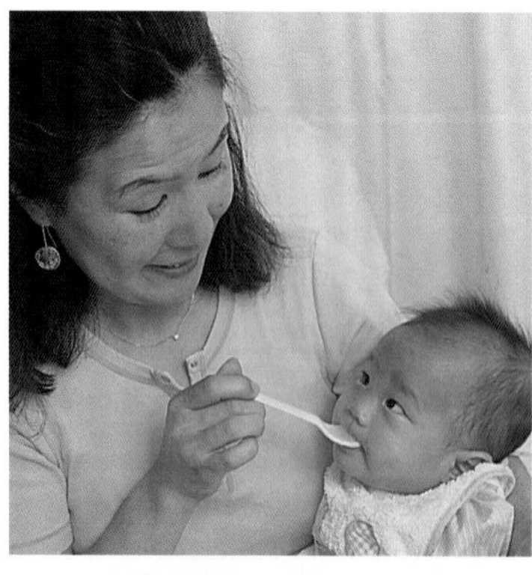

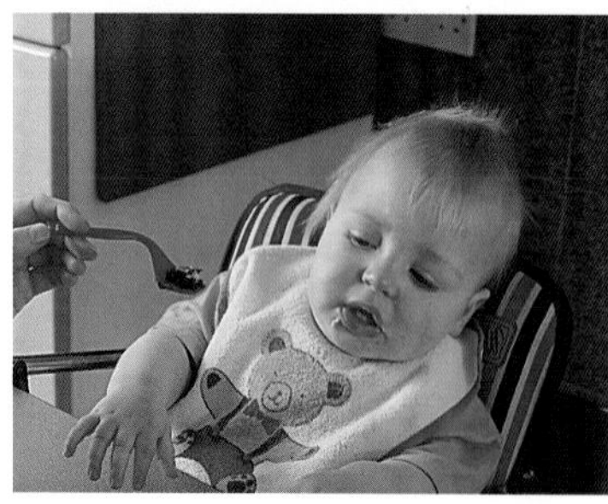

Hints for successful weaning

The idea of weaning is to introduce your baby gradually to a wider range of foods so that by the age of one your baby will be joining in family meals. All babies are different. Some take to it quickly, some take longer. Some are more choosy and may need a new food offered several times before it is accepted.

- Allow plenty of time for feeding, particularly at first. Until now your baby has known only food that comes in a continuous flow from nipple or teat. Your baby needs to learn to move solid food from the front of the tongue to the back in order to swallow it. The food tastes and feels different – it's bound to take time.

- Make sure everything you use for feeding your baby is really clean. Spoon out a small amount of food and heat this, rather than heating a large amount that then goes to waste. You can always heat up more if it is needed. Heat food thoroughly and allow it to cool, stir well and test before offering it to your baby. Throw away any food your baby hasn't eaten as it is not safe to reheat previously warmed food.

- Cover the floor with newspaper and use a bib to catch food spills – weaning can be a messy business!

- **Always stay with your baby when he or she is eating to make sure he or she doesn't choke.**

- Choose a time of day when you are both relaxed.

- Do not rush or 'force feed'. Most babies know when they've had enough to eat. Don't spend a lot of time persuading your baby to take food – they soon learn that refusing food is a good way of getting attention, or of getting sugary pudding instead of a savoury course. Of course it's right to give attention, chat and enjoy meals together, but when food is refused it might be best to call an end to the meal.

- When your baby shows an interest in feeding him or herself, this a good sign. Encourage this by giving your baby one spoon, whilst you try to spoon in most of the meal with another.

- Use mashed-up family food when you can – it's less expensive, you know what the ingredients are (e.g. no added salt or sugar) and it will get your baby used to eating what you eat. Preparing larger quantities than you need and freezing small portions, e.g. in an ice cube tray, can save time and effort. (Commercial baby foods can be useful but don't let them replace family foods altogether. See the box on page 67 for more information about using commercial baby foods.)

- Never add any food to your baby's bottle.

- By the age of one you want your baby to be eating a variety of foods and adapt to your pattern of eating – say three meals a day with a drink at each meal and two or three additional snacks. Offering a wide variety of foods now may help avoid choosiness later on.

Here's how to start

Most babies take time to learn how to take food from a spoon. Be patient and prepared for some spitting and mess. Until now, food has come in one continuous stream. Now there are frustrating pauses.

Don't be surprised if your baby doesn't want the spoon feed at first – this is perfectly normal. Wait until the next meal time. The main aim at this stage is to get your baby used to the idea of taking food from a spoon. Your baby will still be getting most of the nourishment he or she needs from breast milk or 600 ml (around a pint) of infant formula milk a day.

Foods you might try

- Mashed carrot, parsnip, potato, turnips or cauliflower.
- Mashed banana, cooked apple, pear or apricots.
- Plain rice mixed with baby's usual milk.

Milk is still the most important part of your baby's diet, but now gradually increase the amount of solid food you give after the milk feed. At first your baby may be content with only 1-2 teaspoons of mashed food. At the same time, move gradually from solid food at one feed in the day to solid food at two and then three feeds.

Try to keep cereals for one feed only. Begin to add different foods and different tastes, e.g. pureed/mashed meat, chicken with pureed potatoes or vegetables. You'll be able to use lots of the foods you already cook for yourself. Just mash or sieve a small amount (without added salt or sugar) and give it a try. Try to give your baby a variety of foods rich in iron

every day, e.g. beef, pork, lamb, chicken, sardines, egg yolk, green vegetables, beans, peas, lentils, fortified breakfast cereals.

Vitamin C helps the body absorb iron so it is important to include some foods rich in vitamin C at meal times. Vitamin C is found in unsweetened pure orange juice (diluted 1 part juice to 10 parts water), tomato and fresh fruit, e.g. kiwi, orange. This is particularly important if you are weaning your baby onto a vegetarian diet.

You will find that as your baby eats more solid food, his or her milk intake will start to decrease. Once he or she is on three meals a day, you can drop one milk feed, but your baby should still be having breast milk or 500-600 ml (about a pint) of infant formula a day. Full-fat cow's milk products can be used in weaning after six months, e.g. yogurt, custard or cheese sauce. Again, try to follow your baby's appetite and go at your baby's pace.

Baby foods

It can be useful to have a few jars, tins or packets of baby food in the cupboard, but don't let them replace home-made foods altogether. If you buy baby foods:

- *check the expiry date;*
- *check the seals on cans and jars haven't been broken;*
- *read the instructions carefully about how to prepare the food;*
- *avoid these foods before six months: wheat-based foods, gluten, nuts, seeds, eggs, fish, citrus fruits and juices – check the label for these;*
- *choose foods which state they do not contain added sugars;*
- *if your family has asthma, eczema or allergies to foods, talk to your GP or health visitor to see if your baby needs to avoid other foods.*

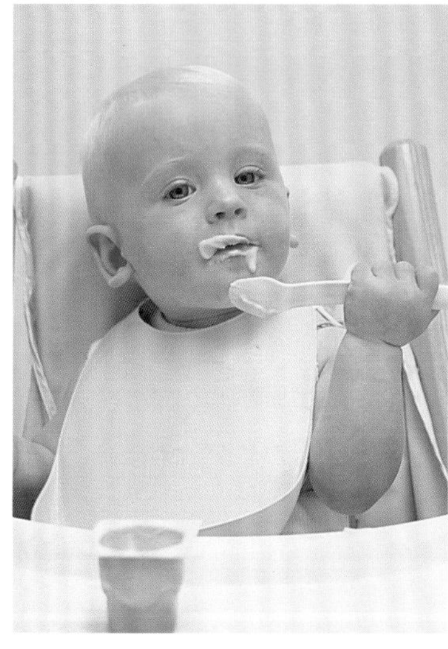

More foods to try
Add to the vegetable, fruit and cereal other foods such as:

- Mashed meat and poultry;
- Mashed hard boiled egg;
- Mashed lentils (dahl) or split pulses, hummus;
- Full-fat milk products (yogurt, fromage frais, custard) unless advised otherwise by your health visitor;

  Full-fat cow's milk can also be used for cooking from six months (e.g. in custard or cheese sauce) but avoid using cow's milk as a drink until your baby is one year old.

Foods to avoid giving your baby

- **Salt.** Do not add **any** salt to foods for young babies as their kidneys can't cope with it. Baby foods are not allowed to contain salt, but such ingredients as bacon will contain some. It's best not to encourage a liking for salt at any age. When you're cooking for the family, leave out the salt so your baby can share the food. It's healthier for you all without any salt anyway.
- **Sugar.** Do not add sugar to the food or drinks you give your baby. Sugar could encourage a sweet tooth and lead to tooth decay when the first teeth start to come through.
- **Honey.** This too is a sugar and can cause the same problems as sugar. Don't give honey until your child is one year old, even for easing coughs. It can contain a type of bacteria which can produce toxins in the baby's intestines and can cause a very serious illness (infant botulism). After the age of one, the baby's intestine matures and the bacteria are not able to grow.
- **Nuts.** Whole nuts should not be given to children under five years in case of choking. See also **Nut allergy**, page 69.

Weaning before six months

Weaning before six months is not recommended. However, if you choose to wean before six months the following foods should also be avoided:

- Foods which contain gluten, e.g. wheat flour, bread, breakfast cereals, rusks, spaghetti or other pastas in tomato sauce, etc.
- Nuts and seeds including ground nuts, peanut butter and other nut spreads.
- Eggs.
- Fish and shellfish.
- Citrus fruits including citrus fruit juices.
- Soft and unpasteurised cheeses.

If you decide to wean your baby before six months, start with a teaspoonful of smooth vegetable or fruit puree (with no added salt or sugar) or cereal (not wheat-based), e.g. sago or baby rice, mixed to a thin consistency. Offer it to your baby before or after one of the milk feeds, or in the middle of the feed if that works better. If the food is hot, make sure you **stir it** and **test it** before giving it to your baby.

As your baby gets used to taking foods from a spoon it is important to move from pureed to mashed and more lumpy foods.

For more information about types and textures see page 67.

Nut allergy

Some people are allergic to nuts or seeds. In recent years, peanut allergy, although still uncommon, appears to be increasing among children. It is not yet known why. The following will help to reduce the risk of developing this life-threatening allergy:

- ***Pregnant or breastfeeding mothers** who are 'atopic', or those for whom the father or any sibling of the baby has an allergy, may wish to avoid eating peanuts or peanut butter products during pregnancy or while breastfeeding.*
- ***Peanuts and foods containing peanuts,** such as peanut butter or **unrefined or cold-pressed groundnut oil**, should not be given to infants from 'atopic' or 'allergic' families until they are at least three years old or to infants who are allergic to peanuts.*
- ***Refined** peanut oil, vegetable oils and cosmetics or creams containing refined groundnut oil are considered safe.*
- *Read contents labels carefully and if you are in doubt, avoid the product.*
- *If there is no allergy in the immediate family, there is no need for children to avoid peanuts after weaning. These can be given from six months but should always be crushed or flaked. Do not give **whole peanuts** or any type of **whole nuts** to children under five in case of choking.*

Allergies

Babies are more likely to develop allergies if there is a family history of eczema, asthma, or hayfever. Introduce new foods one at a time so you can spot any allergic reaction.

MOVING ON

Once your baby has grown used to a variety of foods, give solids first and milk feed second. Your baby should still be having breast milk or a minimum of 500-600 ml (about a pint) of infant formula milk. As solid foods become a large part of your baby's diet, it is important to offer a range of different foods to provide all the vitamins and minerals needed (see page 75).

Try to give **two to three servings** a day of starchy foods, such as potatoes, pasta, yams, rice, bread and unsweetened breakfast cereals. Fruit and vegetables make good finger foods or can be part of the meal. Include them at two or more meals each day.

Your baby should have **one serving** of cooked meat, fish, egg, tofu or pulses, such as beans or lentils (dahl), a day. It is important to include good sources of iron, e.g. red meat (beef, lamb and pork) and liver. Eggs (well cooked until white and yolk are solid) are a quick, nutritious and cheap source of protein.

Finger foods and lumps

Encourage your baby to chew. This will also encourage the development of speech muscles. You can do this by giving foods that have a few lumps. Most babies can start to chew soft lumps, such as baked beans or rice pudding, from six months even if they have no teeth.

Suitable finger foods include toast, bread, pitta bread or chapatti, peeled apple, banana, raw or cooked green beans or carrot sticks, sticks of cheese. Avoid biscuits and rusks so that your baby does not get into the habit of expecting sweet snacks. Even low-sugar rusks contain sugar. Finger foods provide chewing practice and encourage babies to feed themselves.

If you delay giving 'lumpy' or finger foods, you may find that your baby refuses to eat 'lumpy' foods as they get older. **Always stay with your baby during feeding to give encouragement and to make sure he or she doesn't choke.**

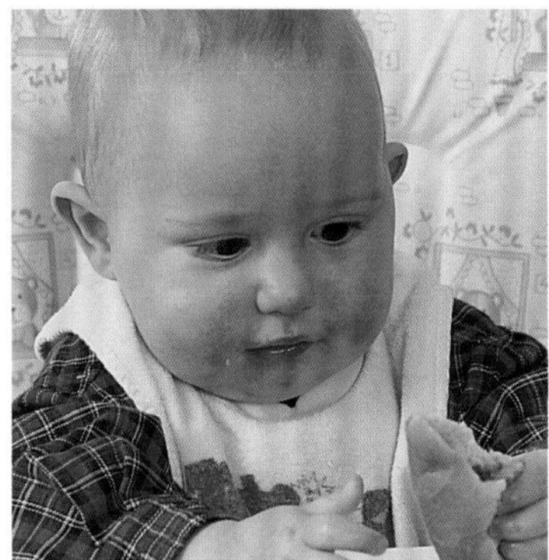

Some meals and snacks to try

Breakfast

- *Porridge or unsweetened cereal mixed with full-fat cow's milk or baby's usual milk*
- *Wholewheat biscuit cereal and milk*
- *Mashed banana and toast fingers*
- *Boiled egg and toast fingers*
- *Stewed apple and yogurt*

Lunch or dinner

- *Mashed cooked lentils with rice*
- *Cauliflower cheese*
- *Minced chicken and vegetable casserole with mashed potato*
- *Mashed pasta with broccoli and cheese*
- *Mashed canned salmon with couscous and peas*
- *Baked beans (reduced salt and sugar) with toast*
- *Scrambled egg with toast, chapatti or pitta bread*
- *Mashed boiled sweet potato with mashed carrot and broccoli*
- *Shepherd's pie with green vegetables*
- *Cottage cheese dip with pitta bread and carrot sticks*
- *Rice and mashed peas.*

Snacks

- *Pieces of fruit or vegetables*
- *Bread, toast, breadsticks, scones, pancakes*
- *Plain yogurt, plain fromage frais*

Drinks

Keep to your baby's usual milk (breast milk or about 500-600 ml (1pt) infant formula milk). Give milk at waking and bedtime. At mealtimes give milk, water or diluted fruit juice. Fruit juice should be given in a cup and diluted 1 part juice with 10 parts water. Do not use fruit drinks, squashes or baby drinks as they tend to be high in sugar and are not needed. After six months, tap water need not be boiled.

Tea and coffee are not suitable for children under five years.

Introduce a cup for drinks at six months and by one year all bottles should be stopped.

Remember that cow's milk should not be given as a drink until your baby is one year old, but it can be used for mixing foods such as cereal or adding to potatoes.

From one year

Once your child is one year old he or she should be learning to fit in with the family by eating three minced or chopped meals a day plus breast milk or whole cow's milk or infant formula milk. Your baby should also have fruit or other healthy snacks in between meals.

If your baby is on the move, you may need to increase the amount of food you give. Babies have small tummies, and they need energy for growth, so make sure you give them **full-fat** dairy products, such as yogurt, fromage frais and cheese. Cutting back on fat is sensible for adults, not for babies.

- Give starchy foods (three to four servings) and fruits and vegetables (three to four servings). Don't encourage a sweet tooth by giving biscuits and cakes – they will fill your baby up without providing the right nutrients.

- If you have decided not to give your child meat or fish, make sure that you give two servings a day of split pulses (red lentils, split peas), tofu, etc. The vitamin C in fruit and vegetables helps to absorb iron so give fruit and vegetables at mealtimes. If you or your family have a history of hayfever, eczema, asthma or other allergies see page 69 for important information.

Drinks

Continue to breastfeed or give 350–600 ml (up to 1 pt) of whole cow's milk or infant formula milk a day. Give milk on waking and at bedtime. Give milk, water or diluted fruit juice at mealtimes. Tea or coffee are not advised for young children.

Your child should be having a good mixed diet by now with probably three meals a day with a couple of healthy snacks in between. You can now start to give your child whole cow's milk as the main drink (not semi-skimmed or skimmed milk).

- If your child doesn't like milk, give at least two servings of full-fat yogurt and cheese or milk-based dishes (cheese sauce, rice pudding, etc.) a day. This will provide calcium for healthy bones.

- Your child's diet should now contain starchy foods such as bread, potatoes, pasta and rice, and a wide range of fruit and vegetables. To give a rough idea of the amounts, aim for about four servings of starchy foods, four servings of fruit and vegetables, and one or two servings of meat, fish or eggs a day.

- Offer a variety of foods. Why not go back to the foods that your child didn't like earlier and try them again?

- Remember, red meat (beef, lamb and pork) and liver are excellent sources of iron. Serving meat and vegetables together rather than at separate meals helps to absorb iron. If your baby has a meat- and fish-free diet, give two servings a day of lentils, peas, beans or eggs. Vitamin C will help the absorption of iron from these foods (see page 73).

Bottle, beaker or cup?

How you give drinks is important. A lidded beaker is better than a bottle with a teat. Drinks flow very slowly through a teat and drinking can take a long time. This means your child spends a lot of time with a teat in the mouth, which may delay speech development and damage teeth, especially if drinking a sweetened drink. Move on from a lidded beaker to drinking from a cup as soon as your child is ready. If you give a bedtime drink in a bottle, make sure it is only water or milk and remember to clean teeth afterwards.

Drinks

Which drinks should I give?

- **Breast milk** is the ideal drink for babies in the first few months, and ideally up to their first birthday. You can go on breastfeeding as long as you want.
- **Infant formula** is based on cow's milk and is the only alternative to breast milk in the first 12 months of your baby's life. Once your baby is six months old you can give follow-on milks, but this change is not necessary.
- **Hydrolysed protein infant formulas** are recommended for babies who are allergic to cow's milk. If you are planning to feed your baby a vegan (strict vegetarian) diet, discuss this with your health visitor and/or GP. Vegan diets are not recommended for young babies.
- **Whole cow's milk** is not suitable as a main drink until your baby is one year old as it doesn't contain sufficient iron and other nutrients to meet your baby's needs. Semi-skimmed milk is not suitable as a drink for children under two, but can be introduced from two years if the child is a good eater and has a varied diet. Skimmed milk is not suitable for children under five.

- **Goat's and sheep's milk** are not suitable as drinks for babies under one year old as they do not contain sufficient iron and other nutrients to keep your baby healthy. Providing they are pasteurised, they can be used once a baby is one year old.
- **Water** is the best alternative drink to milk. Other drinks can fill babies and toddlers up, leaving them with little appetite for more nutritious foods at mealtimes. Take water from the mains tap in the kitchen and boil it for babies under six months (it doesn't need boiling once your baby is six months old). Bottled natural mineral waters vary in the levels of some minerals such as salt, and some with very high levels are not safe for this reason. Fizzy (carbonated) bottled water can damage teeth because it's acidic.

If you have to use bottled water, i.e. when travelling abroad, choose a still bottled water and boil it until your baby is six months old.

- **Citrus fruit juices,** such as orange juice or grapefruit juice, are a good source of vitamin C, but also contain naturally present sugars which can cause tooth decay. They're acidic too. Fruit juices should not be given before your baby is six months old. However, vitamin C helps to absorb any iron in a meal, and so you may be advised to give diluted fruit juice with your child's meals after six months, especially if your baby has a vegetarian diet or you are breastfeeding. **Give very dilute fruit juice (1 part fruit juice with 10 parts water) in a cup at mealtimes only.**

- **Squashes, fizzy drinks, flavoured waters and juice drinks.** Filling up on too much of these drinks can result in a poor appetite, poor weight gain and, in toddlers, loose stools. **They are all unsuitable for babies and young children as they contain a lot of sugars and may cause damage to teeth.**

- **Diet drinks and 'no added sugar' drinks,** whether squashes, flavoured waters or fizzy drinks, are not intended for babies or toddlers. They contain artificial sweeteners and your child could get more of these sweetners than is recommended.

- **Baby and herbal drinks** may contain sugars and their use is **not** recommended.

- **Tea and coffee** are **not** suitable drinks for babies or young children under five years. They reduce iron absorption when taken with meals and, if sugar is added, may contribute to tooth decay.

Start encouraging your child to use a cup after six months. You may find it easier to use a jug with graduated measurements to mix infant formula for use in a cup.

Don't give two supplements at the same time. For example, don't add cod liver oil as well as vitamin drops – one on its own is strong enough. Too much of some vitamins is as harmful as not enough.

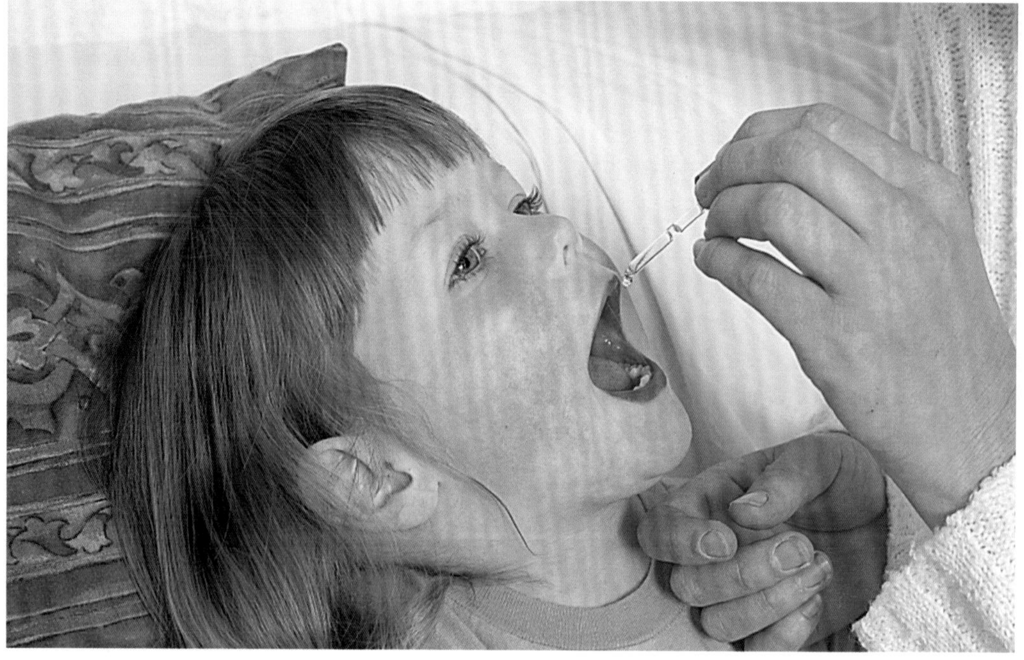

Vitamins

Parents sometimes get confused about whether or not to give vitamin drops. Your health visitor should be able to advise you. If you are still breastfeeding after your baby is six months old, he or she should have baby vitamin drops containing vitamins A, C and D. If your baby is bottle fed, extra vitamins are already added during manufacture. Provided your baby is drinking 500 ml (1 pt) of formula milk per day, vitamin drops are not needed. If your baby is drinking less than this, then it's sensible to give vitamin drops. These can normally be obtained from child health clinics or free if you qualify (see page 145).

It is sensible to give all babies vitamin drops from the age of one to five years old.

Vitamin D is made naturally in the skin when it is exposed to gentle sunlight. As little as half an hour playing outdoors is sufficient to meet your child's daily vitamin D requirements. Remember that children burn easily, especially those with fair skin, so don't expose them to direct sunlight or let them stay out too long in the sun in hot weather (see page 111 for advice about safety in the sun).

Children who wear concealing clothes that cover them throughout the year when outdoors will particularly benefit from starting vitamin drops at one month until they are five.

Sources of vitamin A

- *Dairy products*
- *Fortified fat spreads*
- *Liver*
- *Carrots and dark green vegetables (e.g. spinach, cabbage, broccoli)*

Sources of vitamin C

- *Oranges, pure orange juice (not suitable for babies under six months old)*
- *Kiwi fruit, blackcurrants, mangoes, nectarines, apples*
- *Broccoli, peppers, peas, cauliflower, cabbage, tomatoes*

Sources of vitamin D

- *Summer sunshine*
- *Fortified fat spreads*
- *Fortified breakfast cereals*
- *Salmon, sardines, taramasalata, herring*
- *Meat*

Family Food

For adults and children over five, a healthy, balanced diet usually means eating plenty of bread, breakfast cereals, potatoes, pasta and rice, as well as fruit and vegetables. **The balance of good health** model shown right indicates the types of foods and the proportions you need to eat them in for a well-balanced, healthy diet. Children under the age of five need a diet that is higher in fat and lower in fibre than this, but by five should be eating a diet similar to that recommended for adults.

'Yes, I want my kids to eat the right sorts of things. But wanting is one thing and doing it, or getting them to do it, is something else altogether. Mostly what one will eat the other won't. The only things I know they'll both eat are things like chips and sausages. Family meals almost always mean one of them making a fuss. You can make something for them that takes twice as long as sausages or whatever, and you end up putting it all in the bin.'

Fruit and vegetables
e.g. fresh, frozen and canned fruit and vegetables, salads, dried fruit, fruit juices. *Try to eat at least five servings a day. This can include a glass of fruit juice.*

Bread, other cereals and potatoes
e.g. bread, potatoes, breakfast cereals, pasta, rice, oats, noodles, maize, millet, yams, cornmeal, sweet potatoes. *Make these the main part of every meal, eat wholegrain varieties when you can.*

Milk and dairy products
e.g. milk, yogurt, fromage frais. *Try to eat several servings a day. Do not use low fat varieties for children under two.*

Meat, fish and alternatives
e.g. meat, fish, poultry, eggs, beans, pulses, nuts (except peanuts). *Eat one or two servings a day. Choose lean meat, skin poultry and cook using the minimum of fat. Try to eat oily fish at least once a week.*

Foods containing fat, foods containing sugar
e.g. all spreading fats, oils, salad dressings, cream, chocolate, crisps, biscuits, pastries, ice-cream, cakes, puddings, fizzy drinks. *Limit the amount you eat.*

Some ideas to try if your child won't drink milk

Milk

- *Porridge, hot oat cereal or cornmeal made with full-fat milk*
- *Breakfast cereals with milk*
- *Vermicelli cooked in full-fat milk*
- *Rice pudding, custard, bread-and-butter pudding*
- *Dairy ice-cream made with milk*

Cheese

- *Macaroni cheese, cheese on toast, cheese on vegetables and bakes*
- *Vegetable soup with grated cheese*
- *Chunks of cheese and pieces of fruit*
- *Cottage cheese dips*

Yogurt and fromage frais

- *Add fruit (fresh, frozen or canned) raw, stewed or baked, to full-fat yogurt or fromage frais*
- *Add yogurt to curry*

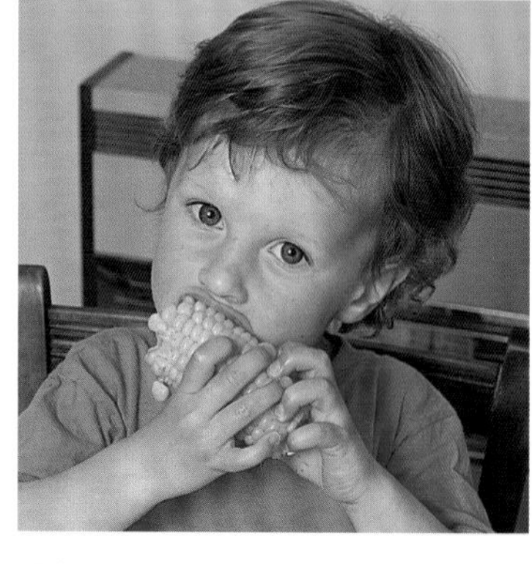

Your Toddler's Diet

By the time your child is starting to stand up and take his/her first steps, he or she will be joining in family meals. They will also be more active and using more energy, and will need a varied, energy-rich diet for good health and growth.

We all need energy (calories) and nutrients (protein, carbohydrate, fat, vitamins and minerals) to grow, for activity, and for the body to work properly and repair itself. Babies and children under two have small tummies and can't eat large amounts of food all in one go, so they need small meals with healthy snacks in between. Like the rest of the family, your toddler needs to eat a variety of foods from the following five groups. By doing so, your child will almost certainly get all the nutrients he or she needs.

- **Milk and dairy foods** – milk, cheese, yoghurt, fromage frais.
- **Bread, other cereals and potatoes** – bread, rice, pasta, maize, potatoes, breakfast cereals, etc.
- **Fruits and vegetables** – all types of fruits and vegetables.
- **Meat, fish and alternatives** – meat, fish, poultry, eggs, beans, lentils etc.
- **Foods containing fat and foods containing sugar** – biscuits, cakes, chocolate, puddings, crisps, sweets, ice-cream, fats and oils. Give only limited amounts.

Milk and dairy products

Milk is important for young children. Milk and dairy products are a good source of vitamin A which helps the body to resist infections and is needed for healthy skin and eyes.

After the age of one, a minimum of 350ml of milk a day will provide energy for growth, and calcium for strong bones and teeth. You can

continue breastfeeding after the age of one if you wish and full-fat cow's milk can now take the place of infant formula and follow-on milk as your baby's main drink. If your child doesn't like drinking milk every day, give at least two servings of milk-based dishes, cheese, yogurt or fromage frais daily, preferably after a main meal.

Use full-fat milk and dairy products until your child is five, although semi-skimmed milk can be introduced from two years of age, provided your child is a good eater and growing well. **Children under two need the extra fat and vitamins in full-fat dairy products. Skimmed milk is not suitable for children under five.**

Families receiving Income Support or an income-based Jobseeker's Allowance with children under five years of age can receive seven pints of milk per week per child, free of charge (for more information see page 145).

Bread, other cereals and potatoes

Whether it is bread or breakfast cereals, potatoes or yams, rice or couscous, pasta or chappatis, most children don't need much encouragement to eat one or more of the foods from this group.

'When you go shopping, your mind's on anything but shopping. You can't stop and think. You grab what you can and get out quick.'

Fat and fibre

Some people wrongly think that small children need a low-fat diet, just like adults. Children under the age of two need fat in their diet to provide energy, and some vitamins are only found in fat. It is therefore more important to make sure that they eat a variety of foods and get enough calories than to worry about fat. Between the ages of two and five their diet will adapt to be more like that of adults. Make sure that both your child, as they get to be five years old, and the rest of your family aim for a healthy diet based on the balance of good health, which is low in fat, especially saturated fat.

It is also a mistake to give babies and toddlers a high-fibre diet as it is quite bulky and can stop important minerals like calcium and iron from being absorbed. High-fibre foods, such as wholemeal bread, pasta and brown rice, can be introduced gradually, so that by the time children are five they are used to a healthy adult diet.

A portion with each meal will provide energy, various nutrients and some fibre. Let your child try lots of different varieties of starchy foods. Try wholemeal bread and pasta every now and then. However, it's not a good idea to give only wholegrain foods because they may fill your child up too quickly to get all the calories they need. Don't add bran to cereals or use bran-enriched cereals as they can interfere with the body's ability to absorb iron. Starchy foods form an important part of anyone's diet. But they can be very filling, so make sure small tummies have room for other foods too.

Some ideas to try

Tasty snacks

- *Breakfast cereals (not sugar-coated)*
- *Popcorn or breadsticks*
- *Toast, bagels, scones or pancakes*
- *Fingers of toasted white bread covered with cheese spread*

More substantial meals

- *Baked potatoes with baked beans and cheese*
- *Pasta with vegetables, meat, fish or cheese sauces*
- *Pitta bread filled with cream cheese, ham or fish*
- *Couscous mixed with peas and flaked fish or cooked minced meat*
- *Noodles or rice mixed with shredded omelette and vegetables*
- *Chapattis with dahl.*

'It's difficult to give them healthy food because of the money. But some of the stuff that's not healthy costs most of all – like sweets. And there are things you can do – like beans and lentils and things are cheap and you can store them. And I slice up fruit and share it between the kids and it goes further.'

'I do feel, you know, I wish she'd eat that. But I'm resigned to it. Because even getting her to try things is hard. So I just serve up the same old things, and it's a fairly good mix, so why worry? I mean, she does eat different sorts of food. She eats baked beans, she loves bread, she'll drink milk. Potatoes and cheese always go down OK. She has orange juice and apples, bananas sometimes. There's nothing wrong with that.'

Fruit and vegetables

Fruit and vegetables contain lots of vitamins, minerals and fibre and they liven up meals with a variety of colours, textures and flavours. Try to introduce lots of different types from an early age, whether fresh, frozen, canned or dried.

Try to ensure children have 5 portions daily of fruit and vegetables. Portion sizes are different for children under 5 years: 1 portion can be 1 tablespoon of cooked vegetables or 1/2 of fruits such as apple, orange, pear, banana, or 1 kiwi or 1 plum. Try to include a wide variety of types and colours of fruit and vegetables.

Different fruits and vegetables contain different vitamins and minerals, so the wider the range your toddler eats, the better. If they are picky, then gradually introduce new varieties on picnics, at granny's or with other familiar food.

Many children don't eat enough fruit and vegetables and it can be hard work persuading them to even eat a mouthful. Obviously, there will always be something they don't like! Use some of the ideas in the box to help you.

Many children don't like cooked vegetables but will nibble on them while you're preparing the meal. Be imaginative about serving vegetables, perhaps mashing different types together or arranging them attractively on the plate.

If your child refuses to eat vegetables, keep offering them but also offer more fruit. Make sure you show that you like eating them. Don't make a big fuss if they refuse. Give vitamin drops as a safeguard (see **Vitamins**, page 74).

Some ideas to try

- *Top pizza with favourite vegetables or canned pineapple.*
- *Give carrot sticks, slices of pepper and peeled apple for snacks.*
- *Mix chopped or mashed vegetables with rice, mashed potatoes, meat sauces or dahl.*
- *Mix fruit, whether fresh, canned or stewed, with yogurt or fromage frais for a tasty dessert.*
- *Chop prunes or dried apricots into cereal or yogurt, or add to a stew.*

Meat, fish and alternatives

Protein is needed by young children to grow and develop. Meat, fish, eggs, nuts, pulses (beans, lentils and peas), foods made from pulses (tofu, hummus, soya mince, etc.) and Quorn are excellent sources of protein, so **give at least one portion from this group each day**. Meat and fish also contain zinc, which is important for healing wounds and making many of the body's processes function properly. Zinc can be in short supply in toddlers' diets.

If you are bringing up your child on a diet without meat (vegetarian) or without any food from an animal (vegan), **two portions of vegetable proteins or nuts** daily will ensure enough protein. Whole nuts should not be given to children under five years of age as there is a risk of choking. Grind nuts finely or use a smooth nut butter (see page 69 for important information about peanut allergy).

Is your child a vegetarian?

Types of vegetarian diets

There are different types of vegetarians. Vegans eat no foods which come from animals. Lacto-vegetarians eat milk and milk products, and lacto-ovo-vegetarians eat milk, milk products and eggs. If your child has a vegetarian or vegan diet, take care to provide enough energy, protein, iron, calcium, vitamin B12 and vitamin D. The principles of weaning for the first six months are the same for vegetarian babies as for non-vegetarians. However, as your child gets older, the iron and energy content of such a diet may be low and the fibre content high (see ***Getting enough iron****, page 80, and* ***Fat and fibre****, page 77). To ensure all your child's nutritional needs are met, smaller and more frequent main meals, with one or two snacks in between, are best. Vitamin drops are especially important up to five years of age.*

Vegan diets

A vegan diet may be very bulky, consisting mainly of fruits, vegetables and beans. Young children may have difficulty in eating enough food to provide the energy and nutrients they need for growth and so may become malnourished. Vegan diets are ***not*** *therefore recommended for young babies. If your child does have a vegan diet, you need to take extra care to ensure he or she has enough of the following nutrients and enough energy. It is also advisable to consult a dietitian or doctor before starting weaning.*

- ***Energy*** *– starchy foods. These need to be eaten in moderation. For extra energy, add vegetable oils or vegetarian fat spreads to foods. Smooth nut or seed butters can also be used, but you will have to avoid some of these products (e.g. peanut butter, tahini paste,* etc.) if there is a risk of your child being allergic to them (see* ***Food allergies****, page 83 and * below).*
- ***Protein*** *– pulses, foods made from pulses, Quorn, but continue with soya-based infant formula until your child is two years of age to ensure she or he has enough protein.*
- ***Iron*** *– see* ***Getting enough iron****, page 80.*
- ***Calcium*** *– soya mince, soya drink that has been fortified with calcium, tahini paste,* tofu and tempeh.*
- ***Vitamin B12*** *– fortified breakfast cereals, some yeast extracts. A supplement of B12 may be needed.*
- ***Vitamin D*** *– see page 74.*

For more information on vegetarian diets, contact: The Vegetarian Society, Parkdale, Dunham Road, Altrincham, Cheshire WA14 4QG, Tel: 0161 925 2000.

* *Tahini paste is made from sesame seeds, and these may cause an allergic reaction in a small number of children.*

Some meals to try

Tasty snacks

- *Canned mashed sardines on fingers of toast*
- *Filled pitta pockets with canned salmon and salad*
- *Scrambled egg on toast with tomato slices*

More substantial meals

- *Beans, lentils and peas make delicious soups or stews*
- *Grilled sausages with baked beans (reduced salt and sugar) and mashed potato*
- *Lean mince for spaghetti bolognese served with vegetables*
- *Chick pea curry with vegetables and chapatti*
- *Grilled fish fingers with potatoes and peas*
- *Stir-fried chicken and vegetables with rice*
- *Ham with baked potatoes and broccoli*
- *Fish curry with vegetables and rice*

Getting enough iron

Iron is essential for your child's health. Lack of iron leads to anaemia, which can hold back your child's physical and mental development. Children who are poor eaters or on restricted diets are most at risk. Iron comes in two forms. One is found in foods from animal sources (especially meat), which is easily absorbed by the body. The other is found in plant foods, which is not quite so easy for the body to absorb.

If you can, try to give your child a portion of meat or fish every day.

Even a small portion of meat or fish is useful because it also helps the body to absorb iron from other food sources. If your child doesn't have meat or fish, make sure that he or she regularly eats plenty of iron-rich alternatives (choose from the list below).

It's also a good idea to give foods or drinks that are high in vitamin C at mealtimes, as it helps the absorption of iron from non-meat sources. Tea and coffee reduce iron absorption, so don't serve these, especially at mealtimes.

Fat, sugar and salt

Foods containing fat and foods containing sugar are the fifth main food group.

Fat Young children, especially the under twos, need the concentrated energy provided by fat in their diet. That is why it is important to give such foods as full-fat milk, yogurt, cheese, and oily fish. Between the ages of two and five you can gradually introduce lower-fat dairy products and cut down on fat in other foods so that by the time children are five they are eating a healthy low-fat diet like that recommended for adults. Make sure you don't increase the fat in the diet by introducing too many high-fat fast foods, e.g. burgers.

Such foods as crisps, chips, biscuits, cakes and fried foods are also high in fat, and they're popular with children and adults alike, but they should be limited at all ages to keep your family healthy. Consider these sorts of foods as 'extras' once your child has eaten well from the four other main groups.

Because fat is such a concentrated source of energy, it is easy to eat too much of it and become overweight. It's a good idea to be aware of the amount of fat contained in foods which the whole family eats and to try to keep it to a minimum. Some ideas for cutting down on fat are shown in the box opposite.

Good sources of iron

Plant sources

- *Fortified breakfast cereals*
- *Dark-green vegetables*
- *Breads*
- *Beans and lentils*
- *Tofu*
- *Dried fruit: apricots, figs, prunes*

Animal sources

- *Lean beef, lamb or pork*
- *Liver pâté, liver or kidney*
- *Chicken or turkey*
- *Canned sardines, pilchards, mackerel or tuna*

Try some of these ideas for cutting down fat in family meals (especially saturated fat)

- *Grill or bake foods instead of frying.*
- *Skim the fat off meat dishes like mince or curry during cooking.*
- *Buy leaner cuts of meat and lower-fat meat products, such as sausages and burgers with low-fat labels.*
- *Take the skin off poultry before cooking – it's the fattiest part.*
- *Use vegetables or soaked dried beans with just a small amount of meat in stews and casseroles.*
- *Use lower-fat dairy products like low-fat spreads and reduced-fat cheeses (e.g. reduced-fat cheddar or edam) rather than full-fat varieties (but not for children under two).*
- *Use as little cooking oil as possible and choose one which is high in polyunsaturates such as rapeseed, sunflower, soya, corn or olive oil.*

Sugar Most young children enjoy sweet foods, such as biscuits, cakes, sweets, chocolates and sweet drinks. A small amount of sugar in foods at mealtimes is OK, but when teeth are in frequent contact with sugary foods and drinks, they will decay. You can reduce the amount of sugar you give by trying the following.

- Reduce the number of foods and drinks you give which taste sweet, whether from sugar or artificial sweeteners as they encourage a sweet tooth.

- Try not to give sweet foods and drinks to your child every day. Keep them for mealtimes and don't use them as a reward.

- Fruit and vegetables contain sugar, but in a form that doesn't damage teeth. However, the sugar in dried fruit and fruit juice can cause decay if consumed frequently.

- Encourage your children to choose breakfast cereals that aren't sugar-coated.

- Beware of other forms of sugars on labels – sucrose, glucose, honey, dextrose, maltose syrup, or concentrated fruit juice.

- Even if diet forms of desserts do not contain these sugars, they are too low in fat for a young child.

- Do not add sugar to milk.

- Jaggery can cause the same damage to teeth as sugar. Limit foods containing this, like Indian sweetmeats.

Salt There is no need to add salt (sodium chloride) to your child's food because there is enough naturally present in foods. Too much salt can lead to a liking for salty foods and contribute towards high blood pressure in later life. The whole family will benefit if you gradually reduce the amount of salt in your cooking. Keep salt off the table and limit the amount of salty foods (crisps, savoury snacks, bombay mix, bacon, ham and other salted meats) your child has. Avoid salt substitutes as these are just as harmful.

Cutlery, chopsticks or fingers?

Be prepared for messy mealtimes with children. It will take time for your child to learn how to behave when eating. You and the rest of the family will set an example, so try to eat and enjoy your food together. Some families prefer to eat with their fingers, while others use chopsticks or cutlery. Whatever tool is preferred, be patient. Your child will need time to get used to them.

By about one year of age, babies should be trying to feed themselves.

'A lot of it is habit. I mean, if your children have never had sugar on their cereal in the morning, then they don't expect it. But then you mustn't have it either. The thing is that I like sweet things myself. In fact, at the moment, the more tired I get the more I want to eat biscuits and that sort of thing. But if I eat them, the children eat them. The only answer is not to buy them in the first place.'

'Everybody knows that sweets aren't good. But they love them. And the fact is, it's a pleasure to treat them.'

Some safety tips

- *Take care that your child only has access to small blunt knives at the meal table.*
- *Unbreakable plates or bowls are ideal for small children, who often decide their meal is finished when their plate hits the floor.*
- *When your child no longer needs the high chair, make sure that he or she is sitting at the right height for the table, otherwise your child will find it difficult to eat. Booster seats, cushions or a lap may be useful, but whatever you use, make sure your child is sitting safely.*

Some babies are very independent and want no help, even if most of the food does not reach their mouths. Others prefer help, but are happy to fiddle with a spoon whilst being fed. Whichever the case, encourage your child to feed him or herself, either with a spoon or by offering suitable finger foods.

How much food do toddlers need?

Children's appetites vary enormously, so common sense is a good guide on how big a portion should be. Be guided by your children – do not force them to eat when they no longer wish to, but do not refuse to give more if they really are hungry. As long as your child eats a range of foods, and your health visitor is happy with his or her progress, try not to be concerned about the amount your child eats.

Finger foods for snacks or with meals

- *Bananas or peeled apple slices*
- *Chapatti or pitta bread fingers*
- *Breadsticks*
- *Wholemeal toast fingers with cheese spread*
- *Cooked pasta twirls*
- *Cooked vegetables, e.g. carrot or green beans*
- *Raw vegetables, e.g. cucumber*
- *Cubes of cheese*
- *Thin-cut sandwiches cut into small pieces*

Food additives

Foods contain additives for a variety of reasons – to prevent food poisoning, to stop foods from going off, to provide colour, flavour or texture. Some food additives are natural substances, others are synthetic. Any additives put into food must, by law, be shown on the label. Many are shown by the European Community 'E number'. Additives with E numbers have been tested and passed as safe for use in EU countries. Numbers without an E in front are allowed in the UK, but not in all EU countries.

A few people suffer from allergic reactions to some additives, but many more people are allergic to ordinary foods such as milk or soya. A diet which is high in processed foods is not only more likely to contain additives, but will probably be higher in salt, sugar and fat than is desirable for adults and children. Replacing these foods with more fruits and vegetables and starchy foods is good advice.

FOOD SAFETY

Young children are especially vulnerable to bacteria that cause food poisoning. So it's very important to store, prepare and cook food safely, and to keep the kitchen clean.
For a healthy, safe diet:

- wash all fruits and vegetables before eating. Peel and top carrots and peel fruits such as apples; remove waxy or furry skins, e.g. peaches;

- avoid raw eggs – they sometimes contain Salmonella bacteria, which may cause food poisoning (also avoid giving your child uncooked cake mixture, home-made ice-creams, mayonnaise, or desserts that contain uncooked raw egg – and, when cooking eggs, the egg yolk and white should be firm;

- when re-heating food, make sure that it is piping hot all the way through, and allow to cool slightly before giving to your child (if you choose to use a microwave to heat your child's food, always stir and check the temperature of the food before feeding your child to avoid burning from hot spots);

- don't give children food or drink when they're sitting on the potty, to avoid passing bacteria to their food and mouth;

- teach your children to wash their hands after touching pets and going to the toilet, and before eating;

- avoid soft and unpasteurised cheeses.

FOOD ALLERGIES

Some children experience unpleasant reactions after eating certain foods. They might be sick, have diarrhoea, cough or wheeze or get an itchy rash or eczema, but they often outgrow these food sensitivities. However, some foods may cause a reaction so severe that it is life-threatening. Thankfully, this affects very few children. The foods most likely to cause a problem for small children are often the ones they first meet at weaning, so it's sensible to avoid giving these foods until a baby is at least six months old. A list of these foods can be found on page 68.

Serious allergies to nuts, nut products and some seeds affect less than 1% of the population. For those who are most at risk (people with allergies such as hayfever, asthma and eczema in the family) it may be best to avoid these foods. Peanut allergy is a particular concern. For children who are at risk of peanut allergy (i.e. those whose parents or siblings suffer from hayfever, asthma, eczema or any food allergy), the advice is to avoid giving peanuts and foods containing peanut products (e.g. peanut butter, ***unrefined*** groundnut oil and some snacks, etc.) until the child is three years old. Read food labels carefully and, if you are still in doubt about the contents, avoid these foods.

If you suspect that your child may be reacting to a food, always seek medical advice. Don't be tempted to experiment by cutting out a major food such as milk. Your child's diet may not provide all the necessary nutrients. Talk about your worries with your doctor and health visitor, who may refer you to a qualified dietitian.

If you suspect your child may be susceptible to food allergic reaction, contact your GP who can refer the child to a specialist clinic.

For advice you can contact the ***National Asthma Campaign*** *Helpline (0845 7010203, www.asthma.org.uk) or* ***Allergy UK*** *www.allergyfoundation.com 020 8303 8583 (allergy helpline Mon-Fri 9am-9pm) 020 8303 8525 (chemical sensitivity helpline Mon-Fri 9am-5pm)*

Problems with eating

It can be a great worry if your child refuses to eat or is terribly choosy, but it is extremely rare for a child to actually starve him or herself. Children will eat enough to keep them going. So try not to worry unless your child is clearly not gaining weight as he or she should (see pages 37-9), or is obviously unwell.

It may be that your child is picking up your own feelings about food. Perhaps you're a dieter or have a weight problem, or maybe you just see healthy eating as a very important goal. If your child is picking up on your anxiety it may be that mealtimes have become an ideal time to get attention.

Just as anxiety may cause problems with toilet training, it can also create problems with eating. So try to take a step back and think about how much of a problem there really is.

Refusing to eat, or eating very little

As long as your child eats some food from each of the five food groups – even if it's always the same old favourites – you shouldn't have to worry. Gradually offer other food choices. Or why not go back to the foods your child didn't like earlier and try them again? Remember, if your child is active and gaining weight, he or she is probably getting enough to eat however little it appears to you.

Tips for success

- Offer your child the same food you're giving your family, and eat your meals together if possible.
- Give smaller portions and praise your child for eating even a little.
- If your child rejects the food, don't force-feed him or her. Remove the food without comment.
- Don't leave meals until your child is too hungry or tired.
- Don't use sweet food as a reward for finishing savouries. To a child this might be saying, 'Here's something nice after eating those nasty greens'. Reward them with a trip to the park or watching a video instead.
- Your child knows that refusing to eat will annoy you, so try to stay calm. Eating with your child and eating the same foods will help to encourage good eating habits.

- If your child fills up with juice or squash between meals and refuses milk or a snack, try gradually reducing the amount, diluting the drink well with water, and offer a small amount of food first. Sometimes too, children mistake thirst for hunger and say they are thirsty when really they are hungry.

- Try to make mealtimes enjoyable and not just about eating. Sit down and have a chat about other things.

- If you know of any other children of the same age who are good eaters, ask them to tea. A good example sometimes works, so long as you don't go on about how good the other children are.

- Ask another adult, whom your child likes, to eat with you. Sometimes a child will eat for, say, a grandparent without any fuss. It may only be for one meal but it can break the habit.

- Your child may just be a naturally slow eater, so lots of patience will be needed.

- Children's tastes change. One day they'll hate something, a month later they'll love it. There will nearly always be enough that your child is willing to eat for some variety (say beans, fish fingers and fruit, potatoes with milk to drink). It may be boring, but it's perfectly healthy.

Party time!

Parties are a great time for children to experience different types of foods. It's a special occasion, so offer foods normally kept for treats as well as some familiar everyday foods.

Try some of the following healthy party food ideas.

- Fill tiny sandwiches and cut them into different shapes. Use fillings that cut easily – wafer thin ham, cheddar cheese, cheese spread, egg mayonnaise, etc.

- Offer bowls of plain popcorn, breadsticks, carrot sticks and baby tomatoes.

- Make reduced-sugar jellies and add canned mandarins or slices of fresh fruit.

- Offer one or two diluted fruit juices to drink rather than carbonated drinks.

- Fruit scones or fruit malt loaf need minimal preparation.

- Decorate small plain biscuits with cheese spread and a small piece of fresh or canned fruit to add colour.

- Serve ice-cream with fresh or canned fruit.

- Don't forget the birthday cake for the end of the meal.

YOUR QUESTIONS ANSWERED

Q. How do I discourage a relative from giving sweets to my child?

A. Suggest a present of a small book, pencil or other non-edible gift instead. You could keep sweets to a special 'treat' day, once a week. Remember that the number of times that teeth come into contact with sugars is as important as the amount of sugar that is eaten. Sweets are best eaten in one go rather than over the course of an hour or two. Keep them for mealtimes, when they do least damage to teeth. If you want more information about caring for your children's teeth ask your health visitor.

Q. What snacks can I give instead of biscuits or crisps?

A. Try some of these:

- a drink of milk;
- a plain yogurt with a banana sliced into it;
- a slice of toast with yeast extract, cheese or a slice of ham;
- some crackers, breadsticks or rice cakes with cheese;
- a bowl of cereal with milk;
- a piece of fruit.

Q. I've heard that a high-fibre diet is unsuitable for young children. Why is this?

A. Foods that contain a lot of fibre (wholemeal bread and pasta, brown rice, bran-based breakfast cereals, etc.) fill up small tummies, leaving little room for other foods. Bran also prevents important minerals from being absorbed. It's good for your child to try different varieties of starchy foods, but don't use only wholegrain foods until your child is five.

Q. What should I pack in a lunchbox for my three-year-old when she goes to nursery?

A. Try to choose two savoury options, some fruit, a sweet option (yogurt, fromage frais, scone, or currant bun) and a drink. Fill sandwiches with canned tuna or salmon, mashed banana, hard or cream cheese, ham, or peanut butter (but beware of food allergies, see page 83). Add a few vegetable sticks of carrots, peppers or cucumber to munch on and a container of ready washed and bite-size fruits – satsuma or seedless grapes. A box of raisins is fine if eaten at lunchtime. If you include a fromage frais or yogurt, don't forget a spoon. A piece of kitchen towel is always useful. If the lunchboxes are not refrigerated at nursery, choose an insulated box with an ice pack to keep food safe and cool. Buy a leak-proof beaker so you can give milk, water or well-diluted fruit juice.

Q. My child refuses to drink anything but sugary drinks.

A. If sugary drinks are drunk frequently, teeth are at high risk of decay. See pages 71–3 for suitable drinks. If your child will only drink sugary drinks, it can take some time to break the habit. Start by diluting these really well with water and offer in smaller quantities, in a beaker at mealtimes.

6 Illness and accidents

Every child gets ill occasionally and every parent has had that feeling of anxiety as they see their normally cheerful child looking sad and listless. Most bouts of illness pass quickly and leave children better able to resist the next attack. Sometimes, if the illness or accident is serious, immediate (and possibly long-term) help is needed. This chapter deals with common childhood illnesses and accidents, the best ways to prevent them, and the action to take in an emergency.

Knowing when your child is ill

Often it's difficult to tell whether a child is ill. Children may be listless, hot and miserable one minute, and running around quite happily the next. Watch out for:

- **some sign of illness**, e.g. vomiting, temperature, runny nose, runny eyes;
- **behaviour that's unusual for your child**, e.g. a lot of crying, being very irritable or refusing food and drink, being listless or drowsy).

Possible signs of illness are always more worrying if your child is a baby or very small. Make sure he/she drinks plenty of fluids and is not too hot. If your baby sleeps a lot, wake him or her regularly for a drink. It may be difficult to judge whether an illness is more serious requiring prompt medical attention. The following guidelines may help you:

Serious illness
There may be serious illness if your baby has any of the following symptoms:

- a high pitched or weak cry, is less responsive, is much less active or more floppy than usual;
- looks very pale all over, grunts with each breath, seems to be working hard to breathe when you look at their chest and tummy;
- takes less than a third of usual fluids, passes much less urine than usual, vomits green fluid, or passes blood in their stools;
- has a high fever or is sweating a lot.

If your baby seems unwell, seek medical advice early and quickly.

Urgent medical attention is needed if your baby shows the following symptoms and signs:

- a fit (convulsion), or if your baby turns blue or very pale (in a dark-skinned baby check the palms of the hands) or seems floppy. Even if your baby recovers without medical attention, still contact your doctor;
- a very high temperature (over 39°C), especially if there's a rash;
- difficulty breathing, breathing fast or grunting breathing, or stops breathing;
- unusually drowsy or hard to wake or doesn't seem to know you;
- glazed eyes and cannot focus;
- a temperature, but the skin of the hands and feet feels cold and clammy;

Always contact your doctor if you think your child's ill, even if you can't make out what's wrong. If you can't contact a GP, go directly to the Accident and Emergency department of the nearest hospital, one with a children's ward if possible. It's worth finding out in advance where this is, in case you ever need it. *See page 152 for what to do in an emergency.*

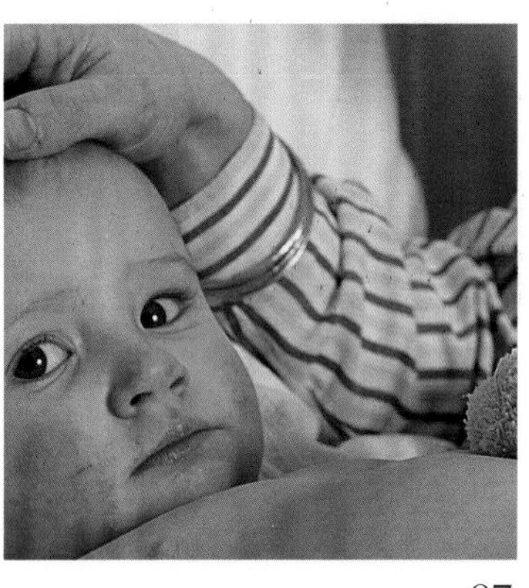

If you've seen your GP or health visitor and your child isn't getting better or is getting worse, contact your GP again the same day. If you become worried and you can't get hold of your GP, or your GP can't come to you quickly enough, then take your child straight to the nearest Accident and Emergency department.

- a purple-red rash anywhere on the body - this could be a sign of meningitis (see photo of the glass test on page 100).

Dial 999 and ask for an ambulance.

If your child is older and you're not sure whether to see the doctor, you might want to carry on normally for a while and see whether the signs of illness or pain continue. **Above all trust your feelings. You know better than anyone what your child is like day-to-day, so you'll know what's unusual or worrying. If you're worried, contact your doctor. Even if it turns out that nothing is wrong, that is exactly what you need to know.**

'He doesn't seem to listen. I'm in and out in no time, and I come home no better off than if I'd stayed at home. In fact, sometimes it makes it worse, because he'll give me something and I'll not know whether it's really needed or not.'

Using your GP

Most practices are very supportive towards parents of small children. Many will fit babies into surgeries without an appointment, or see them at the beginning of surgery hours. Many doctors will give advice over the phone. Others will feel that it is essential to see your child.

'My doctor gives me advice. He said if I had any worries, I could always go and talk to him.'

Some GPs are less helpful and it's not always easy to phone or to get to the surgery. Even so, if you're worried about a particular problem that won't go away, it's right to persist. (See page 133 for information on how to change your GP.)

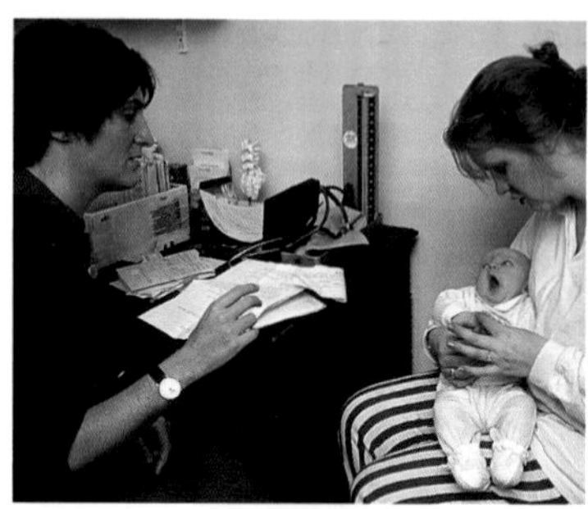

Your health visitor and/or clinic doctor can give you advice and help you decide whether your child is really unwell or not. But it's only your family doctor (your GP) who can treat your child and prescribe medicines. If you think your child is ill, it's best to see your GP.

If you're unsure whether to go to the surgery or ask for a home visit, phone and talk to the receptionist or to your GP. Explain how your child is and what's worrying you. Often it doesn't do a child (or anyone else) any harm to be taken to the surgery, and you're likely to get attention more quickly this way. But explain if it's difficult for you to get there. Wrapping a sick child up and going by car is one thing; going on the bus might be impossible.

Using medicines

Medicine isn't always necessary when your child is ill. Some illnesses simply get better by themselves and make your child stronger and better able to resist similar illness in the future. If you're offered a prescription, talk with your GP about why it's needed, how it will help, and whether there are any alternatives.

- When a medicine is prescribed, ask about any possible side-effects. Could it, for example, make your child sleepy or irritable?
- Make sure you know how much and how often to give a medicine. Write it down if need be. If in doubt, check with your pharmacist or GP.
- Always finish a prescribed course of medicine. A course of antibiotics, for example, usually lasts at least five days. This is to make sure all the bacteria are killed off. Your child may seem better after two or three days, but the illness is more likely to return if you don't finish all the medicine.
- If you think your child is reacting badly to a medicine, for example with a rash or diarrhoea, stop giving it and tell your GP. Keep a note of the name of the medicine so you can tell your GP in the future.
- If you buy medicines at the pharmacist, always say it's for a young child. Give your child's age. Some medicines are for adults only. Always follow the instructions on the label or ask the pharmacist if you're unsure.

- Ask for sugar-free medicines if they are available.
- Look for the date stamp. Don't use out-of-date medicines. Take them back to the pharmacy to be destroyed.
- Only give your child medicine given by your GP or pharmacist. **Never** use medicines prescribed for anyone else.
- Keep all medicines out of your child's reach and preferably out of sight – in the kitchen where you can keep an eye on them, rather than the bathroom.
- In the past, all medicines for children have been diluted to the right strength for each child with a liquid solution so that you could give it to your child on a 5 ml spoon. Now most medicines prescribed by your GP will no longer be diluted in this way. Instead you'll have to measure the correct dose for your child's age. The instructions will be on the bottle.
- Medicines that aren't diluted in liquid may need to be given using a 'liquid medicine measure', which looks like a syringe. It allows you to give small doses of medicine more accurately.

Always read the manufacturer's instructions supplied with the measure, and always give the exact dose stated on the medicine bottle. Some medicines will come with a measure supplied by the manufacturer, in which case that's the right measure to use. If in doubt ask the pharmacist for help.

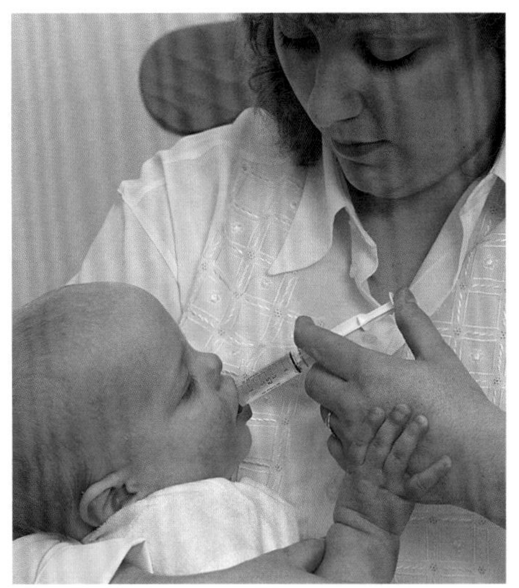

Looking after a sick child

It doesn't matter if your child doesn't want to stay in bed. Children are usually sensible about being ill and if they say they're well enough to be out of bed, they very probably are.

- Don't overheat the room your child is in. Keep it airy without being draughty.
- See page 98 for what to do if your child has a temperature.
- Give your child plenty to drink. For the first day or so don't bother about food unless it's wanted. After that, try to find ways of making a bit of food tempting.
- Try to give your child time for quiet games, stories, company and comfort.
- Sick children are often easily tired and need lots of rest. Encourage your child to doze off when he or she needs to, perhaps with a story read by you or on tape. But do not put your baby to sleep on an armchair or a sofa

Looking after a sick child, even for a couple of days, is exhausting. Make things as easy for yourself as you can. Get rest and sleep when you can, and try to get somebody else to take over every now and then to give you a break.

Symptoms and signs that could be serious:

- *a hoarse cough with noisy breathing;*
- *crying for an unusually long time or in an unusual way or seeming to be in a lot of pain;*
- *refusing feeds;*
- *diarrhoea or vomiting, particularly both together;*
- *unusually hot or cold or listless or more drowsy than normal.*

***Aspirin** should not be given to children under 16 years of age. It has now been linked with a rare but dangerous illness. Seek advice from your GP before taking aspirin if you are breastfeeding.*

***Paracetamol** is safer, but don't give it to children under three months without asking your GP first. Make sure you've got the right strength for your child. Overdosing is dangerous. Read the label and/or check with your pharmacist.*

***Ibuprofen** made for children can be given for pain and fever to children over the age of one who weigh more than 7 kg (15 lbs). Avoid if your child has asthma unless advised by your GP. Check the correct dose for your child's age. Don't give adult ibuprofen to children under the age of 12.*

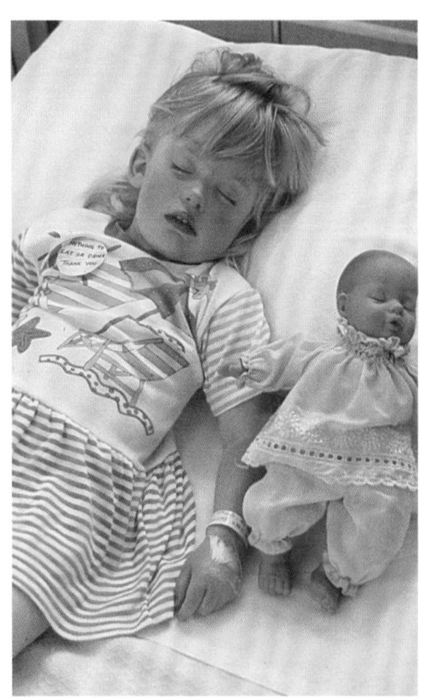

Children in hospital

Hospitals can be strange, frightening places for children. Being ill or in pain is frightening too. There's no parent who isn't anxious to do all they can to help their child.

- **Prepare your child as best you can.** You could play 'doctors and nurses' or 'operations' with teddies and dolls and read story books about being in hospital. It's worth doing this even if you don't know your child is going into hospital. Quite a large number of under fives do have to go into hospital at some stage, and many go in as emergencies.

- **Be with your child in hospital as much as possible.** It's extremely important for you to be with your child in hospital as much as possible and, with young children especially, to sleep there. Do all you can to arrange this. All hospital children's departments now have some provision for parents to stay overnight with their children. Talk to hospital staff beforehand and be clear about arrangements, what will happen, and so on. You may then be able to explain at least a part of it to your child.

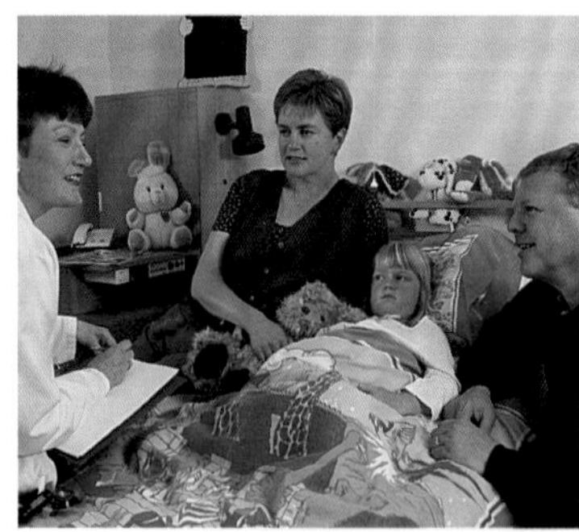

- **Explain as much as possible to your child.** Even quite young children need to know about what is happening to them, so explaining as much as possible is important. What children imagine is often worse than reality. Be truthful, too. Don't, for example, say something won't hurt when it will. Some hospitals will arrange visits for children and their families before the child is admitted for a planned treatment or operation.

- **Talk with hospital staff about anything that will be important for your child.** You may need to explain cultural differences. Staff should know, for example, if hospital food is going to seem very strange to your child. Try to discuss ways of getting over problems like this. Also tell staff about any special words your child uses (such as for needing to go to the lavatory), any special ways of comforting, and so on.

- **Make sure something like a favourite teddy bear or comforter goes into hospital with your child.**

- **Be prepared for your child to be upset by the experience,** and maybe to show it in one way or another for some time afterwards. Reassure as much as you can.

You can get a lot of helpful information and advice on how best to cope when your child is in hospital from Action for Sick Children (address on page 147).

Common complaints

Smoking and childhood illnesses

Children who live in a smoky atmosphere are more likely to get:

- coughs and colds;
- chest infections (temperature with a bad cough);
- asthma attacks;
- ear infections and glue ear.

Every year 17,000 children are admitted to hospital because their parents smoke. If you can't stop smoking or encourage other adults in your house to stop, then try to make sure that your children don't have to smoke too by creating a smoke-free zone. See page 123 for tips on giving up.

Asthma

Asthma is an inflammatory condition of the airways (bronchial tubes) of the lungs. These carry the air we breathe. With asthma the airways are extra sensitive to substances or trigger factors which irritate them, such as dust, animal fur or cigarette smoke. When in contact with a trigger factor, the air passages become narrower and a sticky mucus (phlegm) is produced making it difficult for air to pass through. Asthma is on the increase, especially in children.

The exact cause of asthma is unknown, but an attack can be due to sensitivity (allergy) to a trigger factor or to non-allergic causes. It is known that asthma often runs in families. Viral infections are a very common trigger of an asthma attack – more common than allergy.

Some symptoms of asthma

- Repeated attacks of coughing and wheezing, usually with colds, shortness of breath and production of phlegm. The symptoms are often worse at night or after exercise. Not everyone with asthma gets all the symptoms. And for many young children, a dry irritating cough may be the only symptom. See your GP if you think your child has asthma.

- Smoking during pregnancy or around a child can increase the child's risk of asthma.

- Breastfeeding your child for as long as possible can help protect against asthma developing.

Colds

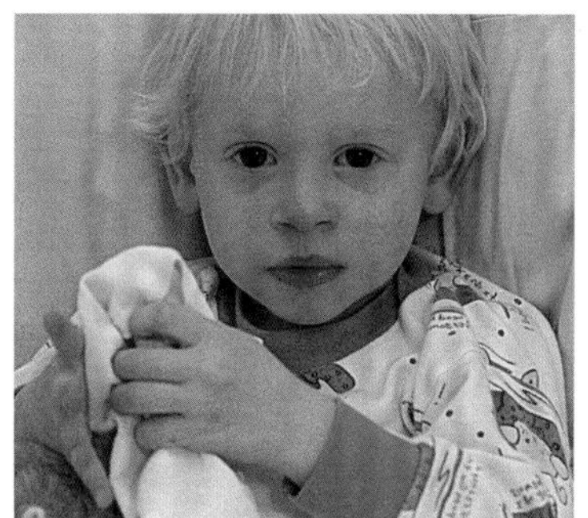

It may seem that your child always has a cold or upper respiratory tract infection. In fact it is normal for a child to have a cold eight or more times a year. This is because there are hundreds of different viruses and young children are meeting each one of them for the first time. Gradually they build up immunity and get fewer colds. Here are some suggestions on how to treat colds.

- Because colds are caused by viruses, not bacteria, antibiotics don't help. It is also best for antibiotics to be used only for more serious illnesses.

- Most colds will get better in five to seven days.

- Cough and cold medicines have not been shown to work and may produce side-effects in young children. They may also cause poisoning if your child accidentally swallows more than the right dose.

- Stuffiness may be made worse by nasal decongestants; if these are necessary they should only be used for two to three days.

- Saline nose drops may help to loosen dried nasal secretions or a stuffy nose – ask your pharmacist, GP or health visitor about these.

- Tickling the nose with a teased cotton bud causes sneezing and is helpful for clearing the nose before feeding.

- Increase the amount of fluid your child normally drinks.

- A pillow or blanket put *under* the baby's mattress to raise the head may help snuffly babies breathe more easily.

Antibiotics

Many doctors are now reluctant to prescribe antibiotics for common illnesses such as colds, or may adopt a 'wait-and-see' policy to make sure an infection is caused by bacteria. Not only are antibiotics ineffective against viruses, but inappropriate use of these can result in the child developing a resistant infection in the future.
If your child is prescribed antibiotics, always make sure the course is finished, even if your child seems better.

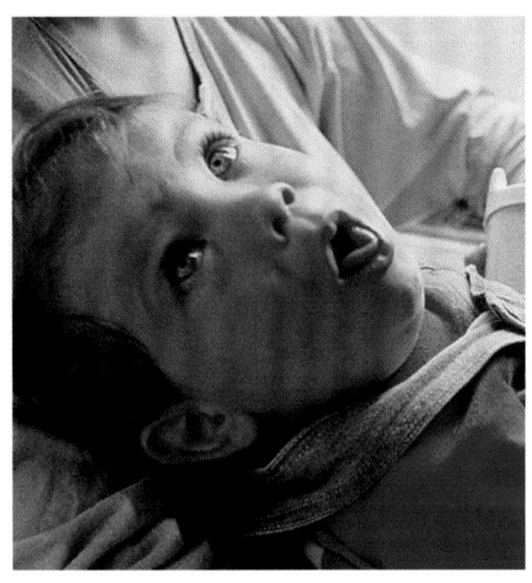

- Fever and pain can be treated with *the correct dose of* paracetamol for your child's age or with junior ibuprofen if your child is over the age of one and weighs 7 kg (15 lbs) or over.
- Encourage all the family to wash their hands to prevent the spread of colds from infected secretions.

Coughs

- Children may also cough when they have a cold because of mucus trickling down the back of the throat. If your child is feeding, eating and breathing normally and there is no wheezing, a cough is not usually anything to worry about. But if your child has a bad cough that won't go away, see your GP.
  If your child has a temperature and cough and/or is breathless, this may indicate an infection on the chest. If the cause is bacteria and not a virus, your GP will prescribe antibiotics to treat this – although it won't soothe or stop the cough straight away.
- If a cough continues for a long time, especially if it is more troublesome at night or is brought on by your child running about, it might be a sign of asthma. Some children with asthma also have a wheeze or some breathlessness. If your child has any of these symptoms, he or she should be seen by your GP. If your child seems to be having trouble breathing, contact your GP, even in the middle of the night.
- Although it is distressing to hear your child cough, in fact coughing serves a purpose. When there is phlegm on the chest, or mucus from the nose runs down the back of the throat, coughing clears it away. Most doctors believe cough mixtures do not work and are a waste of money. To ease your child's cough, give him or her plenty of warm, clear fluids to drink. If your child is over the age of one, try a warm drink of lemon and honey. There is no need to try to stop the cough completely.

Croup

Croup is a result of inflammation of the larynx (voicebox). Your child will have a hoarse, barking cough and noisy breathing. Contact your GP if you think your child has croup. Sometimes, though not often, croup can be life-threatening. Therefore, it is important to watch out for danger signals like:

- indrawing between the ribs or below the ribs with breathing;
- restlessness and lots of saliva;
- irritability;
- blueness of the lips or face.

If you notice any of these signs, call your GP or, if a doctor is not available, take your child straight to the nearest hospital with an Accident and Emergency department.

- If your child has croup a steamy atmosphere may help to relieve a 'croupy' cough and ease breathing. If your child has an attack of croup sit with him or her in the bathroom with the hot tap running or in the kitchen with water boiling. But be careful: very hot water, even if it isn't boiling, can scald. Keep the door and windows closed.

Diarrhoea

Young babies

Most young children have occasional loose stools. Diarrhoea means the frequent passage of unformed watery stools. Diarrhoea, together with vomiting, is called gastro-enteritis. The main problem is that, if diarrhoea or gastro-enteritis continues for more than a few hours, your baby can lose too much fluid from the body and may then become **dehydrated**. The baby becomes lethargic, has a dry mouth, the skin becomes loose and the eyes and fontanelle (soft spot on the top of the head) may become sunken. The baby will also pass very little urine.

To prevent or treat dehydration your baby will need extra fluids. There are special fluids available which can be bought from your local pharmacy or chemist or prescribed by your doctor. These are called **oral rehydration fluids** and include Dioralyte, Electrolade and Rehidrat.

If the diarrhoea continues for more than a few hours, or your baby is also vomiting or is unwell, contact your doctor or health visitor urgently for advice.

In general, for mild diarrhoea:

- give extra fluids in the form of **oral rehydration fluids** – for example, in between feeds or after each watery stool;
- **don't stop breastfeeding** – give the extra fluid in addition to breast milk;
- **if you are bottle feeding** offer normal formula feeds and give extra fluids in the form of *oral rehydration fluid.*

For more severe diarrhoea or for diarrhoea and vomiting:

- **don't stop breastfeeding** – give oral rehydration fluid in addition to breast milk;
- stop formula feeds and **give oral rehydration fluid for three–four hours**;
- **start giving normal formula feeds** after giving oral rehydration fluid for three to four hours.

Your doctor will give you further advice. Many no longer advise that you should stop bottle feeding for 24 hours, and also advise that toddlers can go back on to a normal diet three–four hours after having rehydration fluids.

Remember, if your baby is unwell, or if watery diarrhoea has lasted more than a day, seek your doctor's advice straight away.

Toddler diarrhoea

Some children between the ages of one and five pass frequent, smelly, loose stools with mucus or bits of vegetables in them. Usually these children are otherwise perfectly healthy and are growing fine, and the doctor cannot find any serious cause. This type of diarrhoea is known as 'toddler diarrhoea'. If your toddler has diarrhoea for which there is no obvious cause the following may help.

- **Giving less fluid between meals and at meals if your child drinks a lot.** In particular, cut down on low-calorie drinks with artificial sweeteners and clear apple juice if your child drinks these. If your child is used to drinking a lot, you may have to do this gradually by offering smaller amounts. Also, if your child wants a drink in between meals, try offering some snack food too, such as a piece of bread and butter with a smaller drink.
- **Try to introduce more foods with fat,** such as full-fat yoghurt, cheese, fromage frais and butter.

- **If your child is having foods with a lot of fibre, or wholemeal foods, reduce these.** Give white bread, pasta and white rice instead of wholemeal varieties.

Older children

Contact your GP if your child is vomiting at the same time, or if the diarrhoea is particularly watery, has blood in it or goes on for longer than two or three days or your child has severe or continuous tummy ache.

- Otherwise diarrhoea isn't usually worrying – just give your child plenty of clear drinks to replace the fluid that's been lost, but only give food if it's wanted. Do not give anti-diarrhoeal drugs unless prescribed by your GP.

- Help to prevent any infection spreading by using separate towels for your child and by reminding everyone in the family to wash their hands after using the toilet and before eating.

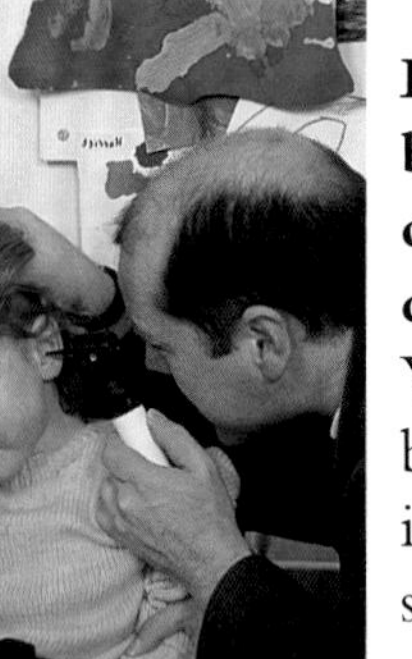

Ear infections

Ear infections are common in babies and small children. They often follow a cold and sometimes cause a bit of a temperature. Your child may pull or rub at an ear, but babies can't always tell where pain is coming from and may just cry and seem unwell and uncomfortable.

- If your child has earache but is otherwise well, paracetamol can be given for 12–24 hours. A covered hot-water bottle can also be placed under your child's ear for warmth.

- Do not put any oil or eardrops into your child's ear unless advised to do so by the GP.

- Some doctors prefer to treat ear infections with antibiotics, others feel the infection will clear up with paracetamol and decongestant nose drops.

After an ear infection your child may have a hearing problem for two to six weeks. If the problem persists after this time you should see your GP for further advice.

Repeated ear infections

Repeated bouts of middle ear infections (called otitis media) may lead to 'glue ear' (otitis media with effusion). Here sticky fluid builds up and can affect your child's hearing. Your child may also have behaviour problems. If you smoke, your child is more likely to develop glue ear and will not get better so quickly. Never bottle feed your baby if he or she is lying down nor let your child drink milk lying down if he or she has repeated ear infections. The milk may go into the short tube between the ear and throat (Eustachian tube) and cause irritation. It is also better if your baby can be weaned from a bottle on to a cup. Your GP will give you further advice about the treatment for glue ear.

Eczema

Atopic eczema (which occurs mainly where there is a family history of eczema, asthma or hayfever) is thought to affect one in eight children. It often starts between the ages of two and four months with patches of red, dry and irritable skin on the face or behind the ears, and in the creases of the neck, knees and elbows. It can be very itchy. This can lead to your baby scratching and the eczema may sometimes become infected. If you think your child has eczema, speak to your GP or health visitor.

Tips on managing eczema

- *Keep your child cool and the bedroom temperature cool.*
- *The faeces of the house dust mite can sometimes cause an allergic reaction and make eczema worse.*
- *If your child has fluffy or furry toys in the cot or bedroom, the house dust mite collects on them. Limit these toys to one or two favourites, and either wash them weekly at 60°C or put them in a plastic bag in the freezer for 24 hours to kill the house dust mite.*
- *Wash your child's bedlinen at 60°C to kill the house dust mite.*
- *Parents sometimes get worried about using topical steroids. However, used properly for short periods they are safe and may prevent the eczema getting worse.*
- ***Don't cut out important foods, such as milk, dairy products, wheat or eggs, without consulting your GP or health visitor.** It's fine to cut out such foods as citrus fruits, juice or tomatoes if you think these are irritating the skin.*
- *Don't let your child's skin get dry. Apply a moisturising cream or emollient to the skin several times a day. (Try to put some cream on when you feed your baby or change a nappy.)*
- *Apply the cream with downward strokes – don't rub it up and down.*
- *Avoid using substances that dry or irritate your baby's skin, such as soap, baby bath, bubble bath or detergents.*
- *Bath your child in cool water with a suitable skin oil added.*
- *Aqueous cream, which can be bought cheaply from pharmacists, is often as effective a moisturiser as more expensive creams. It can also be used for washing instead of soap.*
- *Try to identify and avoid anything that irritates the skin or makes the problem worse. For example, soap powder, animals, chemical sprays, cigarette smoke or some clothing.*
- *Avoid wool and nylon clothing – cotton is best.*

Fits or convulsions

Febrile convulsions or 'fever fits' are common in children under the age of three, but can seem very alarming to parents. Although there are other reasons why children 'fit', fits are most commonly triggered by a high temperature. If your baby or child seems feverish or has a high temperature it is important to cool him or her down immediately. See **Temperatures** on page 98 to find out how to do this.

What to do if your child has a fit
If your child has a fit he or she may suddenly turn blue and become rigid and staring. Sometimes the eyes will roll and the limbs start to twitch and jerk.

- Keep calm.
- Lie your child on his or her side to make sure he or she does not vomit or choke. Remove any objects from your child's mouth. Do not put anything in the mouth.
- Remove your child's clothing and any covering, and ensure your child is cool but not chilly.
- Sponge your child with tepid water if possible, starting from the head and working downwards.

Most fits will stop within three minutes. When it is over, reassure your child, make him or her comfortable, and then call a doctor.

- If the fit hasn't stopped, dial 999, or get someone else to go for help. Carry your child with you if there is no one to help you. If your GP isn't immediately available take your child to a hospital or call an ambulance. Stay with the child to prevent injury and move objects away from where the child is lying.
- Tell your GP that your child has had a fit.

Febrile convulsions become increasingly less common after the age of three and are almost unknown after the age of five. Children with *epilepsy,* which causes fits or seizures, may also grow out of these.

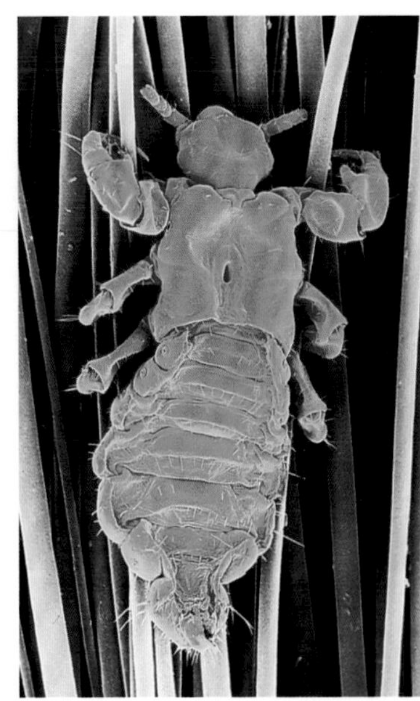

Head lice

Head lice are tiny insects and are slightly smaller than a match head. They can be difficult to see. Lots of children get head lice. It makes no difference whether their hair is clean or dirty. They catch them just by coming into contact with someone who is infested. When heads touch, the lice simply walk from one head to the other. They cannot jump or fly.

Signs of head lice

- A rash on the scalp.
- Lice droppings (a black powder, like fine pepper, may be seen on pillowcases).
- Eggs/nits – the lice lay eggs that are dull and well camouflaged, and hatch after about seven–ten days. Nits are the empty eggshells, about the size of a small pinhead. They are white and shiny and may be found further down the scalp, particularly behind the ears. They may be mistaken for dandruff, but, unlike dandruff, they're firmly glued to the hair and cannot be shaken off.
- Head itching – this is not always the first sign. Lice have usually been on the scalp for three or four months before the head starts to itch, or they may not cause itching.

Checking for head lice
Lice are most easily detected by fine toothcombing really wet hair. Wet your child's hair and part it about 30 times. Comb each section carefully with a plastic, fine-tooth nit comb. This should be done over a pale surface, such as a paper towel or white paper, or over a basin of water or when your child is in the bath. Any lice present may be seen on the scalp or the comb, or may fall on the paper or in the water. They are usually grey or brown in colour.

Treatment of head lice
There are two ways of dealing with the problem.

'Wet combing' or non-insecticide method

- Wash the hair in the normal way with an ordinary shampoo.
- Using lots of hair conditioner and while the hair is very wet, comb through the hair from the roots with a fine tooth comb. Make sure the teeth of the comb slot into the hair at the roots with every stroke.
- Clear the comb of lice between each stroke with a tissue or paper towel.
- Wet lice find it difficult to escape, and the hair conditioner makes the hair slippy and harder for them to keep a grip, so that removal with the comb is easier.
- Repeat this routine every three to four days for two weeks so that any lice emerging from the eggs are removed before they can spread.

Lotions and rinses. Lotions and rinses currently available to treat head lice contain either malathion, phenothrin, permethrin or carbaryl. Lotions containing carbaryl can only be obtained on prescription from your doctor.
The others may be bought from pharmacists or obtained on prescription. Your school nurse, health visitor, pharmacist or GP can advise you on which one to use.

Alternative treatments. 'Natural' methods of treating head lice using essential or aromatherapy oils, such as lavender, rosemary or tea tree oil, or blends of different oils, are popular with some parents. However, little research has been done on their effectiveness or whether these can be toxic if used repeatedly or in the incorrect amount. Some oils can also irritate the skin or may not be suitable for children. **If you do use essential oils to treat head lice it is therefore wise to use these cautiously and not as a preventative measure against lice. It is also known that some essential oils should not be used in pregnancy, so always check that any oil used to treat head lice during pregnancy is safe to use.**

Remember

- One infected child can infect an entire nursery – so do treat your child as soon as you discover head lice.
- Tell the nursery and other parents.
- Check your child's hair regularly, and always check if there is an outbreak at the nursery or school.
- If your child has head lice, check the whole family (including dad!) and treat them if necessary.
- Older people, such as grandparents, may have head lice without knowing it and may pass these on to children.
- Brush and comb your child's hair often – it may help prevent head lice taking hold.

TREATING HEAD LICE USING LOTIONS OR RINSES

Only use these when head lice have been detected and never as a preventative. A fine-tooth *plastic* comb is better for detection than a metal one.

- *Head lice shampoos are not recommended as they are generally ineffective.*
- *Head lice repellants are not recommended.*
- *Follow the instructions on how to use the lotion or rinse carefully.*
- *To make sure all the head is covered, use an adequate amount of lotion. A minimum of 50 ml is needed for each application.*
- *Make a small parting, pour a few drops of lotion on to this and spread over the scalp and hair with the fingers.*
- *Repeat this process making small partings systematically about every 2 cm or ½ in until the whole head is covered.*
- *If after you have rinsed the product off,* ***live lice*** *can still be seen on the head, or seen within a day or two of treatment, the lice may be resistant to the insecticide. In this case, use the 'wet combing' method as described, or switch to a product with a different ingredient. If you have used a product containing phenothrin or permethrin, do not switch to another product containing either of these as they belong to the same insecticide group.*
- *A second application of the same treatment is recommended seven days later.*
- *Do not use any product containing malathion or carbaryl more than once a week for three weeks at a time.*
- *Once the lice are dead, if you want to remove empty eggshells ('nits') from the head, metal tooth combs are best.*

Taking your child's temperature

There is a range of simple devices available which can be used to take a child's temperature. If purchasing one of these, take care to check that it will be easy to use, suitable for your child's age, and capable of producing an accurate reading. Always read and follow the instructions carefully.

Strip-type thermometers

Strip-type thermometers, which you hold on your child's forehead, are not an accurate way of taking temperatures. They show the skin and not the body temperature.

Digital thermometers

A digital thermometer can be of the infrared type that is put in the child's ear or a probe type which is held under the armpit or tongue in the same way as a mercury filled glass thermometer.

Normal body temperature

- *Under the arm, normal temperature is slightly lower than under the tongue – about 36.4°C (97.4°F).*
- *Under the tongue, normal temperature is about 37°C (98.4°F), but may vary a bit.*

Nappy rash

See page 25.

Sore throat

Many sore throats are caused by viral illnesses like colds or flu. Your child's throat may be dry and sore for a day or so before the cold starts.

Sometimes a sore throat is caused by tonsillitis. Your child may find it hard and painful to swallow, have a high temperature and swollen glands at the front of the neck, high up under the jaw.

The majority of sore throats will clear up on their own after a few days. Paracetamol can be given to help reduce the pain.

If your child has a sore throat for more than four days, has a high temperature and is generally unwell or is unable to swallow fluids or saliva, see your GP.

Teething

See page 33.

Temperatures

Babies under six months

Always contact your GP if your baby has other signs of illness (see box on page 88) as well as a raised temperature and/or if your baby's temperature is 39°C (102°F) or higher.

If the doctor doesn't find a reason for the temperature, he or she will almost certainly want to send a urine specimen to the laboratory. A detailed test will show if your baby has a urine infection.

Older children

A little fever isn't usually a worry. **Contact your GP if your child seems unusually ill, or has a high temperature which doesn't come down.**

- It's important to encourage your child to drink as much fluid as possible. Cold, clear drinks are best. Even if your child isn't thirsty, try to get him or her to drink a little and often, to keep fluids up. Don't bother about food unless it's wanted.

Bringing a temperature down is important because a continuing high temperature can be very unpleasant and, in a small child, occasionally brings on a fit or convulsion (see page 95).

- Give your child plenty of cool clear fluids.
- Undress your child to his or her nappy or pants and vest.
- Cover with a sheet if necessary.
- Keep the room cool by turning the radiators down or opening a window.
- Give paracetamol in the *correct* recommended dose for your child's age every four hours.

After these measures, take your child's temperature if you have a thermometer. If the temperature is above 40-41°C (104–105°F), or your child still feels feverish, try sponging your child's body, arms and legs with *tepid* water. **Do not use cold water** as this causes the blood vessels to contract and less heat will be lost. Always give the paracetamol before starting sponging.

Vomiting

Babies

Babies often sick up a bit of milk, some a lot, without distress. But if your baby is vomiting often or violently and/or there are other signs of illness, contact your GP straight away.

Your baby can lose a dangerous amount of fluid if he or she is sick often, especially if your baby has diarrhoea as well. See **Diarrhoea** page 93 for how to make sure your baby is getting enough fluid.

Older children

Older children can be sick once or twice without any bother and be well again quickly afterwards, or after a night's sleep. If your older child goes on vomiting, and/or there are other signs of illness, contact your GP.

- Give your child plenty to drink – clear drinks rather than milk. Don't bother about food unless he or she wants it.

Threadworms

Many children get threadworms. They spread by producing large numbers of tiny eggs which cannot be seen with the eye. The eggs are present in dust and stick to food, carpets, towels, bedlinen and toilet seats. Because they are so small and widespread they get on fingers and under fingernails and are easily swallowed. In the bowel they hatch into worms which lay eggs around the bottom. You'll see them in your child's stools, looking like tiny white threads. Your child may have an itchy bottom and may scratch it a lot, especially at night.

If you think your child has worms, see your GP or health visitor, or ask your pharmacist for treatment. Everybody in the family has to be treated because the threadworm eggs spread very easily. To prevent the infection spreading:

- keep your child's nails short;
- let your child wear pyjamas or pants in bed;
- bath your child or wash around the bottom each morning;
- keep your child's towel separate;
- make sure everyone in the family washes their hands and scrubs their nails before every meal and after going to the toilet;
- disinfect the toilet seat, toilet handle or chain regularly;
- vacuum and dust bedrooms thoroughly.

Spotting a rash

Rashes look different on different people. The colour of spots can vary and, on a black skin, rashes may be less easy to see. If in doubt, check with your GP.

Small children and babies sometimes get rashes that are not due to infectious illnesses and which soon go without treatment. For information about meningitis and septicaemia see page 100.

Kawasaki disease

This disease affects up to 2000 children a year, mainly the under fives, but is not very well known. A diagnosis is important because of the risk of serious complications, which include coronary artery disease.

Although it affects all children, it appears to be more common in children of Asian and African-Caribbean origin. The child has a high fever lasting more than five days without any obvious cause and at least four of the following symptoms:

- *conjunctivitis (red infected eyes);*
- *a rash;*
- *dry, red, swollen lips or a 'strawberry tongue';*
- *redness and/or swelling of the arms and legs or general peeling of the skin;*
- *swollen glands.*

Infectious illnesses

Meningitis and septicaemia – what to look for

Meningitis is an inflammation of the lining of the brain. It is a very serious illness but, if it's picked up and treated early, most children make a full recovery. **Septicaemia** is blood poisoning, which may be caused by the same germs that cause meningitis. Septicaemia is also very serious and must be treated straight away.

In recent years there has been a lot of concern about meningitis in children. There are several different types of meningitis and septicaemia and some can be prevented by immunisation (see page 104).

The early symptoms of meningitis, such as fever, irritability, restlessness, vomiting and refusing feeds, are also common with colds and flu. A baby with meningitis or septicaemia can become seriously ill within hours. Some of the symptoms, such as a severe headache, are difficult to see in babies because they cannot tell you how they feel. The important signs to look out for are shown in the box to the left. **If your child has a red or purple rash, look at it through a glass tumbler. The meningitis rash does not blanch (that is fade or turn white) when the bottom or side of the tumbler is pressed firmly against it, whereas almost all other childhood rashes do.**

If you can't get in touch with your GP, or if you are still worried after getting advice, trust your instincts – take your child to the accident and emergency department of your nearest hospital.

Meningitis and septicaemia

These symptoms may not all appear at the same time. In babies look for the following:

- *a high-pitched, moaning cry;*
- *the baby being difficult to wake;*
- *refusing to feed;*
- *pale or blotchy skin;*
- *very high temperature (39°C and above);*
- *very cold hands and feet;*
- *red or purple spots/marks anywhere on the body that do not fade under pressure – do the 'Glass Test' (see below).*

In older children look for the following signs:

- *stiffness in the neck – can the child kiss his or her knee, or touch the forehead to the knee?*
- *drowsiness or confusion;*
- *a severe headache;*
- *a dislike of bright light;*
- *very cold hands and feet;*
- *red or purple spots/marks that do not fade under pressure – do the 'Glass Test' (see below);*

The rash can be more difficult to see on black skin so check carefully for spots, especially on the soles of the feet, palms of the hands and inside the eyelids.

The 'Glass Test'

*Press the side of a clear glass **firmly** against the rash – you will be able to see if the rash fades and loses colour under the pressure. If it **doesn't change colour**, contact a doctor immediately (see photo below).*

If your child becomes ill with one or more of the above signs, get medical help urgently. If you can't get in touch with the doctor, take your child to the accident and emergency department of your nearest hospital.

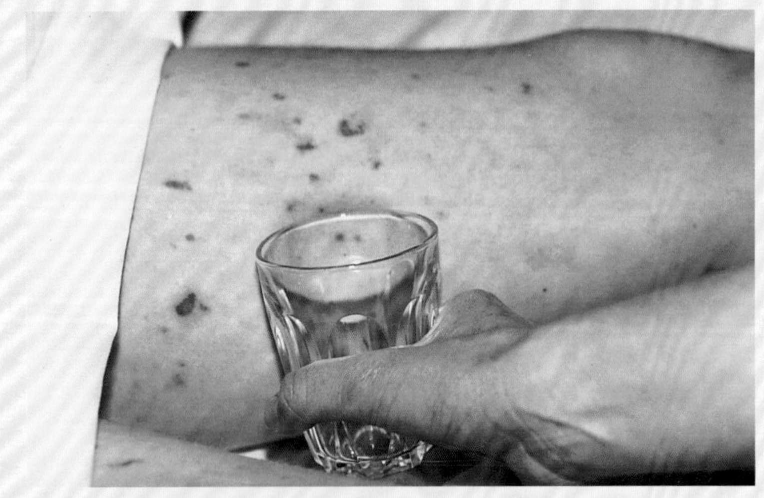

ILLNESS	INCUBATION PERIOD (The time between catching an illness and becoming unwell)	INFECTIOUS PERIOD (When your child can give the illness to someone else)	HOW TO RECOGNISE IT	WHAT TO DO
CHICKEN POX	11–21 DAYS	From the day before the rash appears until all the spots are dry.	Begins with feeling unwell, a rash and maybe a slight temperature. Spots are red and become fluid-filled blisters within a day or so. Appear first on the chest and back, then spread, and eventually dry into scabs, which drop off. Unless spots are badly infected, they don't usually leave a scar.	No need to see your GP unless you're unsure whether it's chicken pox, or your child is very unwell and/or distressed. Give plenty to drink. Paracetamol will help bring down a temperature. Baths, loose comfortable clothes and calamine lotion can all ease the itchiness. You should also inform the school/nursery in case other children are at risk. **Keep your child away from anyone who is, or who is trying to become, pregnant. If your child was with anyone pregnant just before he or she became unwell, let that woman know about the chicken pox (and tell her to see her GP). Sometimes chicken pox in pregnancy can cause miscarriage or the baby may be born with chicken pox.**
MEASLES	7–12 DAYS	From a few days before until 4 days after the appearance of the rash.	Begins like a bad cold and cough with sore, watery eyes. Child becomes gradually more unwell, with a temperature. Rash appears after third or fourth day. Spots are red and slightly raised; may be blotchy, but are not itchy. Begins behind the ears, and spreads to the face and neck and then the rest of the body. Children can become very unwell, with cough and high temperature. The illness usually lasts about a week.	See your GP. If your child is unwell give him or her rest and plenty to drink. Warm drinks will ease the cough. Paracetamol will ease discomfort and lower the temperature. Vaseline around the lips protects the skin. Wash crustiness from eyelids with warm water.
MUMPS	14–21 DAYS	From a few days before becoming unwell until swelling goes down. Maybe 10 days in all.	At first, your child may be mildly unwell with a bit of fever, and may complain of pain around the ear or feel uncomfortable when chewing. Swelling then starts under the jaw up by the ear. Swelling often starts on one side, followed (though not always) by the other. Your child's face is back to normal size in about a week. It's rare for mumps to affect boys' testes (balls). This happens rather more often in adult men with mumps. For both boys and men, the risk of any permanent damage to the testes is very low.	Your child may not feel especially ill and may not want to be in bed. Baby or junior paracetamol will ease pain in the swollen glands. Check correct dosage on pack. Give plenty to drink, but not fruit juices. They make the saliva flow, which can hurt. No need to see your GP unless your child has stomach ache and is being sick, or develops a rash of small red/purple spots or bruises.
PARVOVIRUS B19 (ALSO CALLED FIFTH DISEASE OR SLAPPED CHEEK DISEASE)	Variable 1–20 DAYS	It is most infectious in the days before the rash appears.	Begins with a fever and nasal discharge. A bright red rash similar to a slap appears on the cheeks. Over the next 2-4 days, a lacy type of rash spreads to the trunk and limbs.	Although this is most common in children, it can occur in adults. In the majority of cases it has no serious consequences, but it may cause complications for people with chronic anaemic conditions (e.g. sickle cell disease). Rarely, in pregnant women who are not immune to the disease, the infection may result in stillbirth or affect the baby in the womb. **Pregnant women who come into contact with the infection or develop a rash should see their GP as soon as possible.**
RUBELLA (GERMAN MEASLES)	14–21 DAYS	One week before and at least 4 days after the rash first appears.	Can be difficult to diagnose with certainty. Starts like a mild cold. The rash appears in a day or two, first on the face, then spreading. Spots are flat. On a light skin, they are pale pink. Glands in the back of the neck may be swollen. Your child won't usually feel unwell.	Give plenty to drink. Keep your child away from anybody you know who's up to 4 months pregnant (or trying to get pregnant). If your child was with anyone pregnant before you knew about the illness, let her know. If an unimmunised pregnant woman catches German measles in the first 4 months of pregnancy, there is a risk of damage to her baby. **Any pregnant woman who has had contact with German measles should see her GP. The GP can check whether or not she is immune and, if not, whether there is any sign of her developing the illness.**
WHOOPING COUGH	7–14 DAYS	From the first signs of the illness until about 6 weeks after coughing first starts. If an antibiotic is given, the infectious period is up to 5 days after beginning the course of treatment.	Begins like a cold and cough. The cough gradually gets worse. After about 2 weeks, coughing bouts start. These are exhausting and make it difficult to breathe. Your child may choke and vomit. Sometimes, but not always, there's a whooping noise as the child draws in breath after coughing. It takes some weeks before the coughing fits start to die down.	If your child has a cough that gets worse rather than better and starts to have longer fits of coughing more and more often, see your doctor. It's important for the sake of other children to know whether or not it's whooping cough. Talk to your GP about how best to look after your child and avoid contact with babies, who are most at risk from serious complications.

Immunisation

Immunisation is the safest and most effective way of protecting your child from various infectious diseases

What is immunisation?

Immunisation is a way of protecting ourselves from serious disease. Once we have been immunised, our bodies are more able to fight those diseases if we come into contact with them.

Why do we need immunisation?
Our bodies have a natural defence system against disease. This is called the immune system. The immune system produces substances called antibodies which fight off disease and infection.

There are some diseases that can kill children or cause lasting damage to their health, and sometimes your child's immune system needs help to fight those diseases. Immunisation provides that help.

Research from around the world shows that immunisation is the safest way to protect your child's health.

When to have your child immunised

Your child should have their first immunisations at two months old. They will be given further doses of these immunisations when they are three months old and four months old. Other immunisations are given at around 15 months old, then between three and five years old (before your child starts school), and in their teenage years.

Some immunisations have to be given more than once to build up your child's immunity (protection). This top-up dose is sometimes called a booster.

You will be sent an appointment inviting you to bring your child for their immunisations.

Most doctors' surgeries and health centres run special immunisation or baby clinics. You can often rearrange another time if you can't get to the clinic at the time specified.

It is important that your child has their immunisations at the right age. This will help keep the risk of your child catching these diseases as low as possible. However, if they do miss out it's never too late to catch up.

At the appointment

Your child will be given an injection in their thigh or upper arm.

Common questions about immunisation

How does immunisation work?
Your child will be given a vaccine. A vaccine contains a small part of the bacteria or virus that causes a disease, or tiny amounts of the chemicals that the bacteria produce. Vaccines are specially treated so they do not cause the disease itself. Instead, they work by encouraging the body's immune system to make antibodies. If your child ever comes into contact with the disease, the antibodies will recognise it and be ready to protect your child.

Because vaccines have been used so successfully in the UK, such diseases as polio, diphtheria and measles have almost disappeared from this country.

If these diseases have almost disappeared why do we need to immunise against them?
The diseases are still around in many parts of the world where immunisation is not so widely available, and there are still a few cases in this country. As more people travel abroad, there is a risk that they will bring these diseases back into the UK, and that the diseases will spread to people who haven't been immunised against them. Your child is at risk if they have not been immunised.

Immunisation doesn't just protect your child – it can help to protect your family and the whole community, especially those children who can't be immunised.

It is never too late to have your child immunised. Even if your child is older than the recommended ages, talk to your doctor, practice nurse or health visitor to arrange for them to be protected.

How do we know that the vaccines are safe?
Before anyone can be given a vaccine, it has to go through many tests to check that it is safe and that it works. These checks continue even after a vaccine has been introduced. Only

vaccines that pass all of the safety tests are used. All medicines can cause side-effects, but vaccines are among the very safest.

I am a bit worried that my child will be upset by having an injection.
Your child may cry and be upset for a few minutes, but they will usually settle down after a cuddle. Many children don't get upset at all.

How will my child feel afterwards?
All children are different. Most will not have any side-effects. Some children will

- get redness or swelling where they had the injection, which will slowly disappear on its own;
- feel a bit irritable and unwell and develop a temperature (fever).

Your practice nurse, GP or health visitor may suggest you give your child a dose of paracetamol or ibuprofen liquid if they get a fever. Read the information on the bottle very carefully and give the correct dose for your child's age. You may need to give a second dose four to six hours later.

Very occasionally, children can have allergic reactions straight after immunisation. If they are treated quickly, they will recover completely. The people who give immunisations are trained to deal with allergic reactions.

Are there any reasons why my child should not be immunised?
There are very few reasons why a child should not be immunised. But when you take your child for their immunisation, you should let your health visitor, doctor or practice nurse know if your child

- has a high fever;
- has had a bad reaction to any other immunisation;
- has had treatment for cancer or other serious conditions;
- has a severe (anaphylactic) allergy to anything;
- has a bleeding disorder;
- has had convulsions (fits).

You should also let them know if your child or any other close family member:

- has any illness which affects the immune system, e.g. leukaemia, HIV or AIDS;
- is taking any medicine which affects the immune system, for example, immunosuppressants (given after organ transplant or for cancer) or high-dose steroids.

Most of these will not stop your child from being immunised but will help make the decision as to what is best for your child.

Are there other ways to immunise my child?
There is no other proven, effective way to immunise your child.
The Faculty of Homeopathy (the registered organisation for doctors qualified in homeopathy) follows the Department of Health guidelines and advises parents to have their children immunised with standard vaccines, unless there are medical contraindications.

If my child has a fever what should I do?
A few children may develop a fever after immunisation.

A fever is a temperature over 37.5°C. If your child's face feels hot to the touch and they look red or flushed, they may have a fever. You could check their temperature with a thermometer.

Fevers are fairly common in children. They are usually mild, but it is important to know what to do if your child gets one (see the box *How to treat a fever*).

How to treat a fever

1 Keep your child cool by

- *making sure they don't have too many layers of clothes or blankets on;*
- *giving them plenty of cool drinks.*

2 Give them liquid paracetamol or ibuprofen. Read the instructions on the bottle carefully and give your child the correct dose for their age. You may need to give them a second dose four - six hours later. ***Never give aspirin to children under 16 years old.***

WHEN SHOULD I CALL THE DOCTOR?

Call the doctor immediately if your child

- *has a temperature of 39°C or above;*
- *has a fit.*

If the surgery is closed and you can't contact the duty doctor, go to the accident and emergency department of your nearest hospital. Follow your instincts and speak to your doctor if you are worried about your child.

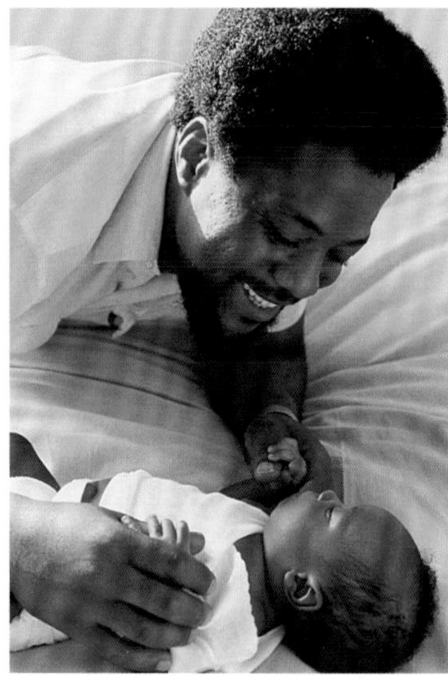

Childhood Immunisations

Around the world, 14 million people die from infectious disease every year. Over half of these people are children under the age of five. Most of these deaths could be prevented with immunisation.

Because of immunisation, many serious diseases have almost disappeared from the UK, but they are still around in other countries, and they could come back.

The childhood immunisation programme gives your child the best protection from these diseases with the following vaccines.

Does my child have to be immunised?
In the UK, parents can decide whether to have their children immunised. Around the world, children are now routinely protected with vaccines. Because of this, some of the world's most serious diseases may soon disappear.

The childhood immunisation programme in the UK offers your child protection against many of these diseases.

DTaP/IPV/Hib vaccine

The DTaP/IPV/Hib vaccine protects against five different diseases: diphtheria, tetanus and pertussis (or whooping cough), polio (inactivated polio vaccine IPV) and *haemophilus influenzae* type b (Hib).

Your baby should have a DTaP/IPV/Hib vaccine at two, three and four months old.

They will be given a booster against diphtheria, tetanus, pertussis and polio before they start school. They will get a further tetanus, diphtheria and polio booster between the ages of 14 and 18.

What is diphtheria?
Diphtheria is a disease that usually begins with a sore throat and can quickly cause problems with breathing. It can damage the heart and nervous system, and, in severe cases, it can kill.

What is tetanus?
Tetanus is a painful disease that affects the muscles and can cause breathing problems. It is caused by germs that are found in soil and manure and can get into the body through open cuts or burns. Tetanus affects the nervous system and can kill.

What is pertussis (whooping cough)?
Whooping cough is a disease that can cause long bouts of coughing and choking which can make it hard to breathe. It can last for up to 10 weeks. It is not usually serious in older children, but it can be very serious and it can kill babies under one year old.

What is polio?
Polio is a virus that attacks the nervous system and can permanently paralyse the muscles. If it affects the chest muscles, polio can kill.

What is Hib?
Hib is an infection that can cause a number of major illnesses like blood poisoning, pneumonia and meningitis. All of these illnesses can kill if they are not treated quickly.

The Hib vaccine only protects your child against one type of meningitis (Hib). It does not protect against any other type of meningitis.

After immunisation
Your child may get some of the following side-effects, which are usually mild.

- It is quite normal for your baby to be miserable within 48 hours of having the injection.
- Your baby may develop a fever (see page 103).
- You may notice a small lump where your baby had the injection. This may last for a few weeks.

If your child has a worse reaction to the DTaP/IPV/Hib vaccine, talk to your doctor, nurse or health visitor.

Rarely, a baby may have a fit a day or two after their DTaP/IPV/Hib vaccination. If your baby has a fit, call your doctor immediately. Babies usually recover from fits quickly and completely. Young babies can have fits at any time, so having a fit after their vaccination may not necessarily be linked to the vaccine. Your doctor will decide whether your baby can have more doses of the vaccine. But if you delay the immunisation, it can increase the chances of fits after DTaP/IPV/Hib, so it's important to make sure your child gets vaccinated at the right age.

MenC vaccine

Your baby should be immunised with the MenC vaccine at two, three and four months old.

This vaccine protects against infection by meningococcal group C. Meningococcal group C is a type of bacteria that can cause meningitis and septicaemia (blood poisoning). The MenC vaccine does not protect against meningitis caused by other bacteria or by viruses.

What is meningitis?
Meningitis is an inflammation of the lining of the brain. The same germs that cause meningitis may cause septicaemia (blood poisoning). Babies and young people aged 15 - 17 are most at risk of getting meningitis or septicaemia from meningococcal group C.

How effective is the MenC vaccine?
Since the MenC vaccine was first used, the number of babies under one year of age with group C disease has fallen by around 95 per cent. About 9 out of 10 babies are protected by this vaccine when it is given to them.

After immunisation
Your baby may have redness and swelling where they had the injection. About half of all babies who have the vaccine may become irritable, and around 1 in 20 may get a mild fever.

MMR vaccine

Your baby should have their first dose of MMR vaccine at around 15 months old and a second dose before they start school.

MMR protects your child against measles, mumps and rubella (German measles).

What is measles?
Measles is caused by a very infectious virus. It is often a mild disease, but if there are complications, it can be dangerous. It causes a high fever and a rash and can go on to cause chest infections, fits and brain damage. About 1 in every 15 children who develops measles is at risk of complications. In serious cases, it can kill. We cannot tell which children may be seriously affected by measles.

What is mumps?
The mumps virus causes headache, fever and painful and swollen glands in the face, neck or under the jaw. It can cause permanent deafness. It can also cause viral meningitis and encephalitis (inflammation of the brain). Very rarely, it causes painful swelling of the testicles in boys and the ovaries in girls.

What is rubella?
Rubella (German measles) usually causes a mild rash, swollen glands and a sore throat in children, but it is very serious for unborn babies. If a pregnant woman catches it early in her pregnancy, it can cause miscarriage or seriously harm her unborn baby's sight, hearing, heart and brain. This condition is called congenital rubella syndrome (CRS). In many cases, pregnant women catch rubella from their own, or their friends' children.

After the vaccine
The three separate vaccines in the MMR immunisation may have different side-effects at different times.

- About a week to 10 days after their MMR vaccine, some children may become feverish, develop a measles-like rash and go off their food as the measles part of the vaccine starts to work.

Your baby does not need any immunisations before going swimming.

MMR – The facts

There have been stories in the press suggesting a link between the MMR vaccine and autism or bowel disease. Extensive scientific research from all over the world agrees that there is no link between MMR and autism or bowel disease. There is a dedicated NHS website that will give you a massive amount of information about the MMR vaccine, covering news stories as they break to detailed scientific research into safety. Visit ***www.mmrthefacts.nhs.uk****.*

Watch out for meningitis and septicaemia

Both meningitis and septicaemia are very serious in babies and young children. It is important that you know the signs and symptoms and what to do if you see them *(see page 100)**. Early symptoms, such as fever, being irritable and restless, vomiting and refusing feeds, are also common with colds and flu. A baby with meningitis or septicaemia can become seriously ill within hours.*

Worldwide, TB kills around two million people every year. Although TB is no longer common in the UK, since the mid-1980s the number of cases each year has risen to around 7,000.

- About two weeks after the vaccine, your child may (very rarely) get a rash of small bruise-like spots due to the rubella part of the vaccine. If you see spots like these, show them to your doctor.

- Very rarely, children may get a mild form of mumps about three weeks after their immunisation. They will not be infectious and they can mix with other people as normal.

- About one child in every 1,000 who have the immunisation may have a fit, which is usually caused by a fever and is called a 'febrile convulsion'. But if a child has not been immunised and they get measles, they are 10 times more likely to have a fit.

Although encephalitis (inflammation of the brain) has been reported (one case in a million doses), the risk of children getting encephalitis after the MMR vaccine is no higher than the risk of getting it if they have not had the vaccine. However, the risk of a child developing encephalitis as a result of having measles is more common – about 1 in every 5,000 cases.

Egg allergies

The MMR vaccine is made using eggs. Research has shown that even children with a severe egg allergy can be given MMR safely. However, if your child has a severe allergy to eggs (rashes on the face and body, a swollen mouth and throat, breathing problems and shock), tell your doctor or practice nurse. If necessary, they can make special arrangements to give your child the vaccine safely.

Other immunisations

BCG vaccine

The BCG vaccine protects against TB (tuberculosis). The BCG vaccine is routinely given to children between 10 and 14 years old. However, it is sometimes offered to babies if it is thought they may be more at risk of coming into contact with TB.

What is TB?

TB is an infection that usually affects the lungs. It can also affect other parts of the body, such as the brain and bones. With treatment, it is possible to make a full recovery.

After immunisation

Depending on how the BCG is given, a blister or sore may or may not appear. If it does appear, it heals gradually, especially if you do not cover it up. It may leave a small scar.

Hepatitis B vaccine

This vaccine is given to babies whose mothers or close family have been infected with hepatitis B.

- The first dose is given within two days of birth.

- A second dose is given at one month old.

- A third dose is given at two months old.

- A booster dose and blood test are given at 12 months old.

What is hepatitis?

There are several different types of the virus. The hepatitis B virus is passed through infected blood and may also be passed on during sex with an infected partner. It can cause the liver to become inflamed.

If you are pregnant and you are a hepatitis B carrier, or if you get the disease during your pregnancy, you could pass it on to your child. Your child may not be ill but they have a high chance of becoming a carrier and developing liver disease later in life. Some people carry the virus in their blood without knowing it.

Pregnant women in the UK are tested for hepatitis B during their antenatal care. If you have the virus, you should have your baby vaccinated. It is safe to breastfeed your baby as long as they have been vaccinated.

After immunisation

The side effects of the vaccine tend to be quite mild. The place where your baby had the injection may sometimes be red, and it may be a bit sore for a few days afterwards.

Travel immunisation

Your child may need extra immunisations if they are going abroad. Contact your doctor or a travel clinic for up-to-date information on the immunisations your child may need.

For more information see the leaflet *E111/T6/ Health advice for travellers* available from post offices in Northern Ireland.

Watch out for malaria

Malaria is a serious infection which you can catch from mosquito bites. It is a major problem in tropical countries. If you are travelling to an area where there is malaria, your child will need protection. There isn't an immunisation against malaria, but your doctor may be able to give you some anti-malarial drugs.

Malaria – avoiding the bug bites

Do all you can to avoid your child getting bitten by mosquitoes.

- *Use insect repellent and mosquito nets soaked in repellent.*
- *Make sure their arms and legs are covered between sunset and sunrise.*
- *Use a repellent that is specially made for children. Ask your pharmacist for advice.*

Timetable of routine childhood immunisations

When to immunise	Diseases vaccine protects against	How it is given
Two, three and four months old	Diphtheria, tetanus, pertussis, polio and Hib Meningitis C	One injection One injection
Around 15 months old	Measles, mumps and rubella (MMR)	One injection
Three to five years old (pre-school)	Diphtheria, tetanus, pertussis and polio Measles, mumps and rubella	One injection One injection
10–14 years old (and sometimes shortly after birth)	Tuberculosis (BCG vaccine)	Skin test, then, if needed, one injection
14–18 years old	Tetanus, diphtheria and polio	One injection

For more information on immunisation, visit **www.immunisation.nhs.uk**
www.dhsspsni.gov.uk/phealth
For more information on MMR, visit **www.mmrthefacts.nhs.uk**

Safety

- Accidents are the most common cause of death among children aged between one and five years.

- Every year about 600,000 children under five go to hospital because of an accident in the home.

Children need to explore and to learn about the things around them. The safer you make your home, the less likely it is that their exploration will land them in hospital. Outside your home it's not so easy to make sure that the world is a safe place, but by getting together with other parents you can make a difference.

You can put pressure on your local council as follows:

- to make road crossings safer;

- to mend stairs and walkways and improve lighting;

- to clear rubbish tips and board up old buildings.

Protect and teach

- **Under-threes** can't be expected to understand or remember safety advice. They need to have an adult nearby at all times.

- **Three-year-olds** can start learning how to do things safely, but expect your child to forget if she or he is excited or distracted.

- **Eight-year-olds** can usually remember and act on safety instructions, though they are not yet safe enough to cross a busy road alone. They need adults around at all times to call on for help.

- **Under eleven-year-old** children are unable to judge speed and distance, so they should never cross busy roads alone. From the age of eight or nine children could cross quiet roads alone but they must wait until there are no cars at all. They should know and understand the Green Cross Code.

Safety checklist

Use this list to check whether you're doing everything you can to prevent accidents. It's impossible to list all dangers, but thinking about some of these should start you thinking about others. Tick off the things you've done.

Danger – choking and suffocation

- ❑ Do you store small objects away from babies and small children who might put them in their mouths?
- ❑ Have you got rid of ribbons and strings that might, either in play or by accident, get wound around a child's neck?

- ❑ Do you keep peanuts away from children in your house? They often cause choking.

❑ Do you store polythene bags out of children's reach?

Danger – fires, burns and scalds

❑ Have you fitted a smoke detector?

❑ Have you checked your smoke detector battery this week?

❑ Could you get out of your house in a fire?

❑ Have you shortened your kettle flex or bought a coiled flex? Dangling flexes from irons and kettles can be pulled.

❑ Do you have a fire guard fixed to the wall round any kind of open fire (coal, gas or electric) or a hot stove?

❑ Do you always use the back rings on the cooker and turn pan handles away from the front of a cooker? A flat work surface on either side of the cooker will prevent your child reaching pan handles at the side of the cooker. Or you could fit a cooker hob guard.

❑ Do you use a playpen, cot or high chair (with restraints) to keep your child safe while you cook?

❑ Do you keep your child away when you're drinking or carrying hot drinks and put mugs and cups, coffee jugs and teapots out of reach?

❑ Have you put your tablecloths away? A child pulling at the edges can bring a hot drink or teapot down.

❑ Do you always run the cold tap first in the bath and test the temperature before your child gets in? Be especially careful once your child is big enough to get into the bath without help and can play with the taps.

❑ Have you turned down the hot water thermostat to 54°C or 130°F to avoid scalds?

❑ Do you always cover hot-water bottles to prevent burns and remove them from the bed before your child gets in?

Danger – falls

❑ Do you always put bouncing chairs on the floor rather than a table or worktop?

❑ Do you have a properly fixed stair gate or barrier, preferably at both the top and bottom of your stairs?

❑ Baby walkers are dangerous. They tip babies down stairs and on to fires and radiators. Don't tick this box until you have thrown yours out.

❑ Have you checked the rails round your landing and balconies? Could your child fall through, crawl under, climb over? Horizontal railings are especially dangerous.

❑ Do you have safety catches or locks on your upstairs windows to stop your child falling out? Are you sure you won't be locked or nailed in if there is a fire?

Danger – cuts

❑ Low-level glass in doors and windows is dangerous, especially once your child is on the move. Have you boarded it up, fitted safety film, or safety glass?

❑ Do you keep all sharp things somewhere safe (away from children)?

❑ Do you make sure your children never walk around holding anything made of glass or with anything like a pencil or lollipop stick in their mouths?

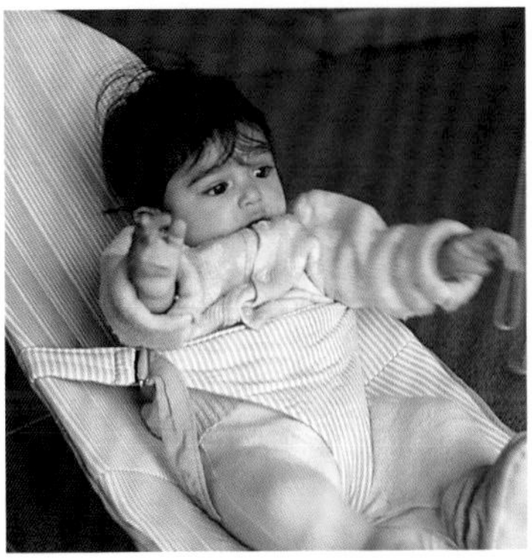

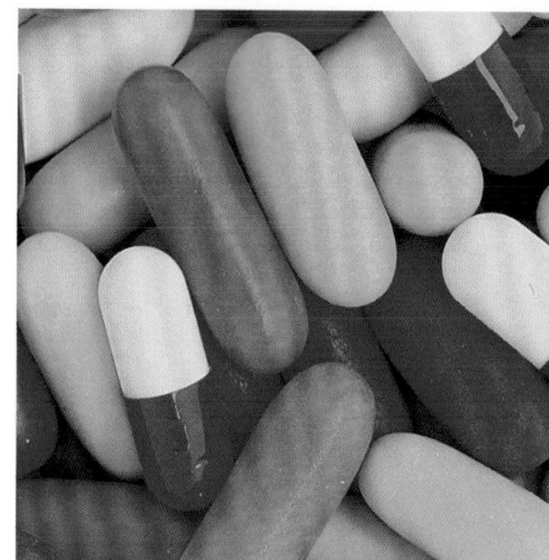

Danger – poisoning

- ❑ Have you locked all alcohol and medicines away or stored them high up, out of sight and where the child can't climb?
- ❑ Are your medicines in child-resistant containers? In other people's houses watch out for dangers like tablets in drawers and handbags.
- ❑ Are your household and garden chemicals in a safe place, high up, or locked away? Some chemicals are sold with child-resistant caps. Make sure you replace the cap properly after use.
- ❑ Are you sure there are no dangerous liquids in a bottle or jar that could make them look like drink?
- ❑ Are you teaching your children not to eat any plants, fungi, berries or seeds?
- ❑ If you use surma on your child's eyes, is it one of the safe, lead-free brands? Talk to your pharmacist. Some surma can be dangerous.

Danger – electricity

- ❑ Are your electric sockets covered by heavy furniture or safety covers when not in use?
- ❑ Have you repaired all worn flexes?
- ❑ Are you careful not to plug too many appliances into one socket?

Danger – drowning

- ❑ Do you know you should never leave a baby or young child under four alone in the bath for a moment? If the phone or doorbell rings, take your child with you, or let it ring.
- ❑ Is your garden pond covered or fenced off? Never leave your child alone near water.
- ❑ Does your child know how to swim? Children who can swim are safer, but it is still no guarantee of safety, so you should still keep a close watch when your children are near water.

Danger – cars

- ❑ Do you know the law?

- It's illegal to carry an unrestrained child in the front seat.
- It's illegal to carry an unrestrained child if there is a suitable restraint in the car.
- If there's a child restraint in the front but not in the back, then children under three must use it.
- If there's an adult restraint in the front but not in the back, children over three years must use it.
- You can only carry unrestrained passengers if there are more passengers than seat belts.

In general, it's safer for a child over three to use an adult belt than not to use a belt at all. Children should never be allowed to travel in the back of a hatchback (unless it has been specially adapted and fitted with seat belts) or to stand in a moving car.

- ❑ Do you have a rear-facing baby seat or a special restraint system for your carrycot?
- ❑ Do you have a child safety seat for toddlers?
- ❑ Do you have a booster cushion for bigger children to use with an adult safety belt?
- ❑ Do you always make sure you get your children out of the car on the pavement side?
- ❑ If you have air bags fitted to your car, do you make sure your baby always travels in the back seat?

In a growing number of areas there are loan schemes for baby safety seats. Through these schemes, you can get the seats more cheaply. Some schemes are run by local maternity hospitals. Or ask your midwife, health visitor or road safety officer.

Danger – roads

- Never let a child on or near roads alone. Young children don't understand the danger of traffic.
- Hold your child's hand when you're near roads. Walking reins are useful for toddlers.
- Teach your child to cross roads safely by always crossing safely yourself and explaining what you're doing. Don't expect any child under the age of eight to cross a road alone.

Danger – strangers

Parents are often very worried about the possibility that their child will be abducted or murdered by a stranger. In fact this is a rare occurrence compared, for example, with the risk of a traffic accident. Nevertheless it's sensible to teach your children the following.

- Never go with anyone (even someone they know well) without telling the grown-up who is looking after them.
- If someone they don't know tries to take them away, it's OK to scream and kick.
- Tell your children always to tell you if they've been approached by someone they don't know.
- Make sure your child knows what to do if he or she is lost.
- In a crowded place, it's safest to stand still and wait to be found.

Otherwise:

- tell a police officer;
- go into a shop and tell someone behind the counter;
- tell someone who has other children with them.

Teach your child his or her address and phone number or the phone number of some other responsible person.

Safety in the sun

The amount of sun your child is exposed to may increase his or her risk of skin cancer later in life. Do the following to protect your child.

- Keep your child out of the sun between 11 am and 3 pm when the sun is highest and most dangerous.
- Keep babies under the age of six months out of the sun altogether.
- Make the most of shade, e.g trees.
- Don't let your child run around all day in a swimsuit or without any clothes on.
- Cover your child up in loose baggy cotton clothes such as an oversized T-shirt with sleeves.
- In particular, protect your child's shoulders and back of neck when playing, as these are the most common areas for sunburn.
- Let your child wear a 'legionnaire's hat' or a floppy hat with a wide brim that shades the face and neck.
- Cover exposed parts of your child's skin with a sunscreen, even on cloudy or overcast days. Use one with a sun protection factor (SPF) of 15 or above and which is effective against UVA and UVB. Re-apply often.
- Protect your child's eyes with sunglasses with an ultraviolet filter made to British Standard 2724.
- Use waterproof sunblock if your child is swimming.

Emergency first aid

Coping with accidents

You'll have to cope with some accidents while your child is young, mostly minor, but some may be major.

- *Learn basic first aid, or revise what you already know. There's information on the following pages. You can also buy books.*
- *Better still, do a first aid course. Courses are run by the St John Ambulance and your local NHS Ambulance Service. These organisations have local branches. Look in your phone book, or contact the address on page 150 or ask your health visitor to organise a course.*
- *The Royal Life Saving Society UK arranges courses in baby resuscitation skills. If you would like to enquire about courses in your area, or would like further information, then telephone 01789 773994 or fax 01789 773995. A step-by-step emergency sequence leaflet* Save a baby's life *on the steps to take when a baby is choking or stops breathing is available for £3 from River House, High Street, Broom, Warwickshire B50 4HN – please send a large stamped addressed envelope.*
- *Make sure you know what to do to get help in an emergency. See inside the back cover.*

If, for whatever reason, you think your child may have stopped breathing, first you must make sure that it is safe for yourself and any other child to approach. For example, if your child has had an electric shock, you will need to turn the power off before approaching. If this is not possible, push the child away from the source of the shock with a wooden object, such as a broom handle or other non-conducting object, then try gentle stimulation by tapping the feet or stroking your child's neck and **shouting** 'hello' or 'wake up'. If you get no response from your child, then he or she is unconscious and you must follow the **ABC of resuscitation** shown below. **You should also call for help**.

A Open the airway

1. Place your child on any firm surface.
2. Put one hand on your child's forehead and the other under the chin and gently lift the chin with two fingers.

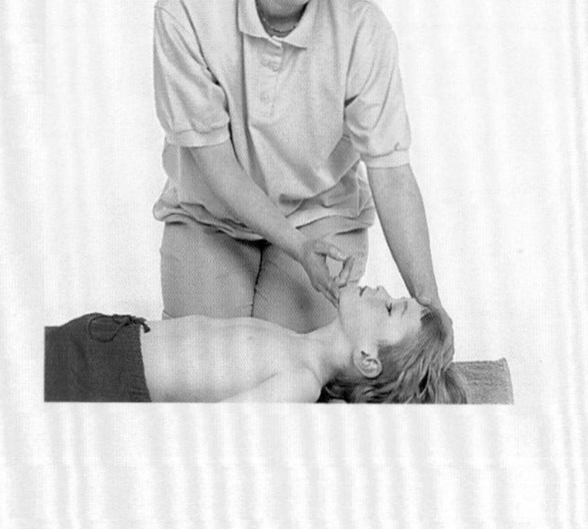

B Check breathing for up to 10 seconds

1. Put your ear close to your child's mouth.
2. Look to see if the chest is rising and falling.
3. Listen for sounds of breathing.
4. Feel for breath on your cheek.
5. Do this for up to 10 seconds.
6. Look inside the mouth for any obvious obstruction which can be removed easily.
7. Do not touch the back of the throat: young children's palates are very soft and may swell or bleed, further blocking the airway.
8. If your child is not breathing, give five breaths of mouth-to-mouth ventilation (see page 113), then check circulation.

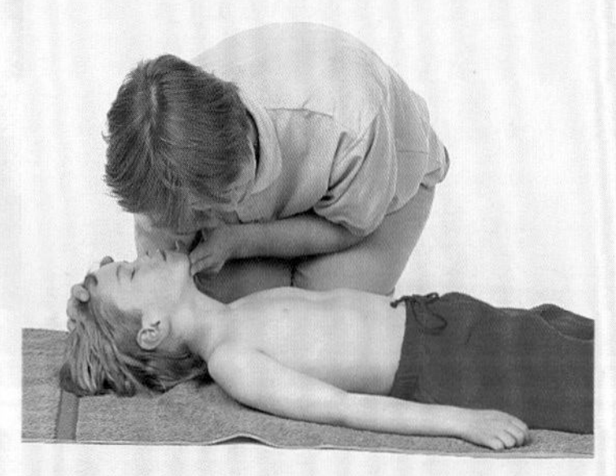

C Check circulation for up to 10 seconds

For babies (under one year)

Assess for signs of life. Check the pulse inside the upper arm by lightly pressing two fingers towards the bone. Look for movement including swallowing and breathing for up to 10 seconds.

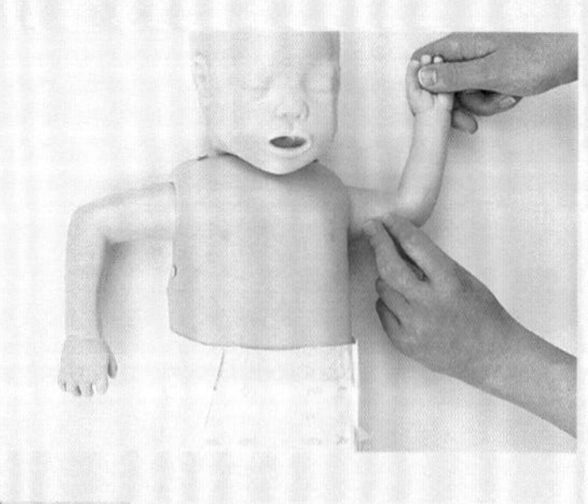

For children (over one year)

Assess for signs of life. Check the pulse in the neck by lightly pressing two fingers to one side of the windpipe. Look for movement including swallowing and breathing for up to 10 seconds.

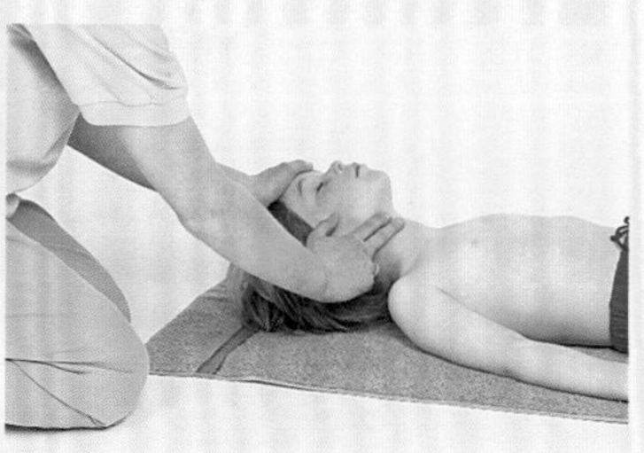

If your child has a pulse but is not breathing

1 Start mouth-to-mouth ventilation (see below).
2 Continue for one minute, then carry your child to a phone and dial 999 for an ambulance, or get someone else to call for you.
3 Continue mouth-to-mouth ventilation. Check pulse every minute.

If your baby or child has no pulse after 10 seconds (or your baby has a pulse slower than one beat per second) and is not breathing

Start chest compression (see page 114) together with mouth to mouth ventilation (see below).

If your child has a pulse and is breathing

1 Place your child in the recovery position (see page 114).
2 Dial 999 for an ambulance.
3 Check breathing and pulse frequently.

Mouth-to-mouth ventilation

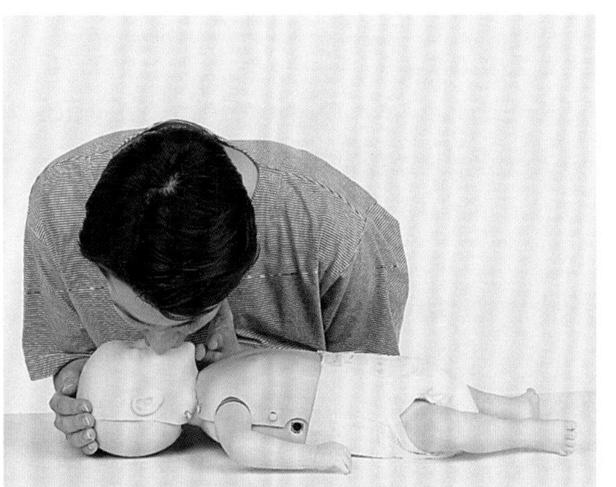

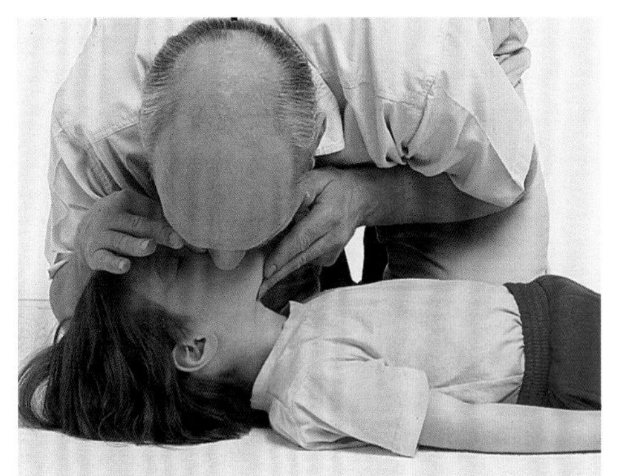

Babies (under one year)

1 Place the baby on any firm surface.
2 Look in the mouth and carefully remove any obvious obstruction.
3 Put one hand on the forehead and two fingers of the other hand under the chin as shown.
4 Gently tilt the head backwards.
5 Seal your lips around your baby's mouth and nose.
6 Blow gently over 1–1.5 seconds, looking at the chest to see if it rises.
7 As the chest rises, stop blowing and allow the chest to fall.
8 Do this at a rate of 20 breaths per minute.
9 Check pulse after 20 breaths. If a pulse is present and above 60 beats per minute, continue mouth to mouth ventilation.
10 If breathing starts, place your baby on its side in your arms or lap with the head held low.

Children (over one year)

1 Place the child on any firm surface.
2 Look in the mouth and carefully remove any obvious obstruction.
3 Put one hand on the forehead and two fingers of the other hand under the chin as shown.
4 Gently tilt the head backwards.
5 Seal your lips around your child's mouth while pinching the nose.
6 Blow gently over 1–1.5 seconds, looking at the chest to see if it rises. Take shallow breaths and do not empty your lungs completely.
7 As the chest rises, stop blowing and allow the chest to fall.
8 Do this at a rate of 20 breaths per minute.
9 Check pulse after 20 breaths. If still present continue mouth-to-mouth ventilation. If absent, commence chest compression.
10 If breathing starts, place your child in the recovery position.

Chest compression together with mouth-to-mouth ventilation

Chest compression must always be combined with mouth-to-mouth ventilation.

Babies (under one year)

1 Place your baby on a firm surface.
2 Find the correct position – a finger's width below the nipple line, in the middle of the chest.
3 Use two fingers and press down on the chest about $\frac{1}{3}$ of the depth of the baby's chest.
4 Press five times in about three seconds, then blow once gently into the lungs.
5 Continue for one minute.
6 Take your baby to a phone and dial 999, unless someone else has already done this.
7 Continue resuscitation (five compressions followed by one breath) until help arrives.
8 Only if colour improves check the pulse. If present, stop chest compressions but continue to give mouth-to-mouth ventilation if necessary.

Children (over one year)

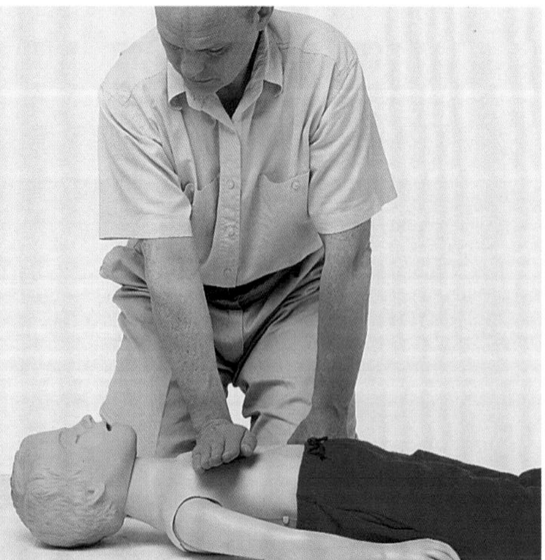

1 Place one hand two fingers' width above where the edge of the ribs meet the breastbone.
2 Use the heel of that hand and press down on the chest about $\frac{1}{3}$ of the depth of the child's chest.
3 Press five times in about three seconds, then blow once gently into the lungs.
4 Continue this process for one minute.
5 Take your child to a phone and dial 999, or get someone else to call for you.
6 Continue resuscitation (five compressions followed by one breath) until help arrives.
7 Only if colour improves check the pulse. If present, stop chest compressions but continue to give mouth-to-mouth ventilation if necessary.

Recovery position

The aim of the recovery position is to keep the airway open and minimise further injury.

Babies (under one year)

1 Don't use the recovery position.
2 Hold your baby on its side in your arms or your lap, in each case with the head held low.

Children (over one year)

Note: For small toddlers it may be more practical to follow the guidelines for babies. Otherwise:

1 Place the arm nearest you at right-angles to the body, elbow bent. Bring the other arm across the chest. Hold the hand, palm out, against the cheek.
2 Roll your child on to his or her side so that the upper leg is bent at the knee and the arms remain in the position described above.

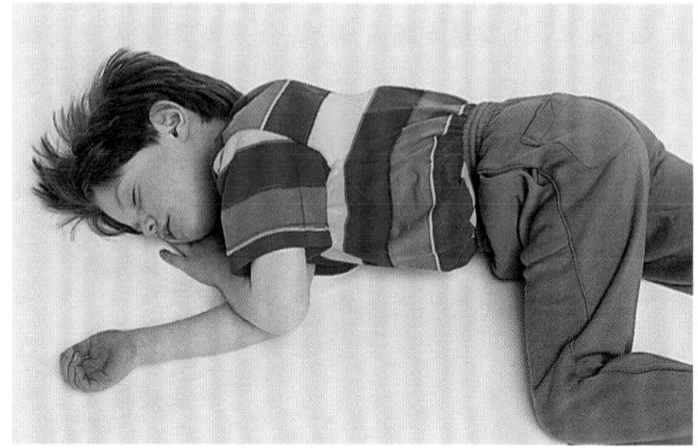

3 Tilt the head back gently to maintain the open airway.
4 If in the correct position, as shown, your child will not roll on to his or her tummy or back.
5 Check breathing and pulse. **If either stops, follow the ABC of resuscitation** (page 112).

If your child has a broken bone

- Don't move your child if you think his or her neck or spine may be injured. Get expert help. Unnecessary movement could cause paralysis.
- A bone in your child's leg or arm may be broken if he or she has pain and swelling, and the limb seems to be lying at a strange angle.
- If you can't easily move your child without causing pain, call an ambulance.
- If you have to move your child be very gentle. Use both hands above and below the injury to steady and support it (using blankets or clothing if necessary). Comfort your child and take him or her to hospital.

If your child is burnt or scalded

- **Immediately** put the burn or scald under running cold water to reduce the heat in the skin. Do this for at least 10 minutes. If running water isn't available, immerse the burn or scald in cold water, or any other cooling fluid, such as milk, or other cold drinks could be used.

- Cover the burn or scald with a clean, non-fluffy cloth like a clean cotton pillow case or linen tea towel or cling film. This cuts down the danger of infection.
- If clothes are stuck to the skin, don't try to take them off.
- Depending on the severity of the burn or scald, see your doctor or call an ambulance or take your child to hospital. You should seek medical help for anything other than a very small burn.
- Don't put butter, oil or ointment on a burn or scald. It only has to be cleaned off again before treatment can be given.
- Don't prick any blisters. You'll delay healing and let in germs.
- Be prepared to treat your child for shock (see page 118).

Don't give your child anything to eat or drink after an accident. Wait until you get to the hospital. He or she may need an anaesthetic later.

Minor accidents

Many general practices are equipped to deal with minor casualties such as cuts or items trapped in the nose or ear. In these sorts of cases, therefore, it may be more appropriate or convenient for you to seek advice from your local practice on where best to go before attending an Accident and Emergency department.

If your child is choking

Choking is caused by an obstruction in the airway and must be treated **immediately**.

- Look inside your child's mouth and remove any object if it is very easy to get at. Do not probe blindly into the mouth – you may push the object further in or damage the soft palate.

- If your child isn't breathing, start mouth-to-mouth ventilation – it may be possible to ventilate your child if the obstruction is only partial. If your child is breathing, follow the instructions below.

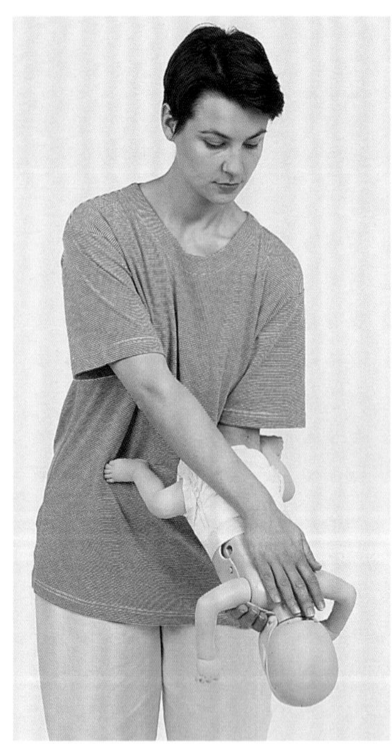

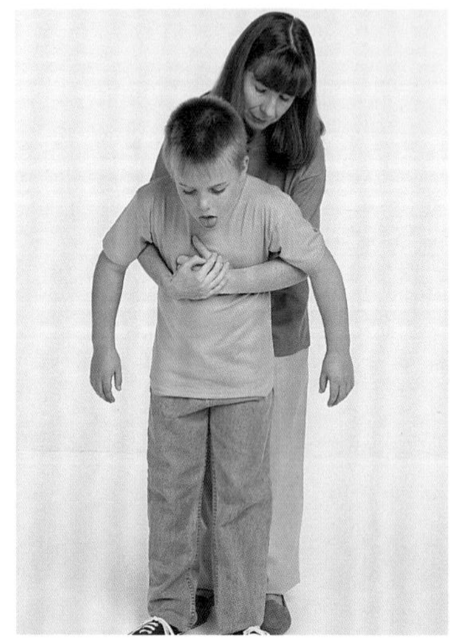

Babies (under one year)

1 Lie the baby along your forearm or thigh with the face down and the head low and supported.
2 Give up to five firm slaps between the shoulder blades.
3 If this does not work, turn your baby head down on his or her back along your thigh. Give five chest thrusts, using the same technique and finger position as for chest compressions (see page 114), but press more sharply at a rate of about 20 per minute.
4 Repeat steps 1, 2, and 3 three times.
5 If this does not work, dial 999 and continue repeating the sequence of back slaps and chest thrusts.
6 **If your baby becomes unconscious follow the ABC of resuscitation** (see page 112).

> **DO NOT USE ABDOMINAL THRUSTS ON BABIES UNDER ONE YEAR.**

Children (over one year)

1 Encourage your child to cough if possible.
2 If this doesn't work, bend your child forwards so that his or her head is lower than the chest and give up to five firm slaps between the shoulder blades. Check the mouth is clear.
3 If this does not work, lie your child on its back and give up to five chest thrusts, using the same technique and finger position as for chest compressions (see page 114) but press more sharply at a rate of about 20 per minute. Check the mouth is clear.
4 If this does not work, give **abdominal thrusts**. Place yourself behind your child and steady him or her with one arm. Put your other arm around your child, placing the heel of your hand in the upper abdomen. Give a sharp pull inwards and upwards below your child's ribs. Repeat up to three times.
5 If this does not work, summon medical aid and continue repeating the sequence of back slaps, chest thrusts, back slaps, abdominal thrusts.
6 **If your child becomes unconscious follow the ABC of resuscitation** (see page 112).

Things stuck up the nose or in the ears

If you suspect that your child has stuck something up his or her nose or into an ear, don't attempt to remove it yourself (you may push it further in). Take your child to the nearest Accident and Emergency department. If the nose is blocked, explain to your child that he or she will have to breathe through the mouth.

If your child has a cut

- If there's a lot of bleeding, press firmly on the wound, using a pad of clean cloth. If you don't have a cloth, use your fingers. Keep pressing until the bleeding stops. This may take 10 minutes or more.
- Don't use a tourniquet or tie anything so tightly that it stops the circulation.
- If possible, raise the injured limb. This helps to stop the bleeding. *Don't do this if you think the limb is broken.*
- Cover the wound with a clean dressing if you can find one. If blood soaks through the pad or dressing, do not remove it. Place another pad or dressing over the top.

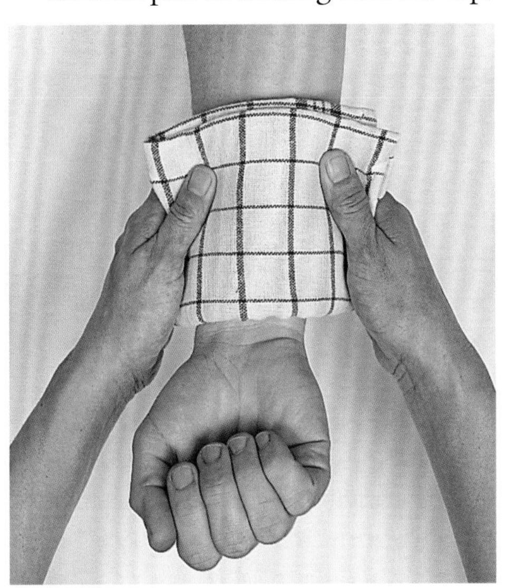

- Then call an ambulance or take your child to hospital.
- Ask your GP about a tetanus injection if your child has not been immunised.

If your child has taken a poison

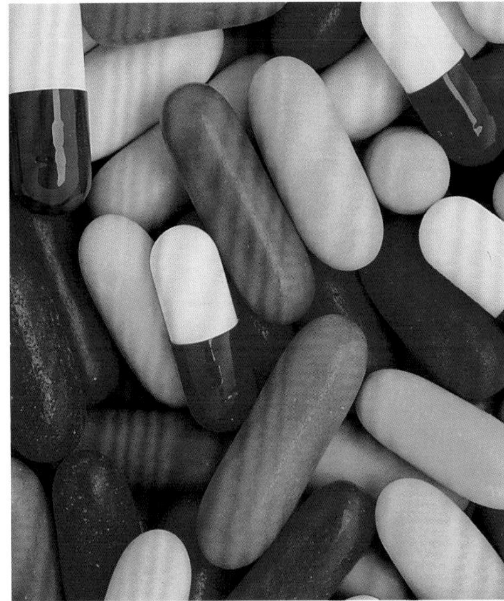

Pills and medicines

- If you're not sure whether your child has swallowed something, spend a minute or two looking for the missing pills. Check they haven't rolled under a chair, for example.
- If you still think something has been swallowed, take your child straight away to your GP or to hospital, whichever is quickest.
- Keep a close watch on your child and be prepared to follow the **ABC of resuscitation if he or she becomes unconscious** (see page 112).
- If possible, take the container (or its label) with you and a sample of whatever you think your child has swallowed.
- Don't give salt and water or do anything else to make your child sick.

When to take your child to hospital after an accident

- *If your child is unconscious.*
- *If your child is vomiting or drowsy.*
- *If your child is bleeding from the ears.*
- *If your child has stopped breathing at some stage.*
- *If your child may have internal injuries.*
- *If your child complains of severe pain anywhere.*
- *If your child is having fits (see page 95).*

If you're worried or uncertain about your child's injuries, get a doctor's advice. If you are unsure whether you should move your child, make him or her warm and call an ambulance. Go to the Accident and Emergency department of your nearest hospital or to a local doctor, whichever is quickest. Not all hospitals have an Accident and Emergency department, so check in advance where your nearest one is. Your health visitor will be able to tell you. (See inside the back cover for how to get help in an emergency.)

Household and garden chemicals

- If you think something poisonous has been swallowed, calm your child as much as you can. You'll do this better if you can keep calm yourself. **But act quickly to get your child to hospital.**
- If possible, take the container (or its label) with you and a sample of whatever you think has been swallowed.
- If your child is in pain or there is any staining, soreness or blistering around the mouth, then he or she has probably swallowed something corrosive. Let him or her sip milk or water to ease the burning in the lips. Get your child to hospital quickly.

If your child is shocked

- If pale, unwell or feeling faint after an accident, help your child to lie down.
- Keep your child covered up and warm, but not too hot.
- If your child has lost a lot of blood, keep his or her head down and raise your child's legs. This makes more blood go to his or her head. **Don't do this if you suspect a head injury or a broken leg.**

If your child suffocates

- Quickly take away whatever is causing the suffocation.
- **If your child has stopped breathing, follow the ABC of resuscitation** (see page 112).

Bereavement

The death of someone you love can turn your world upside down and is one of the most difficult experiences to endure. This may be harder to cope with if you have just had a baby.

Friends and family can help you by spending time with you if you have been bereaved. A sympathetic arm around the shoulders can express love and support when words are not enough.

Grief is not just one feeling but a whole succession of feelings which take time to get through and which cannot be hurried. If you need help or advice, you can contact your GP or any of the organisations listed on page 149.

If your partner dies

If your partner dies during your pregnancy or soon after childbirth, you will feel emotionally numb. It is like no other loss. It is not something you get over, more that you learn, eventually, to live with.

Don't be afraid to lean on family and friends for help and support with your baby.

Financially, you may need urgent advice and support. You could get the three leaflets suggested (see box 'Benefits available if your partner dies' on this page) from your local Jobcentre Plus/Social Security Office (Jobs & Benefits office).

As well as speaking to friends, family and social services, you may like to contact WIDWODS, a small support group set up by young widows (see page 149).

Benefits available if your partner dies

You may find the following leaflets produced by the Jobcentre Plus/Social Security Office (Jobs & Benefits office) helpful:

A Guide to the Social Fund (SB16)

What to Do after Death in England and Wales (D49)

New Bereavement Benefits

Your Guide to Our Services

When a child dies

There's a feeling that children aren't meant to die. That feeling adds great shock (as well as maybe anger, bewilderment, even a kind of guilt) to the enormous grief and sadness brought by death. The grief, sadness and other feelings are important to you. They're not to be set aside quickly or hidden away.

You need to let yourself grieve in your own way. If you need to cry, don't hold back the tears. Crying may be the only way of letting out your feelings. If you feel angry, as many parents do, or find you're blaming yourself or others, it's important to talk about it. Ask the questions you want to ask of, for example, hospital staff, your GP, midwife or health visitor. Often the reasons for a baby's death are never known, not even after a post-mortem. But you need to find out all you can.

After the first shock, it may help you to think about ways of remembering your child. If you don't already have photographs, you may want to have a photograph taken to keep. Talk to the hospital about this. Give a lot of thought to any service or ceremony you may want, and to mementoes you may want to keep.

Try to explain what's happened as simply and honestly as you can to any older children. They need to understand why you're sad, and will have their own feelings to cope with. Sometimes an older child connects the death with something he or she has done, and may be very quiet, or badly behaved, for a time. It's not easy for you to give the love and reassurance that's needed. It may help to get support from others close to your child.

Coping with the outside world and other people is difficult at first. You may find that even people quite close to you don't know what to say, say the wrong thing, or avoid you. Take the support that's given and feels right.

It's best to expect a long time of difficult feelings and ups and downs. Talking may not come easily to you, but even some time after your baby's death, it can help to talk about your feelings. The more you and your partner can talk to each other, the more it'll help you both. A father's experience of a baby's death can be different from a mother's. Although you'll share a lot, your feelings and moods won't be the same all the time. Try to listen to each other so you can support each other as best you can.

Sometimes talking to someone outside the family is helpful – a close friend, your doctor, health visitor, hospital staff, maybe a priest or other religious counsellor.

'There was this huge emptiness, and the only way we could fill the emptiness and begin to understand was to talk and talk, and to cry. The real friends were the ones who let us talk and weren't afraid to see us cry. The last thing we wanted was to be helped to feel better. That would have meant forgetting what had happened to us before we'd even begun to live with it. It would have meant forgetting our baby. You never forget. It will always be part of us, just like any child.'

'Time goes by and gradually, if you grieve enough, you begin to accept it. A time comes when you can make it all right with yourself to feel happy about happy things.'

Talking to other parents who've been through the same loss and grief can be a special help. You can contact other parents through the following organisations.

- ***Stillbirth and Neonatal Death Society***
  Run by and for parents whose baby has died either at birth or shortly afterwards.
- ***Foundation for the Study of Infant Deaths***
  Supports parents bereaved by a cot death or what is called 'Sudden Infant Death Syndrome' (SIDS).
- ***Compassionate Friends***
  An organisation of, and for, all bereaved parents.

Addresses and phone numbers are given on page 149.

7 Your own life

'People say, "How's the baby doing?" And I want to say, "Well she's OK, but do you want to know how I'm feeling?" '

'I'm totally knackered, but I wouldn't give them back for anything!'

'I suppose I'd thought that having a kid wouldn't change that much for me. Obviously it was going to make a difference financially, with Linda giving up work. Apart from that, I'd thought it was Linda's life that was going to change and that I'd be going on much the same as before. Who was I kidding?'

(A FATHER)

Becoming a parent changes your life. Suddenly there seems to be no time for you, for the things you like to do, for quiet moments with your partner or with friends. Sometimes you may feel that there isn't even any time for the basic things in life like eating and sleeping. But if you don't give yourself some time and consideration, your batteries will soon be used up and you simply won't have the energy to make a good job of being a parent. This section is for you.

YOUR BODY AFTER CHILDBIRTH

Having a baby changes your body. You may not like the changes, or you may enjoy feeling different, 'more like a mother'. If you like the way you are, don't let other people tell you differently.

If you feel uncomfortable with your body, you'll want to make some changes. Some things will never be quite the same again – for example, stretch marks will fade, but won't ever go away completely.

Other changes need not be permanent. A saggy tummy can be tightened up with exercise, and weight gain will gradually drop off if you eat and exercise sensibly. But don't expect this to happen overnight. It took nine months to make a baby. Give yourself at least that long to get back into shape again – and it may take longer.

In the meantime, give your body some little treats to cheer you up. For example, if it makes you feel good to paint your toenails, then make time to do it. Maybe for you that's even more important than 20 minutes extra sleep.

Physical problems

A lot of women have physical problems, either as a result of labour and birth, or because of the kind of work involved in caring for young children, or both. Problems like some sort of infection that keeps coming back, back pain, a leaky bladder and painful intercourse are more common than people think.

Helping yourself

For some problems you can do a lot to help yourself. The muscles around your bladder, vagina and back passage (the perineum) may be weak and that could be part of the reason for the 'falling out' feeling or leaky bladder that many women describe. Pelvic floor exercises can help. A bad back can also be helped by exercise, and by learning to use your back carefully.

Pelvic floor exercise
The muscles of the pelvic floor form a hammock underneath the pelvis to support the bladder, womb and bowel. You use these muscles when you pass water, empty your bowels and when you make love. Often they're stretched during pregnancy, labour and birth. If you can improve their strength and function you're less likely to have a leaky bladder and more likely to enjoy intercourse.

You can do this exercise either sitting or standing, when you're washing up, queuing in the supermarket, watching television – anywhere.

- Squeeze and draw in your back passage at the same time. Close up and draw in your vagina (front passage) upwards.
- Do this exercise quickly – tightening and releasing the muscles immediately;
- then do the exercise slowly, holding the contractions for as long as you can (not more than ten seconds) before you relax;
- repeat both exercises ten times four–six times a day.

It helps to imagine you're stopping a bowel movement, holding in a tampon, stopping yourself passing water. In fact, the best way to find the muscles is to try stopping and starting (or slowing down) the flow of urine while you're on the toilet.

Deep stomach exercise
This exercise helps to firm your stomach. (If a gap or bulge line appears vertically down the centre of your stomach, you should ask your physiotherapist for special exercises.)

- Lie on your side with your knees slightly bent;
- let your tummy sag and breathe in gently;
- as you breathe out, gently draw in the lower part of your stomach like a corset, narrowing your waistline;
- squeeze your pelvic floor also;
- hold for the count of 10 then gently release;
- repeat 10 times.

Postnatal check

Don't be so busy looking after your baby that you forget to go for your postnatal check at around six–eight weeks. This is an opportunity for you to talk to your doctor about any health problems following delivery, such as perineal pain or pain following episiotomy, backache, piles, incontinence, etc. It is also an opportunity to talk about how you are feeling, for example, if you are feeling low or depressed, and also to talk about family planning if you wish.

Deep vein thrombosis (DVT)

DVT is a serious condition where clots develop in the deep veins of the legs. It can be fatal if the clot travels from the legs to the lungs. Flights lasting over five hours where you sit still for a long time may increase the risk. Pregnant women and women who have recently had a baby are amongst those more at risk, so if you intend to travel by air, it is important that you consult your GP or health visitor before the trip. You may need advice on in-seat exercises to keep the circulation active. If you do develop swollen, painful legs or have breathing difficulties after the trip, see a doctor urgently or go to the nearest Accident and Emergency department. More information on DVT and travel can be found by searching for DVT on ***www.dh.gov.uk and www.nhsdirect.nhs.uk***

'I think everyone assumes that after the first month or so, you're back to normal again. But I know from talking to friends that I'm not the only one to feel like anything but normal.'

'A frump. That's what I am. But where's the time to do anything about it.'

'I just don't like myself any more. My whole body's completely changed.'

'You think you're the only person in the world with this problem, and you feel embarrassed and, you know, almost a bit ashamed, as though somehow it's your fault. So you just get on and try to forget about it or hope it will go away. And when it doesn't, you get really fed up. It was only because I got talking to a friend, and we found out we both felt the same, it was only then that I started to think, well, maybe I can do something about this. And because there were two of us, we had a bit more courage and could back each other up.'

If you have a problem that is bothering you, don't ignore it – ask for help. Your GP may be able to suggest treatment or might refer you to a specialist at the hospital or to an obstetric physiotherapist who can help with back and bladder problems and painful stitches.

To ease back problems

- While feeding, always sit with your back well supported and straight. Use a pillow or cushion behind your waist.
- Kneel or squat to do low-level jobs like bathing your baby or picking things up off the floor. Avoid bending your back. Make your knees work instead. Change nappies on a waist-level surface or while kneeling on the floor.
- To lift weights like a carrycot or an older child, bend your knees, keep your back straight and hold the weight close to your body. Make your thigh muscles work as you lift.
- Try to keep a straight back when you push a pram or buggy, or carry your baby in a sling.

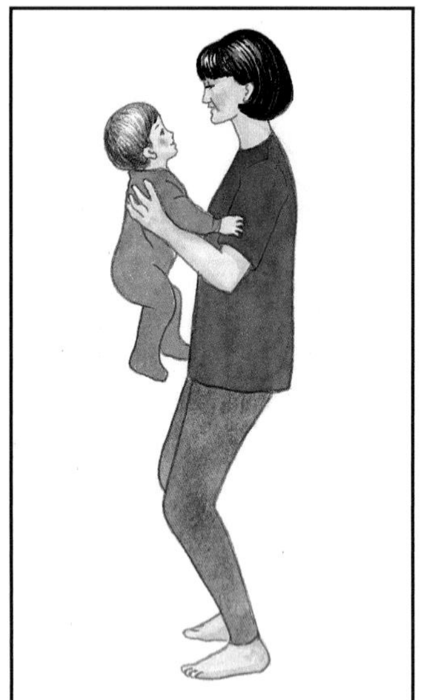

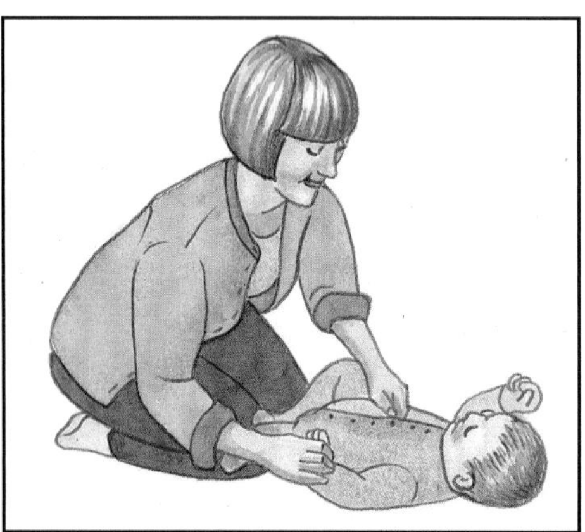

Keeping healthy

Eating

Being a parent is an exhausting business and it is easy to find that you have no time or energy to cook or eat properly. Try to make eating well a priority; it will make you feel better and needn't take lots of time. Try to follow the guidelines about eating a healthy diet explained on page 75.

If you are breastfeeding, make sure you eat and drink plenty and don't go on a diet. The section on page 10 provides information about healthy eating.

If you're not breastfeeding and feel you need to lose weight, talk to your GP about it first. Cut down on fat and sugar and don't go on a crash diet. Small regular meals will keep up your energy levels without adding to your weight.

Physical activity

When you're feeling tired, being more active or taking more exercise may seem like the last thing you need, but activity can relax you, help your body recover after childbirth, keep you fit or improve your fitness, and makes you feel better.

- **Keep up the postnatal exercises you were taught.** Stick at them. They'll strengthen vital muscles and improve your shape. Some important exercises are described on page 121.
- **Join a postnatal exercise class if you've recently had a baby**. Company may help. Find out if your local maternity unit has a class run by an obstetric physiotherapist, or ask your health

visitor about other local classes. If it isn't a special postnatal class, be sure to tell the person running the class if you've had a baby in the last few months. You'll need to take special care of your back and avoid exercises that could damage it.

- **Push the pram or buggy briskly, remembering to keep your back straight**. Get out for walks as much as you can.

- **Play energetic games with older children**. Make yourself run about as well as them. Find outdoor space if there's no space at home.

- **Run upstairs**. You probably find yourself going up and down a hundred times a day in any case. Try to look on it as good exercise!

- **Squat down to pick things up from the floor, holding heavy weights close to your body**. This is also something you're likely to be doing a lot. If you squat rather than stoop, bending your knees and keeping your back straight, you'll improve your thigh muscles. You'll also avoid damaging your back.

- **Join an exercise class**. There may be one locally that welcomes children or has a crèche. Ask your health visitor.

- **Swimming is good, relaxing exercise**. If you take your child with you, try to have someone else there too, so that you get a chance to swim.

- **Borrow or buy an exercise video**. Do a workout at home, perhaps with a friend. Get the children to join in.

Give up smoking

Many people smoke because they believe that it calms their nerves, but it doesn't. It just calms the craving for nicotine that cigarettes create. So here are some useful steps to stop smoking.

- **Know why you want to stop**. It is handy to keep a checklist of your reasons to stop smoking.

- **Change your habits.** Smoking is strongly linked to some situations – the first cigarette of the day, the cigarette with tea or coffee, when the phone rings. Try to break the link by changing your habits. For example, drink orange juice instead of coffee for a while.

- **Be ready to stop**. Choose a day and stop completely on that day. The day before get rid of cigarettes, ashtrays and lighters.

Planning another pregnancy?

Remember to take a daily 400 microgram supplement of folic acid, from the time you stop using contraception until the 12th week of pregnancy. This can help prevent birth defects, such as spina bifida.

Good reasons to stop smoking

- *Your children's health will improve.*
- *Your health will improve.*
- *You'll have money to spend on other things.*

For help

*Contact **NHS Smoking Helpline on 0800 169 0 169** between 7am and 11pm every day. As well as helping you over the phone, the adviser can also tell you where to find support locally and will send you a self-help guide packed with information about how to stop smoking. People who use professional support are more likely to be successful in stopping smoking. In Northern Ireland contact the **Smokers' Helpline** 0800 85 85 85 or the **Ulster Cancer Foundation** (028) 9049 2007 0800 783 3339 (helpline) www.ulstercancer.org*

'I think the tiredness is the worst thing. It goes on and on. And you've got no choice, you've got to keep going. So you feel sort of trapped. And after a bit, it gets you down, feeling so tired all the time.'

'You come in from work and you start right in on another job. And then when you've got them off to bed, there are still other things you've got to do. So you drop into bed and there's been no breathing space. You're probably up in the night as well. And then you get up the next morning and start all over again.'

(A father)

- **Get support.** Tell family and friends you have decided to stop and ask them for their support. For example, ask them not to offer you a cigarette.
- **Anticipate problems**. Which situations will be difficult? Don't just wait for them to happen. Plan how to deal with them.
- **Take one day at a time.** At the beginning of each day, congratulate yourself on having made it so far, but make your goal to get through today without smoking. Never mind tomorrow.
- **If you need to put something in your mouth, try sugar-free gum.** If you need to do something with your hands, find something to fiddle with – a pencil, coin – anything but a cigarette.

Sleep

Most of the time parents just live with tiredness. But when the tiredness begins to make you feel low, bad-tempered, unable to cope and certainly unable to enjoy things, you've got to find ways of getting more sleep or at least more rest. Just one day, one night, one week, could help.

- **Get to bed early, really early, say for a week**. If you can't sleep when you get to bed, do something relaxing for half an hour beforehand, whether it's exercise, soaking in a bath or watching television.
- **Deep relaxation can refresh you after only five or ten minutes**, so it's worth learning a relaxation technique. You may find books, tapes or videos about this at your library.
- **Sleep when your baby sleeps**. Rest when (if) your child has a daytime rest, or is at playgroup or nursery school. Arrange for a relative or friend to take your child for a while, not so that you can get the jobs done, but so you can sleep. Take turns with other parents to give yourself time to rest. Set an alarm if you're worried about sleeping too long.
- **If you can, share getting up in the night with your partner**. Take alternate nights or weeks. If you're on your own, a friend or relative may be prepared to have your children overnight occasionally.
- **Look on page 56 for other ways of coping with disturbed nights**.
- **Do something about any stress**. Tiredness often comes from stress (see below). If you can do something about the stress, you may be able to cope better, even without more sleep.

Coping with stress

Small children ask a lot of you, and there's a limit to what you can ask of them. But perhaps the greatest stress comes from coping with the rest of life at the same time as coping with a baby or small child. You can spend a whole day trying to get one job done, but never managing to fit it in. Just as you start on it, your baby wakes up, or a nappy needs changing, or your child wants attention. Sometimes you can feel as though life is completely out of control. And if you're not the sort of person who can take things as they come and not mind about what is or isn't done, you can get to feel very tense and frustrated.

Stress also comes from worry and unhappiness: maybe to do with the place you live, money, relationships or just a lot of small but important things. You may not be able to change the way your children are or the life you lead, but you may be able to do something about the stress. It's a matter of finding solutions that are right for you.

- You may find that you can relax just by doing something that you enjoy for half an hour in the evening when you can put other things out of your mind for a while. A bath, maybe, or time to look at a magazine or the television. Do whatever will let you unwind. Borrow a book or tape from the library about relaxation. Make yourself do it.

- See other people – it does take off the pressure. Try a mother and baby or parent and toddler group. Ask your health visitor or other parents about local groups. Or, if you're not keen on organised groups, get together with people you meet at the clinic, playgroup or nursery school.

- Relationships can go wrong when you're tense and tired and never seem to see each other, so make time to be with your partner, even if only to fall asleep together in front of the television.

- Talking about the stress you're feeling can help to get rid of it, at least for a while. If you and your partner can understand how each of you is feeling, then take time to talk about how best to support each other. Sometimes it's better to talk with people outside the family (see page 126).

- Make the very most of all the help you can find. And give up a bit. You can't do everything. Try to believe it really doesn't matter.

- There are no prizes for being a supermum or superdad. Compromise if you're a perfectionist.

Feeling depressed

(See also **Postnatal depression** on page 6).

Most of us feel low occasionally and lack of sleep, stress, and maybe the strain of balancing paid work and parenting, and money problems, all contribute to making the early stages of parenthood a difficult, as well as a rewarding, time. Sometimes feeling low takes over completely and becomes depression.

Depression is more than feeling unhappy. It's feeling hopeless about yourself and all that's happening to you. The hopelessness can make you angry, but often you feel too tired even for anger. It can seem as though there's no answer and no end to the way you're feeling. You may feel all, or some, of these things:

- tired, but can't sleep;
- no appetite or are overeating;
- no interest in yourself;
- no interest in your baby;
- the smallest chores are almost impossible to manage;
- you never stop crying.

This kind of depression is like an illness. Nothing seems worth doing, so doing anything as demanding as caring for a baby or child becomes a real struggle. Both for yourself and for the family, it's important to get help.

See your GP or health visitor, or both. Take someone with you if this would help. Make it clear that you're

'It's the two of them. What one wants the other doesn't want. When I'm getting the little one off to sleep, the older one suddenly decides he needs the potty. You can't seem to do right by both of them. You're split in two, and there's no let-up, it's the whole time.'

'It's hard to explain to someone who isn't a parent how, even when you're enjoying it, there's this sort of constant drain on you. You think about them all the time, you have to. You have to think for them all the time. Even when I'm out at work, I have to think about getting back on time, and remembering to tell the childminder something, and buying something for tea ...'

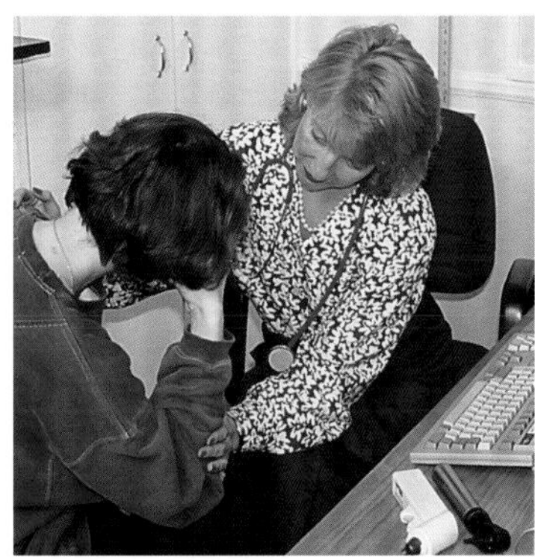

'It gets so frustrating. I wake up in the morning and think, "Right, what have I got today?" And then I give myself a great big long list of all the things I've got to do, and if I can't get them all done in that day, I get really narked about it.'

Alcohol may appear to help you relax and unwind. In fact it's a depressant, affecting moods, judgement, self-control and co-ordination. If you're tired and run down, it affects these even more. So watch how much and when you drink. Never mix alcohol with anti-depressants or tranquillisers.

'It felt like an invasion. All of a sudden, everything was revolving around the baby. For the first month or two I found it really hard. Now it's three of us and it couldn't ever be different, I couldn't imagine it back with just the two of us, but it was a very hard feeling, adjusting to the invasion of our privacy.'

'I think Dave thinks I've got an easy life, you know, just being at home all day. He thinks I can just suit myself and do what I want to do. I get very angry because there are days when I'd give anything to be walking out of the house like he does.'

'There's a lot of pressure, it's true. I think we've had to learn a lot, and learn it fast, about how to get on when there's so much to cope with. But then there's a lot we both enjoy, and more to share, really.'

not talking about just feeling low but something more worrying than that. You may find that you're too low even to make the first step. If this is the case it's important to talk to someone – your partner, a friend or your mother, and ask them to talk to your GP or health visitor on your behalf and arrange an appointment for you.

Talking it through

It does help to talk, but it may be very hard to do so.

- You may want to say things that you're afraid of admitting to the people you love.
- You may feel guilty about your feelings.
- You may believe that you'll be judged as a bad mother for admitting to your feelings.

For all these reasons it's often best to talk to someone who isn't close to you, someone with whom you can be honest without being afraid of shocking them.

You may find that it's enough to talk to your GP or health visitor, or they may be able to refer you to someone else. If you can talk about how you feel, you'll almost certainly find that the things you fear are not as bad as you thought they were.

Medical treatment

If you're feeling totally lost in depression, your doctor may prescribe anti-depressant drugs. They may be enough to give you the lift you need to start coping again, and then to find a way out of your depression, though they can take time to work. Anti-depressants are *not* habit-forming. You should not be concerned about them if they are prescribed for you by your GP. Tranquillisers may also be offered. They are different. They don't help depression and *can* be habit-forming, so they're best avoided.

Relationships

Partnerships under strain

Relationships are often strained by parenthood, no matter what they were like before. Part of the problem is that you have so much less time to spend with each other than you did before the baby arrived and it's so much harder to get out together and enjoy the things you used to do.

- Your partner may feel left out.
- You may feel resentful at what you see as lack of support.

The really hard time, when children take up all your energy, doesn't last for ever. Try to make time for each other when you can and do little things to make each other feel cared for and included.

Time to listen

Don't expect your partner, however close you were before the baby was born, to read your mind. Things are changing in both your lives and you have to talk about it. Your partner will not know what you want unless you say what it is and will not understand why you're resentful or angry unless you explain what's bothering you.

- Ask a friend or relation to babysit so that you can have time together – even if it's just for a walk together in the park.

- Share the housework to make more time just to be together.

- Share the babycare too.

- Talk about how you should bring up your children. You may find that you don't agree about such basic matters as discipline and attitudes. Try to work out a way of not always disagreeing in front of your children.

Sex

Babies and small children don't make for an easy sex life. Often you're tired, maybe too strained, and opportunities are limited. This hardly matters if both you and your partner are content, but if sex is a problem in any way at all, it's important to look at what you can do. Unhappy sex, or just lack of it, can cause a lot of frustration and worry and can really strain relationships.

Immediately after the baby is born many women feel sore as well as tired. They may also be worried about the state of their body or about getting pregnant again.

Men can face problems too. Tiredness apart, a father's sexual feelings will probably be much the same as before his baby's birth. But many men worry about what's right for their partner, are unsure what to do, and feel worried and frustrated.

- **If penetration hurts, say so.** It's not pleasant to have sex if it causes you pain, and if you pretend everything is all right when it isn't you may well start seeing sex as a chore rather than a pleasure, which won't help either of you. You can still give each other pleasure without penetration.

- **Be careful the first few times.** Explore a bit with your own fingers first to reassure yourself that it won't hurt and use plenty of extra lubrication, such as lubricating jelly: hormonal changes after childbirth may mean that you don't lubricate as much as usual.

Getting help

If this is your first baby, you may be feeling very lonely and left out of your old life. Your partner can't supply everything that you used to get from work and friends. You need other people in your life too for support, friendship and a shoulder to cry on. *See **Loneliness** page 129.*

If you feel your relationship is in danger of breaking down, get help.

***RELATE** (National Marriage Guidance) has local branches where you can talk to someone in confidence, either with your partner or alone. Counselling is offered on all sorts of relationship difficulties: you don't have to be married to contact marriage guidance.*

To find your local branch, look under RELATE or Marriage Guidance in your phone book, or write to the address on page 150.

'I couldn't think about it. My mind was on the baby. And it sounds bad, but all my feelings seemed to be taken up by the baby too. And that caused a lot of difficulty for a while. I did feel bad about it, as though it was my fault. But you can't make love as an obligation, can you? I mean, you can, but it's not really any good for either of you.'

(A mother)

'It's not talked about, is it? Except as a sort of joke. So you don't know if you've got a problem or not. At first, Paula found it hurt, and it put us both off and frightened us a bit. We were worried because we didn't know whether that was normal.'
(A FATHER)

'The thing is everything's on your shoulders. When you have to decide something, you know, like whether or not to take him to the doctor, or even everyday small things, there's nobody to share that with. There are so many things it's useful to talk about, and if you're on your own, you can't. If there's a crisis, you're on your own.'

'It's less stressful being your own boss. There's more satisfaction somehow, more achievement. There's no one to disagree with, no conflict over discipline, no competition with other adults.'

DOMESTIC VIOLENCE

If you need to speak to someone or to get help, information or advice, you could ring one of the following helplines.

Women' Aid Federation
0845 702 3468 (24 hours)
In Northern Ireland
028 9033 1818 (24 hours)
In Wales
029 2039 0874
(Mon–Fri 10am–3pm and answerphone)

Rape Crisis Federation
0115 900 3560
(Mon–Fri 9am–5pm and answerphone)

- **Make time to relax together**. There's little point trying to make love when your minds are on anything but each other.
- **Sort out contraception**. It's possible to become pregnant again soon after the birth of a baby, even if you're breastfeeding, and even if you haven't started your period again. So, if you don't want to conceive again quickly, you need to use some kind of contraception from the start. Contraception is usually discussed before you leave hospital after your child's birth, and at the postnatal check-up. But you can go at any time, before or after a check-up, to your GP or family planning clinic, or talk with your health visitor.
- **If your baby sleeps in the same room as you**, you may have to move either yourselves or your baby before you can relax enough to have sex.
- **Don't rush. Take time.**
- **If you're still experiencing pain two months or so after the birth, talk to your doctor or family planning clinic about it.** Treatment is available for a painful episiotomy scar. Ask to see an obstetric physiotherapist.

DOMESTIC VIOLENCE

One in four women experience domestic violence at some point in their lives. This may take the form of physical, sexual, emotional or psychological abuse. Victims are likely to suffer repeated attacks before they seek protection and support. Thirty per cent of this abuse starts in pregnancy or after birth. Domestic violence should not be tolerated. It risks your health and that of your baby before and after birth.

You can speak in confidence to your GP, midwife, health visitor or social worker. If you wish, they can help you take steps to stop the abuse or seek refuge. Or you can contact one of the confidential helplines listed under Domestic violence on page 147.

LONE PARENTS

Bringing a baby into your life changes your relationships with other people whether you're part of a couple or alone with your child.

Some lone mothers feel that their own mothers are taking over, others resent the fact that their mothers won't help them more.

However painful it may be, it's best to try to be very clear about the kind of help you do want, rather than going along with what's offered and then feeling resentful. Remember your mother is also having to get used to a completely new relationship with you and she won't know what to do for the best – unless you tell her!

You may find that your old friends stop coming by or that they seem to expect you just to drop everything and go out for the evening. Try not to get angry with them. They don't understand the changes you are going through. Keep in touch and keep some space for them in your life. Friends can be more valuable than money when the going gets tough.

You may be amazed and delighted at how much help you'll get from relations and friends if you ask! But the best support will probably come from other lone mothers.

- Suggest a 'swap' arrangement with another parent so that you take it in turns to look after both the children, by day to begin with, and later overnight. The children will benefit too from having a close friend, especially if they've no brothers and sisters.

- Suggest a regular evening babysit by a trusted relation or friend. You may well find that they're delighted at the opportunity of making friends with your child.
- Grandparents are often glad to have a baby overnight, even if they don't much care for babysitting.

Making new friends

If you don't already know people locally, try contacting other mothers through local groups.

- Ask your health visitor what's going on locally, and look through the list of support and information organisations on page 146. Many run local groups.
- Gingerbread, a self-help organisation run by and for one-parent families (address on page 149), has local groups around the country. Through these groups you can meet parents in similar situations to your own. And you can often help each other out as well as support each other generally.

Absent fathers

If you'd hoped to bring up your child as a couple you may be feeling very angry and hurt. One of the hardest things for a lone mother is to keep her hurt, angry feelings to herself and let her child make a different relationship with his or her father.

Unless your child's father is violent to you or the child, or you feel he's likely to abuse the child in some way, it's almost certainly better for your child's own development if he or she is able to see his or her father regularly, even if you remarry.

You may find that your child behaves badly at first when he or she gets home. Small children aren't able to understand and explain how they're feeling, and this is the only way they have of letting you know that they're confused. Unless you're convinced that something bad is happening on access visits, the best thing is to be reassuring and calm. In the end your child will learn to look forward to visits and also to coming home.

Money and housing

Money may be a major headache. Look at **Your rights and benefits** (pages 134–45) to check you're claiming all you're entitled to.

The National Council for One Parent Families (address on page 149) offers free advice packs to lone parents and will provide independent advice about maintenance problems to women on benefits.

If you need help with claiming maintenance, contact the Child Support Agency enquiry line on 0845 713 3133 (local call charge or 0845 713 9896 in Northern Ireland). If you're on benefits your case will be handled automatically. If you're not on benefits, and want the agency to assess and collect maintenance on your behalf, there is a fee.

See page 147 for information about help with housing problems. If you are working, or thinking of it, see pages 134–45 for information about available help.

Loneliness

Lots of mothers feel lonely. Especially after the birth of a first baby, many find that they're cut off from old friends, but it's difficult to make new ones. Getting out to see people, even if you've got people to see, is often an effort.

'At home in Pakistan, there's a lot of visiting, lots of people about, and children can go anywhere. Here there isn't so much coming and going. You can feel very isolated.'

'When I was working, there were lots of people to talk to and I had all the company I needed. Now I haven't got any of that, I really miss it. And I think I've lost confidence. I don't find it so easy to talk to people.'

'We first met at a postnatal group which the health visitor organised. We were all really shy at first, but after six weeks of meeting we all wanted to meet again, so we swapped addresses and agreed to meet on Tuesday mornings. That was three years ago. We have had our second babies now and our older ones are great friends – they go to nursery together and stay over at each other's houses. That postnatal group was the best thing that ever happened to me!'

Lone parents – your feelings

You'll almost certainly want (and need) to talk about your own feelings. Try to find another adult to talk to. Your children don't need to hear the details of your feelings about their father and will feel confused and unhappy about loving someone who you clearly do not love.

Some mothers find the answer to feeling lonely and cut off is to take a job. It's not always easy to find the right sort of work with the right sort of hours, or to make childcare arrangements. But if you feel that work outside the home could help, read the ***Going back to work*** *section.*

'At first I hated leaving her. It was much more upsetting than I'd thought – but more for me than for her, really. I'm better about it now, especially as time goes by and I can see that she's happy and well looked after and I've got to know and like the person who cares for her. But I don't think you can ever feel completely right about it. So you just have to live with that and get on with it.'

'There's no doubt it's hard work. I mean, there's no evenings off, because it's then that we have to get all the jobs done round the house. To my mind, families where there's one parent at home all the time have it very easy in comparison.'

'I enjoy the job. It's nothing much, but it earns money we need, and it gets me out and makes me do things I'd not do otherwise. I think I'm a better parent for doing it. I like having contact with people other than mothers. And Darren gets to meet other children, and he thrives on that.'

Meeting new people takes confidence, but it's worth it. Having other people with whom to share the ups and downs of being a parent will help you to cope with the difficult times and make the good times better.

- Ask your health visitor for information about postnatal groups, mother and baby groups, parent and toddler groups, and playgroups. These may be advertised on the clinic noticeboard.
- Chat with other mothers at your baby or child health clinic.
- Talk to your health visitor and ask for an introduction to other new mothers living nearby.
- MAMA, Home-Start, the National Childbirth Trust, and many other local organisations, sometimes based in a church or temple, run local groups where you can meet other people, chat, relax and get a lot of support.

Going back to work

Most mothers go back to work at some point. About half do so before their children start school. It may help to talk to other working mothers. But also try to decide what's right for you and your family. (For information about childcare, see pages 47–50.) You'll need to think about the following.

- **Feeding** – if your baby is still breastfeeding, try to get him or her used to taking milk from a bottle or cup before you return to work. If you need help with combining work and feeding, discuss it with your health visitor, the National Childbirth Trust, La Lèche League, or the Association of Breastfeeding Mothers (see page 146). You can express milk to leave for feeds. It's also

possible to give your baby formula milk in the middle of the day and still breastfeed the rest of the time.

- **Childcare arrangements** – must be as simple as possible to work smoothly. If they don't work smoothly, there's a lot of strain. You also have to be reasonably sure they'll go on working over time.
- **Paying for childcare** – can you afford to pay for childcare out of what you earn? Can you find work that you can do while your partner is at home? Can you fit work into school hours? Can a relation help out? Is there any subsidised childcare in your area? (See page 49.)
- **Housework** – when and who'll do it? If you have a partner you need to talk about how you'll divide responsibilities for housework and childcare.
- **Making time for your child** – even the best childcare isn't a substitute for a parent. Children need to know that they're special. If you work long hours during the week, can you or your partner keep your weekends completely free? If you don't see your child in the day, can you keep him or her up late in the evening and compensate with long daytime sleeps? You may be able to work flexi-time, part-time or a four-day week, and make a special time to be with your child.

8 Your services

There is a wide range of services available from statutory organisations, voluntary organisations and local groups. This chapter will help you find what you need. (Additional information for those living in Northern Ireland can be found on page 133.)

Health services

Child health clinics

Your child health clinic offers regular health and development reviews (see page 36) and immunisation (see pages 102-7) for your baby or child. It's run by health visitors and doctors. You can talk about any problems to do with your child, but if your child is ill and is likely to need treatment, you should go to your GP.

At some child health clinics you can get baby milk and vitamins cheaper than in the shops. If you're entitled to free baby milk and vitamins, or to low-price baby milk, you may be able to get these at your clinic.

Clinics are good places to meet other parents. Some run mother and baby or parent and toddler groups, and sell secondhand baby clothes and equipment.

Community midwives

Your community midwife has a legal duty to care for you and your baby for the first ten days after your baby's birth and will keep you on her books for the first 28 days if you, or the baby, need her. She can help with any problem to do with you or your baby and will give you a phone number to call at any time, day or night, if you need to.

Family doctors

Your family doctor (GP) can be contacted at any time for yourself, your baby, or child. Some doctors will see small babies at the beginning of surgery hours or without an appointment if necessary, but be prepared to wait. Some will give advice over the phone. Most doctors provide developmental reviews and immunisation themselves, or you can go to a child health clinic.

Health visitors

Your health visitor usually makes her first visit some time after your baby is ten days old. After that she may only see you at clinics or when you ask to see her. If you're alone, or struggling, she may make a point of coming by to see whether you need any help.

A health visitor is a qualified nurse who has had extra training to become a health visitor. Part of her role is to help families, especially families with babies and young children, to avoid illness and keep healthy. Talk to your health visitor if you feel anxious, depressed or worried about your children. She may be able to offer advice and suggest where to find help, and may organise groups where you can meet other mothers.

Your health visitor can visit you at home, or you can see her at your child health clinic, doctor's surgery or health centre, depending on where she's based. She'll give you a phone number to get in touch if you need to.

Patient advice and liaison services (PALS)

Your local PALS provides information to patients carers and their families about local health services. For example, they can provide you with a list of local doctors. PALS can advise you on how to get what you need from your health services and tell you about the complaints procedures. You can contact your local PALS by phoning your local NHS Trust or Primary Care Trust, asking to be put through, or phone NHS Direct on 0845 4647.

Local authority services

Children's information service

Your local Children's Information Service (CIS) can provide information about registered childcare, free early education places and other services available in your area. You can

Register your baby with your doctor

Register your baby with your doctor as early as possible with the pink card (yellow card in Northern Ireland) that you'll be given when you register your baby's birth at the local register office. Sign the card and take or send it to your doctor. If you need the doctor to see your baby before you've registered the birth, you can go to the surgery and fill in a registration form for the doctor there. If you move, register with a new doctor close to you as soon as possible (see page 133).

Sure Start is the Government's programme to improve services for children. Sure Start is delivering free part-time early education for 3 and 4 year olds, and it is developing more and better childcare options in England. Find out more through your local Children's Information Service.
Visit: www.surestart.gov.uk
Search for childcare at www.childcarelink.gov.uk

contact them through Sure Start on 0800 006 0296 or on www.surestart.gov.uk

Education departments

Your education department (in your phone book under the name of your local authority) is responsible for all the State-run nursery schools, nursery classes and infant schools in your area and can give you information about them.

The education department also has a responsibility to assess children with special needs and provide suitable education for them.

Housing departments

The housing department (in your phone book under the name of your local authority) is responsible for all council housing in your area and will run the council housing waiting list.

The housing department has a legal duty to house people in certain priority groups who are homeless (or are soon going to be) through no fault of their own. Priority groups include pregnant women and parents of children under 16.

Through your housing department you should also be able to find out about local housing associations, which also provide housing for rent.

Social workers

Social workers are usually found in social services departments. Their job is to provide support for people in need in their area who are having difficulty coping, financially or practically. A social worker may be able to get your child a nursery place, help you find better housing, or give you information about your rights.

To contact a social worker, phone your local social services department, or ask your health visitor to put you in touch.

Advice centres

Advice centres are any non-profit-making agencies that give advice on benefits, housing and other problems. They include citizens advice bureaux, community law centres, welfare rights offices, housing aid centres, neighbourood centres and community projects. Look for them under these names in your phone book, or under the name of your local authority.

Using the services

If you're to get the best from these services, it helps to be clear about what you want.

- Before you meet with any professional, think through exactly what you want to talk about and what information you can give that'll be helpful. You may want to make some notes beforehand and take them with you as a reminder.

- Unless your child needs to be with you, try to get a friend or neighbour to look after him or her so that you can concentrate. It's much easier to talk and listen if you're not distracted.
- If you do have to go with your child or children, take books or toys with you to entertain them.

- Try to consider the answers or advice given to you. If your immediate feeling is 'but that wouldn't work for me' or 'that isn't what I'm looking for', then say so and try to talk about it. You're less likely to come away with an answer you're not happy with or can't put into practice.

- If a problem is making life difficult or is really worrying you, it's worth keeping going until you get some kind of answer, if not a solution. So if the first person you talk to can't help, ask if they can suggest where else you might go. Or if the doctor or health visitor suggests a remedy that doesn't work, go back and ask again.

- Some professionals aren't good at explaining things. If you don't understand, then say so. It's their responsibility to be clear, not yours to guess what they mean. Go back over what's said to you to get it straight.

- If your first language is not English, you may be able to get the help of a linkworker or health advocate. Their job is not just to translate the words, but to act as a friend and make sure that the professionals understand just what you need. Ask your health visitor if there's a linkworker or health advocate in your area.

How to change your GP

You may need to change your GP if you move. You may want to change for other reasons, even if you're not moving house.

First find a GP who will accept you. See if anybody can recommend one. The Central Services Agency or HSSC can give you a list of the doctors in your area. You may have to try more than one GP before you find one willing to accept you, especially if you live in a heavily populated area. If you can't find someone after several attempts, your local health authority will do it for you and you should send them your medical card if you have it, or the address of your previous GP if not.

When you call at the surgery of the GP you've chosen, you may be asked why you want to change. You don't have to give a reason but if you do, try to avoid criticising your old GP. Say something good about the new one instead. For example, the surgery may be easier to get to, the hours may be better, the GP may have a good reputation for treating young children, the practice may be larger and provide more, or you may prefer a woman doctor or one who shares your cultural background.

Once you've found a GP to accept you, leave your medical card with the receptionist. You don't have to contact your old GP at all. If you've lost your medical card, your new GP will probably ask you to complete a form instead, although sometimes you may be asked to contact the primary care trust (in the phone book under the name of your primary care trust) giving the name and address of your previous GP to obtain a medical card first. If you don't know your old GP's name and address, this may take a while, but if you need treatment in the meantime, you can approach any GP, who must take you on, at least temporarily. It's best to say from the beginning that you need treatment now if you're also asking to be permanently registered with that GP.

Finding other help

The help you want may not come from the services of professionals. There are many other sources of help available to parents – not only family and friends, but also many different kinds of local groups and voluntary organisations.

Local groups

To find out about local groups, try the following:

- Ask your health visitor or GP.
- Ask at your citizens advice bureau or other advice centre, your local library, your social services department, or your local Council for Voluntary Service (in your phone book, maybe as Voluntary Action Group, Rural Community Council or Volunteer Bureau). (In Northern Ireland, contact the Northern Ireland Council for Voluntary Action.)
- Look on noticeboards in your child health clinic, health centre, GP's waiting room, local library, advice centres, supermarket, newsagent or toy shop.
- Look through the list of national organisations (pages 146-51). Many run local groups.

In many areas there are now groups offering support to parents who share the same background and culture. Many of these are women's or mothers' groups. Your health visitor may know if there's such a group in your area. Or ask at places like your local library, your citizens advice bureau or other advice or community centre, your local Council for Voluntary Service or your Community Relations Council (in your phone book, maybe as Council for Racial Equality or Community Relations Office).

Starting a group

If you can't find a local group that suits you or can't find the support you need, think about setting it up yourself. Many local groups have begun through a couple of mothers (say with crying babies or sleepless toddlers, or just fed up and lonely) getting together and talking. You could advertise on your clinic noticeboard or in a newsagent's window or local newspaper. Or ask your health visitor to put you in touch with others in the same situation as yourself. You don't have to offer any more than a place to meet and a few cups of coffee.

'I think looking after children is the hardest job going and the one you get least preparation for.'

Northern Ireland

Patient Advice and Liaison Services
In Northern Ireland these services are provided by the Health and Social Services Councils (HSSC). Look in your phone book under Health and Social Services Council.

Social Services departments
In Northern Ireland, look in your phone book under your local Health and Social Services Trust.

Housing departments
In Northern Ireland, the housing department is called the Northern Ireland Housing Executive (in your phone book under Housing Executive).

Education departments
In Northern Ireland, the education department is called the Education and Library Board (in your phone book under Education and Library Board).

Note: In this publication, the NHS also refers to the Northern Ireland Health and Personal Social Services.

9 Your rights and benefits

The following pages are a guide to the main benefits available to families with young children. You may qualify for other benefits too. Benefits have to be claimed on many different forms, from many different offices, and the situation is always changing. The rates given here are accurate from April 2004. It's always worth checking that you're claiming everything to which you are entitled. There are many voluntary organisations that are happy to help. Don't hesitate to ask for advice. If in doubt, get a second opinion. See the box below on where to get advice.

Where to get advice and help

Working out what benefits and rights you are entitled to and making claims can be complicated. Get help if you need it.

- *You can go to your local Jobcentre Plus or in Northern Ireland 'Social Security Office'/Jobs & Benefits office or to their Benefit Shop, Castle Court, Royal Avenue, Belfast. Tel: 028 9033 6958. Or go to your local citizens advice bureau, library or other advice centre (see page 150).*
- *Some local authorities have welfare officers. Phone your social services department (in Northern Ireland local Health and Social Services Board) and ask.*
- *Some voluntary organisations offer information and advice on benefits and rights at work, e.g. the National Council for One Parent Families, Maternity Alliance and Parents at Work (see pages 149 and 150).*

Leaflets giving general information

Rates of benefits change every year, but you can find them in leaflet GL23, Social security benefit rates. *Some other useful leaflets that you can get are:*

- BC1 Babies and children.
  A guide to benefits for anyone expecting a baby or caring for children.
- BC2 Expecting a baby?
  Benefits you may be able to get.
- BC3 Bringing up children?
  Benefits you may be able to get.
- SD1 Sick or disabled?
  A guide for people who have a physical or mental illness or disability, including children – and people who look after them.

There are also leaflets which give more information about particular benefits. You can get all these leaflets from your local Jobcentre Plus/Social Security Office (Jobs & Benefits office), some large post offices, your citizens advice bureau or other advice centre.

Benefits for all parents

Prescriptions and NHS dental treatment

Who gets them?

These are free while you are pregnant and for 12 months after you have given birth. Your child also gets free prescriptions until age 16. To claim for free prescriptions, ask your doctor or midwife for form FW8 and send it to your primary care trust (in Northern Ireland, ask for form HC11A and send it to the Central Services Agency). You will be sent an Exemption Certificate which lasts until a year after your due date.

How do I claim?

To claim after your baby is born (if you didn't claim while you were pregnant) fill in form A in leaflet P11 *NHS Prescriptions* (in Northern Ireland read HC11 *Help with health costs*), which you can get from your doctor or Jobcentre Plus/ Social Security office (Jobs & Benefits office).

To claim for dental treatment, tick a box on a form provided by the dentist or show your Exemption Certificate.

Child Benefit

What is it?
A tax-free benefit to help parents with the cost of caring for their children. It is payable for each child from birth until at least age 16.

Who gets it?
The mother, or the person responsible for the care of a child, but you must generally have been living in the United Kingdom for at least six months.

How much is it?
For your first child, £16.05 per week. (If you are a single parent who has been claiming since before June 1998, you get £17.55 per week for your first child.) For other children you get £10.75 a week per child.

How do I claim?
You may get a claim pack inside the Bounty Pack which most new mothers are given in hospital. You can also get a claim pack from your Jobcentre Plus/Social Security office (Jobs & Benefits office) or post office (also from the General Register office in Northern Ireland). Fill in the forms and send them with your baby's birth certificate to the Child Benefit Centre (Child Benefit Office in Northern Ireland). The birth certificate will be returned to you. You can also apply online, or notify a change of circumstances, at http://esd.dwp.gov.uk/dwp/index.jsp (not available for Northern Ireland residents).

Child Benefit can be paid directly into your bank account or by a book of orders which you cash at the post office. It is usually paid every four weeks in arrears, but single parents and families on low incomes can choose to be paid weekly. You should start to claim Child Benefit within three months of your baby's birth, otherwise you will lose some of the benefit.

Anything else?
Child Benefit can help to protect your State Retirement Pension if you stay at home to look after your child. For every complete year that you get Child Benefit, but you don't pay enough National Insurance contributions to count towards the basic pension, you automatically get 'Home Responsibilities Protection'.

Maternity leave

What is it?
It is 26 weeks' **Ordinary Maternity Leave** (OML) from work for all pregnant employees. It doesn't matter how many hours a week you work or how long you've worked for your employer.

Also, if you've worked for your employer for at least 26 weeks by the end of the 15th week before your baby is due, you qualify for **Additional Maternity Leave** (AML). This means you can take an additional 26 weeks unpaid leave at the end of your Ordinary Maternity Leave. **You must give your employer the correct notice.** See box on page 136 giving notice for Ordinary Maternity Leave and Additional Maternity Leave.

When can I start my leave?
The earliest you can start your leave is 11 weeks before the expected week of childbirth (this is when you are about 29 weeks). You have to use the due date on your MAT B1 certificate which your midwife or GP will give you from about 20 weeks. Find the Sunday before your baby is due (or the due date if it is a Sunday) and count back 11 Sundays from there. **It is for you to decide when you want to stop work.** You can even work right up until the date the baby is due, unless:

- You have a **pregnancy-related illness/absence in the last four weeks of your pregnancy**. In this case your employer can start your maternity leave even if you are absent for only one day. However, if you are ill only for a short time, your employer may agree to let you start your maternity leave when you had planned.
- Your baby is born before the day you were planning to start your leave. In this case, leave will start on the day of birth.

Do I have to give notice of my return?
You do not need to give any notice of return if you are going back to work at the end of your Ordinary Maternity Leave or Additional Maternity Leave. You simply go to work on the day that you are due back. If you want to return to work early you must give your employer 28 days' notice of the date you will be returning. If you do not give this notice and just turn up at work, your employer can send you away for 28 days or until the end of your leave, whichever is earlier. If you are entitled to Additional Maternity Leave but want to return to work after Ordinary Maternity Leave, you must give 28 days' notice of your return, as you are in fact returning early.

Giving notice for Ordinary Maternity Leave and Additional Maternity Leave

To give notice of your maternity leave, tell your employer the following things, in or before the 15th week before your baby is due:

- That you are pregnant.
- The expected week of childbirth.
- The date on which you intend to start your maternity leave (if your employer asks you to, you must put this in writing).

If you want to change the start date for your maternity leave, you must give your employer notice of the new date at least 28 days before the new date or the old date, whichever is the earlier. If there is a good reason why this is not possible, tell your employer as soon as you can.

What happens when I go back?
When you go back after Ordinary Maternity Leave it will be to **exactly the same job**. When you go back after Additional Maternity Leave your employer must give you

- the same job; or
- only if that is not reasonably practicable, a suitable job on very similar terms and conditions.

What will I get while I'm away?
During the first 26 weeks of leave (your Ordinary Maternity Leave period) your *contractual rights,* i.e. any special rights that apply to your particular workplace, such as a company car or pension continue as if you were still at work, apart from your normal pay.

During the first 26 weeks of your leave you will probably be entitled to either Maternity Allowance or Statutory Maternity Pay (see page 138). After that your leave will be unpaid. Some employers also offer extra maternity pay: you need to check your contract, or ask the human resources department or your union representative.

During the rest of your time on leave (your Additional Maternity Leave period) you will continue to be an employee, but the only **contractual rights** which will continue automatically will be:

- the notice period in your contract of employment will still apply (if either you or your employer wish to terminate your employment);
- you will be entitled to redundancy pay;
- disciplinary and grievance procedures will apply; and
- if your contract has a section which states that you must not work for any other company, this will still apply.

It might be possible to negotiate with your employer for other contractual rights to continue.

These rules do not apply to your statutory rights, i.e. rights that apply by law to all employees in this country. For example, everyone has a legal right to 20 days paid annual leave whether they are on maternity leave or not. Also, your employer must not discriminate against you by failing to consider you for such opportunities as promotion or when paying some bonuses.

If you are made redundant whilst on maternity leave, your employer must offer you any suitable alternative work that is available. If there is none, they must give you any notice and redundancy pay that you are entitled to.

Return to work on child-friendly hours

What are my rights?
If you need to change your working hours because of childcare, you have the right to have your request seriously considered. Since April 2003, parents with a child six years old or under, or a disabled child of 18 years old or under, have the right to ask their employers for flexible working arrangements. Under the new right, both you and your employer will have to follow a set procedure. Also, according to the Sex Discrimination Act (Sex Discrimination Order, Northern Ireland), employers must have a good business reason for refusing to let women work flexibly in order to look after their children.

It is not yet clear how the two rights will work together, so where possible you should carefully follow the procedure for asking for flexible work under the new right.

Under the new right, you will need to send a written request to your employer giving details of the new working pattern you want to work. Your employer can only refuse your request for one of the business reasons set out in the rules, e.g. if it would have a detrimental effect on quality.

Your employer must explain why a particular reason applies in your circumstances. If your employer refuses your request, there is an appeal procedure that you must use.

If your employer does not follow the procedure, or refuses for a reason not stated in the rules, or without an explanation, or makes the decision based on incorrect facts, you can make a claim in an Employment Tribunal (Industrial Tribunal in Northern Ireland). The tribunal will not question whether your employer was justified in refusing unless you can show that your employer got the facts wrong. You must make a tribunal claim within three months of the refusal.

If you cannot use the procedure, e.g. if you have not worked for your employer for long enough, you may be able to rely on your rights under sex discrimination law. You may also be able to rely on sex discrimination law even if you have used the new procedure, if you do not believe that your employer had good business reasons for refusing your request.

Your employer must seriously consider your request to change your working pattern. They will only know if they have a good reason for refusing your request by giving it a lot of thought. People often assume a job has to be done full-time or at certain fixed times of day. But, if you and your employer look carefully at your job, you may be able to work out a more child-friendly option – perhaps one that neither of you had considered before.

Does all this apply to me?
The new right, which became law on 6 April 2003, applies to you if:

- you are an employee;
- you are the parent, adoptive parent or foster carer of a child under six, or a disabled child under 18 (or married to, living with or the partner of that person);
- you have worked for your employer for 26 weeks by the time you make your request; and
- you have not made a request in the last 12 months.

The Sex Discrimination Act 1975 (Sex Discrimination Order 1976 in Northern Ireland) applies to all employers and parents with childcare responsibilities. If you need to rely on sex discrimination law, you will need to show that you would be disadvantaged by not being allowed to work the child-friendly hours you need to. You must have a good reason for asking to work differently. Some good reasons for asking are:

- you can't find or afford full-time childcare;
- you can't find or afford childcare outside 9am–5pm, Monday to Friday;
- you have to be there when your children come home from school;
- you are suffering from severe stress from working long hours.

What do I do next?
Before making your request, look at the job you do now and how it could be done differently. You will then need to make your application in writing. Your application must:

- state that this is an application for flexible work and that you are applying as a parent or as someone with parental responsibility;
- state the working pattern you are asking for and the date you want it to start;
- explain how you think the new working pattern may affect the employer and how you think it could be dealt with;
- state whether you have asked before and, if so, when;
- sign and date the application.

Your employer must arrange a meeting with you to discuss your application within 28 days of receiving it. They must give you notice of their decision in writing within 14 days of the meeting. If your employer agrees to your request, the new arrangement should start on the date agreed between you. Your terms and conditions, such as pay and leave, will remain the same until the date the new arrangement starts, when they will be reduced pro-rata to reflect your new working pattern.

If your employer refuses, they must give you a reason (this must be one of those allowed under the regulations) and they must inform you of your right to appeal. You must appeal within 14 days of receiving their notice of refusal. Your employer then has 14 days from the date they receive your notice of appeal to hold the appeal meeting. Again they must notify you of their decision in writing, within 14 days of the appeal, giving reasons for their decision.

What counts as a good reason for refusing?
Many of the arguments employers use do not count as justification at an Employment Tribunal (Industrial Tribunal). For example:

- there are no part-time vacancies (they should look at whether your own job could be done part-time or as a job-share);

- the job is too senior (the law applies to all women, no matter how senior);
- last-minute overtime is an essential part of the job (your employer should consider setting up a job-share, or an 'on call' rota);
- it is too expensive (costs are not usually any higher for part-timers); or
- continuity is crucial (there are usually practical ways around this, like keeping good records and ways of communicating).

An employer probably would be justified in refusing flexible work if there were good business reasons and there was no alternative solution, e.g. if particular opening hours are necessary for business.

If you think your employer has unreasonably refused your request, you should get advice about whether you can get compensation under the new right and/or under sex discrimination law. You must make a tribunal claim within three months of the refusal.

Parental Leave

This is unpaid leave from work of 13 weeks per parent per child, to be taken before the child's fifth birthday. Parents of children born or adopted after 15 December 1999 can get this leave. Adoptive parents can take it either within five years of the placement for adoption or by the child's 18th birthday, whichever is earlier. For children on Disability Living Allowance (DLA) leave has been extended to 18 weeks and must be taken before the child is 18. Parental leave has been extended to include parents of all children who were under five years old on 15 December 1999, to be taken by the end of March 2005.

Every worker is also entitled to emergency unpaid leave to make arrangements for the care for a dependant who falls ill, gives birth or is injured. This leave can be used if there is a sudden problem with care arrangements for the dependant, e.g. if your childminder falls ill.

Dismissal or unfair treatment

It is against the law for your employer to treat you unfairly, dismiss you or select you for redundancy for any reason connected with pregnancy, childbirth, maternity or parental leave.

If you are dismissed while you are pregnant or on maternity leave, your employer must give you a written statement of the reasons. You can make a claim for unfair dismissal, and sex discrimination, in an employment tribunal (industrial tribunal) within three months. You can also claim unfair dismissal if you are dismissed in connection with parental leave or time off for dependants.

Statutory Maternity Pay (SMP)

What is it?

Maternity pay for 26 weeks. Your employer pays it to you and then claims most or all of it back from the Inland Revenue. **You can get it even if you don't plan to go back to work. You will not have to pay Statutory Maternity Pay back if you don't return to work.** You may qualify for Statutory Maternity Pay from more than one employer.

Who gets it?

You get Statutory Maternity Pay if:

- you have worked for the same employer for at least 26 weeks by the end of the qualifying week (the 15th week before the expected week of childbirth, i.e. you started the job before you got pregnant), **and**
- you are still in your job in this qualifying week (it doesn't matter if you are off work sick, or on holiday), **and**
- you actually receive at least £77 (before tax) per week in earnings, on average, in the eight weeks (if you are paid weekly) or two months (if you are paid monthly) up to the last pay day before the end of the qualifying week.

> To find out which is the qualifying week, look on a calendar for the Sunday before your baby is due (or the due date if that is a Sunday) and count back 15 Sundays from there. You should use the due date on the MAT B1 certificate which your midwife or GP will give you when you are about 20 weeks pregnant.

If you are not sure if you're entitled to Statutory Maternity Pay, ask anyway. Your employer will work out whether or not you should get it, and if you don't qualify, they will give you form SMP1 to explain why. If your employer is not sure how to work out your Statutory Maternity Pay or how to claim it back, they can ring the Employers' Helpline on 0845 714 3143 for advice.

How much is it?

For the first six weeks you get 90% of your average pay. After that you get the basic rate of Statutory Maternity Pay, which is £100 (or 90% of average if less) per week for 20 weeks. The average is calculated from the pay you actually received in the eight weeks or two months up to the last payday before the end of the qualifying week. Your employer normally pays your Statutory Maternity Pay in the same way as your salary is paid. S/he deducts any tax and National Insurance contributions.

When is it paid?
The earliest you can start your Statutory Maternity Pay is 11 weeks before the expected week of childbirth. This is when you are about 29 weeks pregnant, but you have to use the due date on your MAT B1 certificate which your midwife or GP will give you. Find the Sunday before your baby is due (or the due date if it is a Sunday) and count back 11 Sundays from there. It is for you to decide when you want to stop work. You can even work right up until the date the baby is due, unless:

- You have a pregnancy-related illness/absence in the last four weeks of your pregnancy. In this case your employer can start your maternity leave even if you are absent for only one day. However, if you are ill only for a short time your employer may agree to let you start your maternity leave when you had planned.
- Your baby is born before the day you were planning to start your leave. In this case leave will start on the day of birth. Statutory Maternity Pay is paid for 26 weeks. You cannot get any Statutory Maternity Pay for any week in which you work, even part of a week. So if you return to work early your Statutory Maternity Pay will stop.

How do I claim?
You must give your employer at least 28 days notice of the date you want to start your pay. You cannot then change your mind. You must also send your maternity certificate (MAT B1 form), which your GP or midwife will give you when you are about 20 weeks pregnant. You can give notice for leave and pay together in the 15th week before your baby is due but if you do that you cannot change your mind about pay later.

Maternity Allowance (MA)

What is it?
A weekly allowance for women who work just before or during their pregnancy and who can't get Statutory Maternity Pay (see above). You may get Maternity Allowance if you are self-employed, if you stopped work or if you changed jobs during pregnancy.

Who gets it?
You can claim Maternity Allowance if you have worked in at least 26 of the 66 weeks before your expected week of childbirth. You have to have earned at least £30 per week for 13 weeks. You should choose the 13 weeks in which you earned the most. In your chosen weeks, you can add together earnings from more than one job, including any self-employed work.

How much is it?
Maternity Allowance is paid at a flat rate of £100 a week, or 90% of your average earnings if this is less, for 26 weeks.

When is it paid?
Maternity Allowance is paid for up to 26 weeks, but only for weeks in which you are not working. The earliest you can claim Maternity Allowance is 15 weeks before your baby is due, and the earliest it can start is 11 weeks before your baby is due. The latest it can start is your expected week of childbirth. If you are employed or self-employed, you can choose when to start your Maternity Allowance, but if you are unemployed your Maternity Allowance must start 11 weeks before your baby is due.

How do I claim?
The rules are complicated, so if you are not sure whether you qualify, make a claim. Your local Jobcentre Plus (in Northern Ireland, Incapacity Benefits Branch, Castle Court, Royal Avenue, Belfast BT1 1SB) will work out whether or not you can get the benefit.

You must claim within three months of giving birth or you may lose the benefit. Fill in form MA1, available from your Jobcentre Plus/Social Security Office (Jobs & Benefits office) or antenatal clinic, and send it to the Jobcentre Plus (Northern Ireland customers **only** should send form MA1 to Incapacity Benefits Branch). You must also send your maternity certificate (form MAT B1), which you get from your GP or midwife; and, if you are employed, form SMP1 from your employer to show why you don't qualify for Statutory Maternity Pay. Send in form MA1 as soon as you are 26 weeks pregnant. You can always send the other forms later.

If you have not earned enough, have not worked for enough weeks or have not paid enough National Insurance contributions by the time you are 26 weeks pregnant, then you can decide to apply for Maternity Allowance later in your pregnancy. You should send off the MA1 form as soon as you have fulfilled all the qualifying conditions.

Maternity Allowance is paid by a book of orders which you cash, or paid directly into your bank account. If you are not entitled to Maternity Allowance, the Jobcentre Plus/Incapacity Benefits Branch will use the same claim form to check whether you might be entitled to Incapacity Benefit (see below).

Incapacity Benefit (IB)

What is it?

A weekly allowance which can be paid to women who don't qualify for Statutory Maternity Pay or Maternity Allowance.

Who gets it?

You get Incapacity Benefit if you have enough National Insurance contributions in earlier tax years. Claim if you have paid any National Insurance contributions during the last three tax years that do not overlap the current calendar year. If you are not sure whether or not you qualify, claim and your local Jobcentre Plus/Incapacity Benefits Branch will work out whether you can get the benefit.

How much is it and when is it paid?

It is £55.90 per week. It is paid from six weeks before your baby is due, until two weeks after your baby is actually born. You won't get Incapacity Benefit for any week in which you work.

How do I claim?

Make a claim for Maternity Allowance using form MA1, which you can get from your Jobcentre Plus/Social Security Office (Jobs & Benefits office) or your antenatal clinic. You also have to send your maternity certificate (form MAT B1), which you get from your midwife or GP when you are about 26 weeks pregnant. You don't need to send in a sick note from your doctor.

If you are not entitled to Maternity Allowance, the Jobcentre Plus, or in Northern Ireland the Incapacity Benefits Branch, will check automatically to see if you qualify for Incapacity Benefit. It can be paid directly into your bank or by a book of orders that you cash. You must claim within three months of giving birth or you may lose the benefit.

Contribution-based Jobseeker's Allowance (JSA)

What is it?

An allowance which lasts for up to 26 weeks for people who are unemployed or working less than 16 hours a week.

Who gets it?

You get it if you have paid enough National Insurance contributions during the last two tax years that do not overlap the current calendar year. You have to be available for work for at least 16 hours and actively seeking work.

How much is it?

If you are under 18 you get £32.90 a week; if you are aged 18-24 you get £43.25 a week; if you are 25 or over you get £54.65 a week. Your partner's earnings are not taken into account but, if you are in part-time work, your earnings are.

How do I claim?

Go to your local Jobcentre Plus/Social Security Office (Jobs & Benefits office) in person, or you can claim by post if you live too far away. You will have to go to the Jobcentre Plus/Social Security Office (Jobs & Benefits office) every fortnight to 'sign on' to show that you are available for work.

The benefit is paid directly into your bank account, or by Giro normally every two weeks.

Anything else?

If your family has no other income, you will probably be entitled to income-based Jobseeker's Allowance and other benefits for families on low incomes (see section overleaf).

If I resign from my job and don't go back to work after maternity leave, can I claim anything?

You may be able to claim contribution-based Jobseeker's Allowance for up to six months. However, you will have to show that you had 'just cause' for voluntarily leaving your job. You will also have to be available for work for as many hours a week as your caring responsibilities permit (and not less than 16).

If you haven't paid enough National Insurance contributions, you may be able to claim income-based Jobseeker's Allowance instead (see below), depending on your personal circumstances. Apply in person at the Jobcentre Plus/Social Security Office (Jobs & Benefits office). If you are a single parent you may be able to claim Income Support or tax credits once the baby is born. If you are in a couple and your partner has a low income, you may be able to claim tax credits (see page 141).

Benefits for families

Child Tax Credit and Working Tax Credit

Two new tax credits were introduced in April 2003 – Child Tax Credit and Working Tax Credit. The Child Tax Credit is financial support for children, bringing together the child elements from Income Support, Income-based Jobseeker's Allowance, Working Families Tax Credit, Disabled Persons Tax Credit and the Children's Tax Credit. It is paid to the main carer (usually the mother), and the same rules will apply to all families whether or not they work.

Who gets it?

Child Tax Credit gives financial support for children. It can be claimed by lone parents or couples with one or more children. Nine out of ten families with children will get this new tax credit.

Working Tax Credit will help people in lower paid jobs by topping up their wages. It will be paid through the wage packet and can be claimed by single people or couples, with or without children, who work enough hours each week. You must be working at least 16 hours each week if:

- you have dependant children and/or
- you have a disability.

Otherwise, you must be 25 or over and work at least 30 hours a week.

You can be treated as if you are working during Ordinary Maternity Leave if you are getting Statutory Maternity Pay or Maternity Allowance, and were working enough hours immediately before starting your maternity leave.

Help with child care?

Working Tax Credit can include a childcare element to help with the cost of approved childcare where a lone parent or both partners in a couple work for at least 16 hours a week or one partner works and the other is disabled.

The childcare element is worth up to 70% of eligible childcare costs, up to a weekly maximum of £135 for one child and £200 for two or more children, paid to the main carer.

How do I claim tax credits?

Both Child Tax and Working Tax credits can be claimed using the same form, obtained by phoning the helpline on 0845 300 3900 (in Northern Ireland 0845 603 2000/textphone 0845 607 6078) or online at www.inlandrevenue.gov.uk/taxcredits.

How much will I get?

The amount you get will depend on your current circumstances, e.g. the number of children in your household, the number of hours you and your partner work, and your household's gross income for the last tax year. Claims for the tax year 2003-4 will initially be based on income for 2001-2.

Awards will run until the end of the tax year, but if there is a change affecting the amount, you can ask for the award to be adjusted from the date of the change; for example, if your wages fall significantly during the current tax year because you are going on maternity leave, or following the birth of your baby.

Maternity Allowance or the first £100 a week of Statutory Maternity Pay will be ignored as income. Families with children, with an annual income of £50,000 or less, will get at least £545 a year. A single parent staying at home to look after a child under one year old will get £2,535 a year (£48.75 a week).

Anything else?

If you get tax credits you may also be able to get the £500 Sure Start Maternity Grant, reduced price formula milk for a baby under one and help with fares to hospital for treatment (including antenatal appointments).

Income-based Jobseeker's Allowance (JSA) and Income Support

What are they?

Weekly payments for people who are not in work and do not have enough to live on. If your family income falls below a set level the benefit will 'top it up'. This means that you may be able to get Income Support even if you are already getting Statutory Maternity Pay, Maternity Allowance, Incapacity Benefit or some income from part-time work.

Who gets them?

You can claim income-based Jobseeker's Allowance if you are 18 or over and you are actively seeking work. Usually you would claim this benefit if you are living with your partner and you are either unemployed or working less than 16 hours per week. You should also claim it if you are single and unemployed but your baby has not been born yet.

If you are 16 or 17 years old and face severe hardship you may be able to claim before your baby is born. You should get further advice about this.

You can claim Income Support if you are 16 or over and cannot be available for work. This would be because you are a single parent or because you are 29 weeks pregnant or more. You may also get Income Support if you are single and pregnant and you are too sick to work.

You **cannot claim either income-based Jobseeker's Allowance or Income Support** if you have a partner who lives with you and who works for 24 hours or more a week, or if you work for more than 16 hours a week, or if you have savings of more than £8000.

How much is it?
This depends on your age and the size of your family, and on what other income you have. If you are under 25 or have more than £3000 in savings you get a lower rate. If you are claiming during pregnancy you should let the Jobcentre Plus/Social Security Office (Jobs & Benefits office) know as soon as the baby is born.

Any new claim to Income Support or income-based Jobseeker's Allowance awarded from 6th April 2004 will not include child-related elements because support for children will be provided by Child Tax Credit. Families already in receipt of Income Support or income based Jobseeker's Allowance in April 2004, who have not already claimed Child Tax Credit, will have their details transferred to Child Tax Credit from April 2005.

How do I claim?
To claim income-based Jobseeker's Allowance, either you or your partner must go to the Jobcentre Plus/Social Security Office (Jobs & Benefits office) in person.

To claim Income Support, fill in form A1, which you may get from a post office or a Jobcentre Plus/Social Security Office (Jobs & Benefits office).
The benefit is paid directly into your bank account, or by cheque or by orderbook. If you are claiming income-based Jobseeker's Allowance, you will have to go to the Jobcentre Plus/Social Security Office (Jobs & Benefits office) every fortnight to 'sign on' to show that you are available for work. If you are claiming Income Support, you do not need to 'sign on'.

Anything else?
If you get Income Support or income-based Jobseeker's Allowance, or Pension Credit guarantee credit you can claim other benefits, such as a £500 Sure Start Maternity Grant, free milk and vitamins, help with fares to hospital, Housing Benefit and Council Tax Benefit. You may be able to get help with mortgage interest payments. See below for more information on all these benefits.

£500 Sure Start Maternity Grant from the Social Fund

What is it?
A lump sum payment (a grant which you do not have to pay back) to help buy things for a new baby.

Who gets it?
Pregnant women and new parents who are getting income-based Jobseeker's Allowance, Income Support, Pension Credit or Working Tax Credit, where a disability or severe disability element is included in the award or Child Tax Credit at a rate higher than the family element.

How much is it?
£500 for each baby. If you have more than £500 in savings the payment will be reduced. This means that all women getting one of the qualifying benefits above will get the full grant of £500.

How do I claim?
Claim using form SF100 (Sure Start), which you can get from your local Jobcentre Plus/Social Security Office (Jobs & Benefits office). You can normally claim at any time from 11 weeks before the first day of the week in which the baby is due and up to three months from the date of birth, adoption or Parental Order. Those adopting can apply for a payment if the baby is not more than 12 months old when they apply and they apply within three months of the Adoption Order. Married couples who have a child by a surrogate mother are eligible for a Sure Start Maternity Grant, provided they have been granted a Parental Order. A claim must be made within three months from the date of the Parental Order.

Part of the form will need to be completed by your midwife, GP or health visitor – this is to confirm when your baby is due or actually born, and that you have received advice about the health and welfare of yourself and your baby.

If you can't get income-based Jobseeker's Allowance, Income Support, Pension Credit, Working Tax Credit or Child Tax Credit until after your baby is born, claim the Sure Start Maternity Grant before your baby is three months old.

The Discretionary Social Fund

What is the Discretionary Social Fund?
The discretionary social fund provides grants and interest-free loans for needs that are difficult for people to meet out of their weekly benefits or regular income.

What are they and who gets them?
There are three types of payments available:

- Community care grants for people getting Pension Credit, Income Support (IS) or income-based Jobseeker's Allowance.
- Budgeting loans are interest-free, repayable loans for getting Pension Credit, Income Support or income-based Jobseeker's Allowance for at least 26 weeks.
- Crisis loans are interest-free, repayable loans for people (whether on benefits or not) unable to meet their immediate short-term needs in a crisis.

How much are they?
This depends on your personal circumstances, your ability to pay and on how much money is available. Social Fund payments are not a right and there is a limited amount of money to be distributed to all those who apply.

How do I claim?
For information about which Social Fund payment to claim and how, contact your local Jobcentre Plus/Social Security Office (Jobs & Benefits office). More information is also available in leaflets SB16 (Guide to the Social Fund) and GL18 (Help from the Social Fund).

Loans have to be repaid at a set amount per week, which will be taken directly from your income if you are claiming other benefits. The amount you have to repay per week depends on the size of the loan, the size of your income and any other debts you may have.

Anything else?

- The Social Fund can also provide Community Care Grants to families receiving Pension Credit, income-based Jobseeker's Allowance or Income Support under certain circumstances, such as to help pay fares to visit a mother and baby in hospital or to help a family under exceptional pressure. Grants do not have to be paid back.
- You cannot get a Budgeting Loan or a Crisis Loan for more than £1,000, and the total you owe the Social Fund cannot be more than £1,000.
- Savings of more than £500 will usually affect how much you can get (£1,000) if you or your partner are aged 60 or over.

Housing Benefit – help with your rent

(In Northern Ireland this will help with your rent and/or rates.)

What is it?
Housing Benefit will help you pay your rent (in Northern Ireland rent and/or rates) if you're on income-based Jobseeker's Allowance, Income Support, or have a low income. If you are a council/Housing Executive tenant, it will be paid direct to the council/Housing Executive; if you are a private tenant, it will be paid either to you or direct to your landlord. In Northern Ireland, if you are an owner occupier, Housing Benefit will be in the form of a rate rebate administered by the Rate Collection Agency.

How much is it?
It depends on the rent and/or rates you pay, average rents in your area, the size of your home, your income, savings, other benefits, your age and your family size. It may not be the same amount as the rent you are actually paying. You cannot get Housing Benefit if you have savings of more than £16,000, and the amount you get is reduced if you have savings of more than £3000.

How do I claim?
If you're getting income-based Jobseeker's Allowance or Income Support, you will get a Housing Benefit claim pack with your Jobseeker's Allowance/Income Support claim form. Otherwise get a form from your local council. In Northern Ireland get a claim form HB1 from your Northern Ireland Housing Executive district

office. If you are an owner occupier get claim form F1 from the Rate Collection Agency (RCA), 21-27 Chichester Street, Belfast BT1 4JJ, or call 028 9025 2525 or your local RCA.

Help with mortgage interest repayments

Who gets it?
If you've got a mortgage and you're on income-based Jobseeker's Allowance or Income Support, you may be able to get help with your interest payments, although there is usually a waiting period during which you won't get any help.

How much is it?
You can only get help with interest payments (not repayments of capital or contributions to a linked PEP, endowment or insurance policy), and the amount is usually based on a standard average interest rate (which may not be the same as the interest you are paying).

If you took out your mortgage before 2 October 1995, you will get no help for eight weeks, half of the allowable interest for the next 18 weeks and then all the allowable interest after that.

If you took out your mortgage after 1 October 1995, you will get no help for 39 weeks and then all the allowable interest from week 40 of your claim. If you claim benefit because of the death of your partner or because your partner has left you and you have at least one child under 16, you are treated as if you took out your mortgage before 2 October 1995.

How do I claim?
Once you have claimed income-based Jobseeker's Allowance or Income Support, your Jobcentre Plus/Social Security office (Jobs & Benefits office) will automatically send you a form MI12 about your housing costs shortly before they become payable. You fill out part of the form and then send it to your mortgage lender to fill out the rest.

The money will either be paid to you as part of your income-based Jobseeker's Allowance or Income Support, or paid directly to your mortgage lender.

Anything else?
Tell your mortgage lender as soon as you get into difficulties with your mortgage. If you are unable to meet your repayments, you may be able to negotiate a temporary agreement for reduced repayments, e.g. during your maternity leave. Some mortgage lenders allow a few months 'repayment holiday' once during the life of the mortgage.

If you have mortgage protection insurance, contact your insurer immediately. Most insurance policies will pay out if you are receiving Jobseeker's Allowance or Income Support, but not if you are only receiving Statutory Maternity Pay or Maternity Allowance, so check carefully.

Council Tax Benefit

(Not applicable in Northern Ireland.)

What is it?
A benefit to help you pay your Council Tax if your income is low.

Who gets it?
If your income is low or you're getting income-based Jobseeker's Allowance or Income Support, you may get Council Tax Benefit.

How much is it?
You may get all of your Council Tax paid or just part of it. It will depend on your income, savings, whether other adults live with you, and an assessment of your circumstances.

Have you claimed everything?

You can claim → If you get ↓	Child Benefits	Free prescriptions	Free dental treatment	£500 Sure Start Maternity Grant	Social Fund loans	Council Tax Benefit (not NI) & Housing Benefit	Help with mortgage	Free milk	Free vitamins	Fares to hospital
Income-based JSA	✓	✓	✓	✓	✓	✓	✓	✓	✓	✓
Income Support	✓	✓	✓	✓	✓	✓	✓	✓	✓	✓
Low income	✓	✓	✓	✗	✓	✓	✗	✗	✗	✓
All mothers	✓	✓	✓	✗	✗	✗	✗	✗	✗	✗

How do I claim?
If you're getting income-based Jobseeker's Allowance or Income Support, you will get a Council Tax Benefit claim form with your Jobseeker's Allowance/Income Support claim form. Otherwise get a form from your local council.

Free milk and vitamins

Who gets them?
You can get these free if you are pregnant and in a family receiving Income Support, income-based Jobseeker's Allowance or Pension Credit guarantee credit. If you have a child under five, receive Child Tax Credit ONLY and have a family income of £13,230 or less (2003/4) you qualify.

How do I claim?
Your local Jobcentre Plus/Social Security Office (Jobs & Benefits office) will arrange for these to be issued to you once you tell them that you are pregnant and the date your baby is due. You will get milk tokens, which can be exchanged for one pint of milk a day from shops and milkmen who have been approved by the Department of Health, Social Services and Public Safety (DHSSPS). From November 2004 responsibility for issuing the tokens will change. For more information, contact Welfare Foods Team on 028 9052 2836.

Once your baby is born you should claim Child Tax Credit from the Inland Revenue. They will review your financial situation and if you fulfil the qualifying criteria, which is to receive Child Tax Credit ONLY with a family income of £13,230 or less (2003/4), they will pass your details to the Token Distribution Unit (TDU) so that tokens can be issued to you. Apart from claiming Child Tax Credit for your baby there is nothing more you need to do. If you qualify, the TDU will send you tokens that you can use for liquid milk if you are breastfeeding or infant formula if you are bottle-feeding every four weeks. When your baby is a year old, the tokens will change to liquid milk only.

Infant formula milk and vitamins are available from Child Health Centres/Clinics and, in some areas, pharmacies. Your midwife/health visitor should know what the local arrangements are.

When obtaining supplies from the Child Health Centres/Clinics you will need to show your benefit book or award letter and proof of your child/children's age(s) (your Child Benefit order book, the birth certificate or your parent-held child health record).

Reduced-price formula milk

You may buy infant formula milk at a reduced price if you have a baby aged under one year and receive Working Tax Credit with a family income of £14,600 or less (2003/4). The Inland Revenue will automatically assess you for this and will arrange for you to be issued with an NHS Tax Credit Exemption Certificate if you qualify.

Help with hospital fares

Who gets it?
If your family gets income-based Jobseeker's Allowance, Income Support, you can get a refund for fares to and from the hospital (including visits for antenatal care). This can cover normal public transport fares, estimated petrol costs and taxi fares if there is no alternative. You may also be entitled to help if your family has a low income or if you are getting tax credits (check your tax credits letter to see if this applies to you).

How do I claim?
If you are claiming one of the benefits mentioned above, you can claim at the hospital at the time of your visit by showing proof that you get the benefit. Alternatively, you can claim within three months of your visit by filling in form HC5 which you can get from the hospital or the Jobcentre Plus/Social Security Office (Jobs & Benefits office).

If your income is low, you must first fill in form HC1, which you can get from your doctor, hospital or Jobcentre Plus/Social Security Office (Jobs & Benefits office). Depending on how low your income is, you will then be given either certificate HC2, which means you qualify for free services, or certificate HC3, which means that you qualify for some help. You show the certificate when you go to the hospital, or you can claim within three months of your visit, on form HC5.

Further information

Some useful websites include:

www.ssani.gov.uk (Social Security Agency for general benefit information)

www.inlandrevenue.gov.uk (Inland Revenue for details on lower earnings limit)

www.delni.gov.uk/employmentbill (Department of Education and Learning for guidance on employment rights)

www.hseni.gov.uk (Health and Safety Executive for Northern Ireland)

www.ratecollectionagency.gov.uk

www.nihe.gov.uk (Northern Ireland Housing Executive)

USEFUL ORGANISATIONS

Some of these organisations are large. Many are small. Some can put you in touch with local groups or a local contact.

When you write for information, please enclose a large stamped addressed envelope for a reply.

An organisation specific to Northern Ireland is indicated by 'NI'. Some organisations have a Northern Ireland branch and the contact details are listed below the national details.

ADDICTIVE DRUGS

In Northern Ireland see also *Dunlewey Substance Advice Centre, Northlands* and *NICAS* under 'Alcohol'.

Drugaid

Drug and Alcohol Misuse Service

1a Bartlett Street
Caerphilly CF83 1JS
(029) 2088 1000
Provides counselling and information to drug, alcohol and solvent misusers and the general public.

National Drugs Helpline

0800 77 66 00
0800 917 87 65 (minicom/text phone)
www.talktofrank.com
Offers free, confidential advice and counselling about any drugs issue, 24 hours a day.

Narcotics Anonymous

202 City Road
London EC1V 2PH
(020) 7251 4007
(020) 7730 0009 (helpline 10am-10pm)
www.ukna.org
Self-help organisations whose members help each other to stay clear of drugs. Local groups. Some groups have a crèche.

ALCOHOL

Alcohol Concern

Waterbridge House
32-36 Loman Street
London SE1 0EE
(020) 7928 7377
www.alcoholconcern.org.uk

In Wales:
Welsh Substance Misuse Intervention Branch
National Assembly for Wales
Crown Building
Cathays Park
Cardiff CF10 3NQ
(029) 2082 5111
Can provide a list of organisations offering help and advice.

Alcoholics Anonymous (AA)

AA General Service Office
PO Box 1
Stonebow House
Stonebow
York YO1 7NJ
(01904) 644 026
0845 7697 555 (helpline)
www.alcoholics-anonymous.org.uk

In Northern Ireland:
(028) 9043 4848
Network of independent self-help groups whose members encourage each other to stop drinking. First names only are used to preserve anonymity. For your nearest group look in the phone book or contact the AA General Service Office.

Drinkline

0800 917 8282
(Fri, Sat, Sun 24 hours, Mon-Thur 9am-11pm)
Helpline offering support advice and counselling on alcohol problems.

Dunlewey Substance Advice Centre (NI)

226 Stewartstown Road
Belfast BT17 0LB
(028) 9061 1162
Help and counselling on alcohol, drug and solvent abuse.

Northern Ireland Community Addiction Service Ltd (NICAS) (NI)

40 Elmwood Avenue
Belfast BT9 6AZ
(028) 9066 4434
Counselling, treatment, education, information and training on dealing with alcohol and drug addiction

Northlands (NI)

Northlands Centre
Shepherds Way
Dungiven Road
Londonderry BT47 2AL
(028) 7131 3232
www.northlands.org.uk
For treatment, training, education and research about alcohol and other drug-related problems.

BEHAVIOURAL DIFFICULTIES

CRY-SIS

BM Cry-SIS
London WC1N 3XX
(020) 7404 5011 (helpline 9am-10pm)
www.cry-sis.org.uk
Self-help and support for families with excessively crying, sleepless and demanding children.

Enuresis Resource and Information Centre

34 Old School House
Britannia Road
Kingswood
Bristol BS15 8DB
(0117) 960 3060
(Mon-Fri 10am-4pm)
www.eric.org.uk
Provides advice and information to children, young adults, parents and professionals on bedwetting and soiling. Also sells bedding protection and enuresis alarms.

Hyperactive Children's Support Group

Dept W
71 Whyke Lane
Chichester PO19 2PD
(01243) 551 313
(Mon-Fri 10am-1pm)
www.hacsg.org.uk
Information to help with problems related to hyperactivity.

SNAP Cymru

10 Coopers Yard
Curran Road
Cardiff CF10 5NB
(029) 2038 8776
(Mon-Fri 9am-5pm)
www.snapcymru.co.uk
Advice and help for children with special educational needs.

West Glamorgan & West Wales AD/HD Family Support Group (UK)

17 Curtis Street
Neath SA11 1UW
0800 0566 267 (helpline)
Information and help with problems relating to attention deficit/hyperactivity disorder. Offers family support.

BREASTFEEDING

Association of Breastfeeding Mothers

PO Box 207
Bridgewater
Somerset TA6 7YT
(020) 7813 1481 (24-hour voluntary helpline)
www.abm.me.uk
Telephone advice service for breastfeeding mothers. Local support groups.

The Breastfeeding Network

PO Box 11126
Paisley
PA2 8YB
0870 900 8787 (helpline)
www.breastfeedingnetwork.org.uk
Help with breastfeeding – local groups and leaflets.

La Lèche League (GB)

PO Box 29
West Bridgford
Nottingham NG2 7NP
(020) 7242 1278
(0845) 120 2918 (24-hour helpline)
www.laleche.org.uk

In Northern Ireland
(028) 2564 7951
Help and information for women who want to breastfeed. Personal counselling. Local groups.

National Childbirth Trust (NCT)

Alexandra House
Oldham Terrace
London W3 6NH
(0870) 444 8707 (enquiry line 9am-5pm)
(0870) 444 8708 (8am-10pm for support on breastfeeding)
www.nctpregnancyandbabycare.com

In Northern Ireland
(028) 6862 1842
Information and support for mothers, including breastfeeding information, antenatal classes, postnatal groups.

CHILDCARE/PLAY, DEVELOPMENT AND EDUCATION

Advisory Centre for Education (ACE)

1c Aberdeen Studios
22 Highbury Grove
London N5 2DQ
0800 800 5793
www.ace-ed.org.uk
Advice for parents on state education, special education, exclusion from school, bullying and school admission appeals.

Child Growth Foundation

2 Mayfield Avenue
London W4 1PW
(020) 8994 7625
www.heightmatters.org.uk
Information and advice for parents concerned about their child's growth.

Children's Information Services (CIS)

08000 96 02 96 (information line)
www.childcarelink.gov.uk/index.asp
Provide up-to-date information and advice on childcare provision and services in your area. For your local office look in the phone book.

Daycare Trust

21 St George's Road
London SE1 6ES
(020) 7840 3350 (helpline Mon-Fri 10am-5pm)
www.daycaretrust.org.uk
Campaigns for the provision of good childcare facilities. The Daycare Trust gives information on all aspects of childcare.

Mudiad Ysgolion Meithrin/The National Association of Welsh Medium Nursery Schools and Playgroups

145 Albany Road
Cardiff CF24 3NT
(029) 2043 6800
www.mym.co.uk
Help and advice on setting up and running parent and toddler groups and playgroups. Contact with local playgroups.

National Association of Toy and Leisure Libraries

68 Churchway
London NW1 1LT
(020) 7255 4600
www.natll.org.uk
Information about local toy libraries (which lend toys). Offers publications and training courses.

National Childminding Association

8 Masons Hill
Bromley BR2 9EY
(020) 8464 6164
www.ncma.org.uk
Infoline 0800 1694486
info@ncma.org.uk

In Northern Ireland:
Northern Ireland Childminding Association (NICMA)
16-18 Mill Street
Newtownards
Belfast BT23 4LU
(028) 9181 1015
www.nicma.org
An organisation for registered childminders; provides training, information and support. Works to improve status and conditions of childminders and standards of childcare.

NIPPA – The Early Years Organisation (NI)

6c Wildflower Way
Apollo Road
Belfast BT12 6TA
(028) 9066 2825
www.nippa.org
Information, advice and training for early years staff and families with young children.

Ofsted Early Years

Alexandra House
33 Kingsway
London WC2B 6SE
0845 601 4771
www.ofsted.gov.uk
Government department responsible for registration, inspection and investigation of childcare settings (childminders and daycare facilities).

Pre-School Learning Alliance

69 King's Cross Road
London WC1X 9LL
(020) 7833 0991
www.pre-school.org.uk
Supports the work of community pre-schools.

Sure Start

Provides information on Government support for children, parents and communities and details of local childcare and early years education.
www.surestart.gov.uk

Wales Pre-School Playgroups Association

Ladywell House
Newton
Powys SY16 1JB
(01686) 624 573
www.walesppa.co.uk
Help and advice on setting up and running parent and toddler groups and playgroups. Contact with local playgroups.

Working Families

1-3 Berry Street
London EC1V 0AA
(020) 7253 7243
0800 013 0313 (legal advice line)
www.workingfamilies.org.uk
Information and advice on flexible working hours, childcare provision and employment rights for working parents. Local groups.

CONTRACEPTION

Brook

421 Highgate Studios
53-79 Highgate Road
London NW5 1TL
(020) 7284 6040 (admin)
0800 0185 023 (helpline Mon-Fri 9am-5pm)
www.brook.org.uk

In Northern Ireland:
Brook Belfast
29a North Street
Belfast BT1 1NA
(028) 9032 8866
(Mon 2.30pm-5pm, Thur 5.30pm-8pm, Fri 2pm-4.30pm, Sat 1.30pm-4pm. Male clinic first Wed of every month, 6pm-8pm)
Advice and practical help with contraception and pregnancy testing, advice on unplanned pregnancies and sexual counselling for young men and women. Free and confidential. For your nearest centre look in the phone book or contact Brook Central Office.

fpa (Family Planning Association)
2-12 Pentonville Road
London N1 9FP
(020) 7837 5432
0845 310 1334 (helpline Mon-Fri 9am-7pm)
www.fpa.org.uk

In Northern Ireland:
113 University Street
Belfast BT7 1HP
Belfast (028) 9032 5488
Londonderry (028) 7126 0016 (Mon-Thur 9am-5pm, Fri 9am-4.30pm)

In North Wales:
Green House
Trevelyan Terrace
Bangor LL57 1AX
(01248) 353 534

In South Wales:
Suite D1
Canton House
435-451 Cowbridge Road East
Cardiff CF5 1JH
(029) 2064 4034
Information on family planning, sexual health and methods of contraception.

Marie Stopes International
153-157 Cleveland Street
London W1T 6QW
(020) 7574 7400
0845 300 8090 (24-hour booking and appointment line)
www.mariestopes.org.uk
Provides family planning, women's health check-ups, male and female sterilisation, pregnancy testing, advice on unplanned pregnancies and sexual counselling for men and women. You don't need to be referred by your doctor, but you do need to book an appointment. A charge is made to cover costs. For centres in Manchester and Leeds and Bristol look in the local phone book.

Sexual Health Line
0800 567 123 (24 hours)
www.playingsafely.co.uk
Information and advice on sexual health matters, HIV, contraception and local services.

DEPRESSION AND STRESS

Association for Postnatal Illness (APNI)
145 Dawes Road
London SW6 7EB
(020) 7386 0868
www.apni.org
Telephone support for mothers with postnatal depression.

Meet-a-Mum Association (MAMA)
376 Bideford Green
Linslade
Leighton Buzzard
Beds LU7 2TY
(01525) 217064
(020) 8768 0123 (helpline Mon-Fri 7pm-10pm)
www.mama.org.uk
Support for mothers suffering from postnatal depression or who feel lonely and isolated. Will try to put you in touch with another mother who has experienced similar problems, or with a group of mothers locally, or help you to find ways of meeting people. Write with an SAE for details of local groups.

MIND (National Association for Mental Health)
Granta House
15-19 Broadway
London E15 4BQ
(020) 8519 2122 (admin)
0845 766 0163 (Mind infoline)
www.mind.org.uk

In Wales:
Mind Cymru
3rd Floor
Quebec House, Castlebridge
Cowbridge Road East
Cardiff CF11 9AB
(029) 2039 5123
Help for people experiencing mental distress, Mind infoline offers confidential help. Local associations.

NI Association for Mental Health (NI)
Beacon House
80 University Street
Belfast BT7 1HE
(028) 9032 8474
Research, training and awareness on mental health issues.

Parentline Plus
520 Highgate Studios
53-57 Highgate Road
London NW5 1TL
0808 800 2222 (helpline Mon-Fri 8am-10pm, Sat 9.30am-5pm, Sun 10am-3pm)
0800 783 6783 (text phone)
www.parentlineplus.org.uk
Free confidential helpline to anyone parenting a child. Runs parenting classes and produces a range of leaflets and publications.

Parents Advice Centre (NI)
Franklin House
12 Brunswick Street
Belfast BT2 7GE
Belfast (028) 9023 8800 (helpline Mon-Fri 10am-4pm)
Londonderry (028) 7126 6663 (helpline Mon-Fri 10am-4pm)
Dungannon (028) 8775 2900 (Mon-Thur 10am-4pm Fri 10am-1pm)
Ballymena (028) 2565 0099 (Mon-Fri 10am-1pm)
(An evening helpline is available on any of the above numbers Mon-Thur 7pm-9pm)
www.pachelp.org
Support, guidance and counselling for parents with any family difficulties.

DOMESTIC VIOLENCE

Belfast Rape Crisis and Sexual Abuse Centre (NI)
29 Donegall Street
Belfast BT1 2FG
(028) 9024 9696 (helpline)
(028) 9024 9696 (text phone)
Support and counselling to all survivors of sexual abuse, rape or incest.

NEXUS Institute (NI)
119 University Street
Belfast BT7 1HP
(028) 9032 6803
www.nexusinstitute.org
Provides a professional counselling service to both male and females over the age of 17 who have been sexually abused or raped. Centres in Portadown, Londonderry and Enniskillen.

NSPCC (National Society for the Prevention of Cruelty to Children)
42 Curtain Road
London EC2A 3NH
(020) 7825 2500
0808 800 5000 (24-hour national helpline)
www.nspcc.org.uk

In Northern Ireland:
Jennymount Business Park
North Derby Street
Belfast BT15 3HN
(028) 9035 1135

In Wales:
Floor 13
Capital Tower
Greyfriars Road
Cardiff CF10 3AG
(029) 2026 7000
0808 100 2524 (bi-lingual helpline Mon-Thur 11am-6.30pm)
Aims to prevent all forms of child abuse. If you're in need of help or know of anyone who needs help, look in the phone book for your nearest NSPCC office.

Rape Crisis Federation
Unit 7
Provident Works
Newdigate Street
Nottingham NG7 4FD
(0115) 900 3560 (Mon-Fri 9am-5pm and answerphone)
www.rapecrisis.co.uk
Refers women seeking help on rape, sexual abuse or violence to local rape crisis centres.

Refuge
2/8 Maltravers Street
London WC2R 3EE
0870 599 5443 (24-hour helpline)
Emergency accommodation and advice for women and children experiencing domestic violence in London.

Women's Aid Federation of England
PO Box 391
Bristol BS99 7WS
(01179) 444 411 (admin)
0845 702 3468 (24-hour helpline)
www.womensaid.org.uk

In Northern Ireland:
129 University Street
Belfast BT7 1HP
(028) 9024 9041 (office)
(028) 9033 1818 (24-hour helpline)
www.niwaf.org

In Wales:
38-48 Crwys Road
Cardiff CF24 4NN
(029) 2039 0874 (Mon-Fri 10am-3pm)
Information, support and refuge for abused women and their children.

HOUSING

Housing Rights Service (NI)
Fourth Floor
Middleton Buildings
10-12 High Street
Belfast BT1 2BA
(028) 9024 5640
Helpline for people with housing problems. Offers advice and information on homelessness, housing debt, in both the private rented sector and Northern Ireland Housing Executive.

Northern Ireland Housing Executive (NI)
2 Adelaide Street
Belfast BT2 8PB
(028) 9024 0588
www.nihe.gov.uk
Advice and information on all aspects of housing.

Shelter
88 Old Street
London EC1V 9HU
(020) 7505 4699
0808 800 4444 (24-hr helpline)
www.shelter.org.uk

In Northern Ireland:
Shelter NI
c/o Housing Rights Service (see above)
(028) 9024 5640

In Wales:
25 Walters Road
Swansea SA1 5NN
(01792) 469400
www.sheltercymru.org.uk
Help for those who are homeless. Advice on any housing problems.

ILLNESS AND DISABILITY (GENERAL)

Action for Sick Children (NAWCH)
c/o National Children's Bureau
8 Wakley Street
London EC1V 7QE
(020) 7843 6444
0800 074 4519 (freephone)
www.actionforsickchildren.org

In Wales:
The Association for the Welfare of Children in Hospitals (AWCH Wales)
31 Penyrheol Drive
Sketty
Swansea SA2 9JT
(01792) 205 227
Aim to ensure sick children receive the highest standard of care at home or in hospital. Information and support to parents and carers.

Benefit Enquiry Line for People with Disabilities
0800 882 200
0800 243 355 (text phone)

Contact a Family
209-211 City Road
London EC1V 1JN
(020) 7608 8700 (admin)
0808 808 3555 (helpline Mon-Fri 10am-4pm)
www.cafamily.org.uk

In Northern Ireland:
Bridge Community Centre
50 Railway Street
Lisburn BT28 1XP
(028) 9262 7552

In Wales:
1st Floor Exchange Building
Mount Stuart Square
Cardiff CF10 5EB
(029) 2049 8001
Links families of children with special needs through contact lines. All disabilities. Local parent support groups.

Disability Action (NI)
Portside Business Park
189 Airport Road West
Belfast BT3 9ED
(028) 9029 7880
www.disabilityaction.org
Information and advice for people with physical disabilities.

Disabled Living Centres Council
Redbank House
4 St Chad's Street
Cheetham
Manchester M8 8QA
(0161) 834 1044
(0161) 839 0885 (text phone)
www.dlcc.org.uk
Disabled Living Centres offer information and advice on products, also the opportunity to try them out and explore other solutions.

In Wales:
Disability Wales/Anabledd Cymru
Wernddu Court
Caerphilly Business Park
Van Road
Caerphilly CF83 3ED
(029) 2088 7325
www.dwac.demon.co.uk
National association of disability groups in Wales. Provide information and training.

Disabled Living Foundation (DLF)
380-384 Harrow Road
London W9 2HU
(020) 7289 6111 (admin)
0845 130 9177 (helpline Mon-Fri 10am-1pm)
0870 603 9176 (text phone Mon-Fri 10am-1pm)
www.dlf.org.uk
Source of information on daily living and disability equipment.

Family Fund Trust for Families with Severely Disabled Children
PO Box 50
York YO1 9ZX
0845 130 4542 (9am-5pm)
www.familyfundtrust.org.uk
Gives cash grants to ease stress on families caring for severely disabled children under 16. Also provides information.

MENCAP (Royal Society for Mentally Handicapped Children and Adults)
MENCAP National Centre
123 Golden Lane
London EC1Y 0RT
(020) 7454 0454
www.mencap.org.uk
In Northern Ireland:
Segal House
4 Annadale Avenue
Belfast BT7 3JH
(028) 9069 1351
In Wales:
31 Lambourne Crescent
Cardiff Business Park
Llanishen
Cardiff CF14 5GF
(029) 2074 7588
Work with people with a learning disability and their families and carers. Local branches.

Northern Ireland Mother and Baby Action (NIMBA) (NI)
Hope House
54 Scotch Quarter
Carrickfergus BT38 7DP
(028) 9332 9933
www.nimba.org.uk
A local charity offering support and advice to parents of premature, ill or disabled babies who need intensive or special care. A parents' support network is available throughout NI alongside practical services for parents.

Parentability
c/o National Childbirth Trust (see under Breastfeeding)
A network within NCT specifically for the support of disabled parents.

Phab
Summit House
50 Wandle Road
Croydon CR0 1DF
(020) 8667 9443
www.phabengland.org.uk
In Northern Ireland:
Jennymount Business Park
North Derby Street
Belfast BT15 3HN
(028) 9050 4800
www.phabni.org
In Wales:
11 Lon Fach Rhiwbina
Cardiff CF14 6DY
(029) 2052 0660
enquiries@phabwales.org
Promotes integration between disabled and non-disabled people through social, leisure and educational activities. Local groups.

Royal Association for Disability and Rehabilitation (RADAR)
12 City Forum
250 City Road
London EC1V 8AF
(020) 7250 3222
(020) 7250 4119 (minicom)
www.radar.org.uk
Information and advice on disability. Local organisations.

ILLNESS AND DISABILITY (SPECIALISED)

AFASIC – Association for All Speech Impaired Children
2nd Floor
50-52 Great Sutton Street
London EC1V 0DJ
(020) 7490 9410 (admin)
0845 355 5577 (helpline Mon-Fri 11am-2pm)
www.afasic.org.uk
Helps children with speech and language disorders. Information and advice for parents. Local groups.

Association for Spina Bifida and Hydrocephalus (ASBAH)
ASBAH House
42 Park Road
Peterborough PE1 2UQ
(01733) 555 988
www.asbah.org
In Northern Ireland:
Graham House
Knockbracken Healthcare Park
Saintfield Road
Belfast BT8 8BH
(028) 9079 8878
In Wales:
Asbah Cymru
4 Llys y Fedwen
Parc Menai
Bangor LL57 4BL
(01248) 671 345
Support for parents of children with spina bifida and/or hydrocephalus. Advice, practical and financial help. Local groups.

Association of Parents of Vaccine Damaged Children
78 Camden Road
Shipston-on-Stour
Warwickshire CV36 4DH
(01608) 661 595
Advises parents on claiming vaccine damage payment.

The Blind Centre for Northern Ireland (NI)
70 North Road
Belfast BT5 5NJ
(028) 9050 0999
www.bcni.co.uk
Aims to enhance the quality of life for blind and visually impaired people through direct local services, leisure and talking books/magazines.

British Deaf Association
1-3 Worship Street
London EC2A 2AB
(020) 7588 3520
(020) 7588 3529 (text phone)
(020) 7496 9539 (video)
www.britishdeafassociation.org.uk
In Northern Ireland:
3rd Floor
Wilton House
5-6 College Square
Belfast BT1 6AR
(028) 9072 7400
(028) 9043 4755 (text phone)
(028) 9043 8796 (video)
In Wales:
Shand House
2 Fitzalan Place
Cardiff CF24 0BE
(029) 2030 2216
(029) 2030 2217 (text phone)
(029) 2030 2219 (video)
Provides advocacy and youth services for deaf people whose first language is British Sign Language; also advice and counselling.

The Cedar Foundation (NI)
31 Ulsterville Avenue
Belfast BT9 7AS
(028) 9066 6188
www.cedar-foundation.org
Works in partnership with people with physical disability. Children's Services provide advice and support to children and young people with motor disabilities and their families.

Changing Faces
1-2 Junction Mews
London W2 1PN
(020) 7706 4232
www.changingfaces.co.uk
Offers advice, information and support to young children with facial disfigurements and their carers. Child specialist available to help young children cope.

Cleft Lip and Palate Association (CLAPA)
235-237 Finchley Road
London NW3 6LS
(020) 7431 0333
www.clapa.com
Voluntary organisation of parents and professionals offering support to families of babies born with cleft lip and/or palate. Feeding equipment available. Local groups.

Climb (Children Living with Inherited Metabolic Diseases)
Climb Building
176 Nantwich Road
Crewe CW2 6BG
(0870) 7700 325 (admin Mon- Fri 10am-3pm)
(0870) 7700 326 (advice line)
www.climb.org.uk
Provides information, advice, support and small grants for the medical treatment and care of children with metabolic diseases. Puts parents in touch with each other. Local groups.

Coeliac Society of the United Kingdom
PO Box 220
High Wycombe
Buckinghamshire HP11 2HY
(01494) 437 278 (admin)
0870 444 8804 (helpline)
www.coeliac.co.uk
Helps parents of children diagnosed as having the coeliac condition or dermatitis herpetiformis.

Council for Disabled Children
8 Wakley Street
London EC1V 7QE
(020) 7843 6000 (admin)
0845 859 1000 (helpline)
www.ncb.org.uk/cdc
Information for parents and details of all organisations offering help with particular disabilities.

Cystic Fibrosis Trust
11 London Road
Bromley BR1 1BY
(020) 8464 7211
0845 859 1000 (helpline)
www.cftrust.org.uk
In Northern Ireland:
12 Selshion Manor
Portadown BT62 1AF
(028) 3833 4491
Information and support for parents of children with cystic fibrosis and for people worried about the possibility of passing on the illness. Local groups.

Diabetes UK
10 Parkway
London NW1 7AA
(020) 7424 1000 (admin)
(020) 7424 1030 (careline)
(020) 7424 1031 (textphone)
www.diabetes.org.uk
In Northern Ireland:
Suite 8
Bridgewood House
Newforge Business Park
Newforge Lane
Belfast BT9 5NW
(028) 9066 6646
In Wales:
Diabetes UK Cymru
Quebec House
Castlebridge
Cowbridge Road East
Cardiff CF11 9AB
(029) 2066 8276
Information and support for all people with diabetes.

Down's Syndrome Association
155 Mitcham Road
London SW17 9PG
(020) 8682 4001
www.downs-syndrome.org.uk
In Northern Ireland:
Graham House
Knockbracken Healthcare Park
Saintfield Road
Belfast BT8 8BH
(028) 9070 4606
In Wales:
Suite 1
206 Whitechurch Road
Heath
Cardiff CF4 3NB
(029) 2052 2511 (Mon-Fri 9am-12.30pm)
Information, advice, counselling and support for parents of children with Down's syndrome. Local groups.

Haemophilia Society
Chesterfield House
385 Euston Road
London NW1 3AU
(020) 7380 0600
(0800) 0186 068 (helpline Mon-Fri 9am-5pm)
www.haemophilia.org.uk
Information, advice and practical help for families affected by haemophilia and other bleeding disorders. Some local groups.

The HIV Support Centre (NI)
3rd floor
7 James Street South
Belfast BT2 8DN
0800 137 437 (Mon-Fri 9am-5pm and 7pm-10pm, Sat 2pm-5pm)
www.thehivsuppportcentre.org.uk
Free confidential helpline for advice on sexual health, HIV, AIDS and all other STIs.

(I CAN) Invalid Children's Aid Nationwide
4 Dyers Buildings
Holborn
London EC1N 2QP
(0845) 225 4071
www.ican.org.uk
Advice and information for parents of children with speech and language difficulties.

Meningitis Cymru
149 Hawthorn Way
Brackla
Bridgend CF31 2PG
(01656) 646 414 (admin)
0800 652 9996 (helpline)
www.meningitiscymru.org.uk
Education, support and information on meningitis for the people of Wales.

Meningitis Research Foundation
Midland Way
Thornbury
Bristol BS35 2BS
(01454) 281 811
(0808) 880 33 44 (24-hour national helpline)
www.meningitis.org
In Northern Ireland:
71 Botanic Avenue
Belfast BT7 1JL
(028) 9032 1283
Provides a support network for families who are bereaved and help and information to families with someone currently ill or recovering from meningitis and septicaemia.

Muscular Dystrophy Campaign
7-11 Prescott Place
London SW4 6BS
(020) 7720 8055
(020) 7720 8055 (helpline Mon-Thur 10am-4pm)
www.muscular-dystrophy.org
Provides support and advice through local branches and a network of Family Care Officers.

National Asthma Campaign
Providence House
Providence Place
London N1 0NT
(020) 7226 2260
0845 7010 203 (helpline operated by nurses 9am-5pm)
www.asthma.org.uk
Information and support for people with asthma, their families and health professionals. Booklets. Over 180 branches nationwide.

National Autistic Society
393 City Road
London EC1V 1NG
(020) 7833 2299
0870 600 8585 (Advice line Mon-Fri 10am-4pm)

In Wales:
Suite C1
William Knox House
Britannic Way
Llandarcy
Neath SA10 6EL
(01792) 815 915
www.nas.org.uk
Provides day and residential centres for the care and education of autistic children. Puts parents in touch with one another. Advice and information. Local groups.

National Deaf Children's Society (NDCS)
15 Dufferin Street
London EC1Y 8UR
(020) 7490 8656 (text/typetalk/voice)
0808 800 8880 (voice/text helpline Mon-Fri 10am-5pm)
www.ndcs.org.uk

In Northern Ireland:
Wilton House
5 College Square North
Belfast BT1 6AR
(028) 9031 3170
(028) 9027 8177 (text)

In Wales:
Room 2
43 Charles Street
Cardiff CF10 2GB
(029) 2037 3474
(029) 2038 4277 (text phone)
Works for deaf children and their families. Information and advice on all aspects of childhood deafness. Local self-help groups.

National Eczema Society(NES)
Hill House
Highgate Hill
London N19 5NA
(020) 7281 3553
0870 241 3604 (helpline Mon-Fri 1pm-4pm)
www.eczema.org

In Northern Ireland:
9 Notting Hill
Malone Road
Belfast BT9 5NS
(028) 9066 6393 (after 6pm)
Support and information for people with eczema and their families. Nationwide network of local contacts offering practical advice and support.

National Meningitis Trust
Fern House
Bath Road
Stroud GL5 3TJ
(01453) 768 000
0845 6000 0800 (24-hour helpline)
www.meningitis-trust.org.uk

In Northern Ireland:
PO Box 549
Belfast BT5 7YN
0845 1200 663

In Wales:
PO Box 16
Neath SA10 8XB
0845 120 4886
Information and support for those already affected by meningitis. Local groups.

Parents and Professionals and Autism (PAPA) (NI)
Donard House
Knockbracken Healthcare Park
Saintfield Road
Belfast BT8 8BH
(028) 9040 1729
www.autismni.org
Provides information, advice, training and research. Raises awareness. Local branches.

Positively Women
347-349 City Road
London EC1V 1LR
(020) 7713 0444 (admin)
(020) 7713 0222 (helpline Mon-Fri 10am-4pm)
www.positivelywomen.org.uk
Offers counselling and support services to HIV positive women.

Reach (The Association for Children with Hand or Arm Deficiency)
Reach Head Office
PO Box 54
Helston
Cornwall TR13 8WD
0845 130 6225 (Mon-Wed, Fri 9.30am-5.30pm)
www.reach.org.uk
Information and support to parents of children with hand or arm problems. Local groups.

Restricted Growth Association
PO Box 4744
Dorchester DT2 9FA
(01308) 898 445
www.rgaonline.org.uk
Aims to help reduce the distress and disadvantages of persons of restricted growth by providing information, counselling, family support, friendship and other forms of practical help.

Royal National Institute for the Blind (RNIB)
105 Judd Street
London WC1H 9NE
(020) 7388 1266
0845 766 9999 (helpline – interpreters available Mon-Fri 9am-5pm)
www.rnib.org.uk

In Northern Ireland:
40 Linenhall Street
Belfast BT2 8BA
(028) 9032 9373

In Wales:
Trident Court
East Moors Road
Cardiff CF24 5TD
(029) 2045 0440 (English and Welsh callers welcome)
Information, advice and services for blind and partially sighted people. Local branches.

Royal National Institute for the Deaf (RNID)
19-23 Featherstone Street
London EC1Y 8SL
(020) 7296 8000
0808 808 0123 (voice Mon-Fri 9am-5pm)
0808 808 9000 (text Mon-Fri 9am-5pm)
www.rnid.org.uk
In Northern Ireland:
Wilton House
5 College Square North
Belfast BT1 6AR
(028) 9023 9619 (voice)
(028) 9031 2033 (text)

In Wales:
4th Floor
Tudor House
16 Cathedral Road
Cardiff CF11 9LJ
(029) 2033 3038
(029) 2033 3036 (text)
Information, advice and services for deaf and hard of hearing people. Local groups.

SCOPE
6 Market Road
London N7 9PW
(0808) 800 3333 (E and W helpline Mon-Fri 9am-9pm, Sat, Sun 2pm-6pm)
www.scope.org.uk

In Wales:
SCOPE Cwmpas Cymru
The Wharf
Schooner Way
Cardiff CF10 4EU
(029) 2046 1703
(029) 2049 5187 (text)
Offers advice and support to parents of children with cerebral palsy. Local groups.

SENSE (National Deaf-Blind and Rubella Association)
11-13 Clifton Terrace
Finsbury Park
London N4 3SR
(020) 7272 7774
(020) 7272 9648 (minicom)
www.sense.org.uk

In Northern Ireland:
The Manor House
51 Mallusk Road
Mallusk BT36 4RU
(028) 9083 3430
(028) 9083 3430 (minicom)

In Wales:
SENSE Cymru
5 Raleigh Walk
Brigantine Place
Atlantic Wharf
Cardiff CF10 4LN
(029) 2045 7641
(029) 2046 4125 (minicom)
Advice and support for families of deaf-blind and rubella-disabled children.

Sexual Health Line
0800 567 123 (24-hour helpline)
www.playingsafely.co.uk
Free and confidential advice about HIV, AIDS, sexual health, sexually transmitted infections, local services, clinics and support services.

Sickle Cell Society
54 Station Road
Harlesden
London NW10 4UA
(020) 8961 7795/4006
www.sicklecellsociety.org

In Wales:
Sickle Cell and Thalassaemia Centre
Butetown Health Centre
Loundon Square
Butetown
Cardiff CF10 5UZ
(029) 2047 1055
Information, advice, and counselling for families affected by sickle cell disease or trait. Financial help when needed. Local groups.

Terrence Higgins Trust
0845 1221 200 (helpline Mon-Fri 10am-10pm, Sat, Sun 12am-6pm)
0800 096 7500 (African AIDS helpline)
www.tht.org.uk
Free and confidential advice about all matters connected with HIV and AIDS

The UK Thalassaemia Society
19 The Broadway
Southgate Circus
London N14 6PH
(020) 8882 0011
0800 731 1109 (24-hour information line)
www.ukts.org
Information, and advice for families affected by thalassaemia.

Wales Council for the Blind (W)
3rd Floor
Shand House
20 Newport Road
Cardiff CF24 0DB
(029) 2047 3954
www.wcb-ccd.org.uk
Information, advice and services for blind people.

LONE PARENTS

Gingerbread
7 Sovereign Close
Sovereign Court
London E1W 3HW
(020) 7488 9300
0800 018 4318 (advice line Mon-Fri 9am-5pm)
www.gingerbread.org.uk

In Northern Ireland:
169 University Street
Belfast BT7 1HR
(028) 9023 1417
0808 808 8090 (advice line 9am-5pm)
www.gingerbreadni.org

In Wales:
4th Floor
Baltic House
Mount Stuart Square
Cardiff CF10 5FH
(029) 2047 1900
Self-help association for one-parent families. Local groups offer support, friendship, information, advice and practical help.

Lone Parent Helpline
0800 018 5026 (Mon-Fri 9am-5pm)

National Council for One Parent Families
255 Kentish Town Road
London NW5 2LX
(020) 7428 5400 (admin)
0800 0185 026 (helpline Mon- Fri 9am-5pm)
0800 018 5026 (Maintenance and money matters advice available Mon, Thur 10.30am-1.30pm)
www.oneparentfamilies.org.uk
Free, confidential information for one-parent families on financial housing and legal problems.

LOSS AND BEREAVEMENT

The Child Bereavement Trust
Aston House
High Street
West Wycombe
Buckinghamshire
HP14 3AG
(01494) 446 648
0845 357 1000 (helpline)
www.childbereavement.org.uk
Resources for bereaved families.

Compassionate Friends
53 North Street
Bristol BS3 1EN
(0117) 953 9639
(10am- 4pm/6.30pm-10.30pm 7 days a week)
www.tcf.org.uk
An organisation of and for bereaved parents and families. Advice and support. Local groups.

CRUSE Bereavement Care
CRUSE House
126 Sheen Road
Richmond
Surrey TW9 1UR
(020) 8939 9530 (admin)
0870 167 1677 (helpline Mon-Fri 9.30am-5pm)
www.crusebereavementcare.org.uk

In Northern Ireland:
Piney Ridge
Knockbracken Healthcare Park
Saintfield Road
Belfast BT8 8BH
(028) 9079 2419

In Wales:
Ty Energlyn
Heol Las
Caerphilly CF83 2WP
(029) 2088 6913
08457 585 565 (helpline 5pm-9pm)
A nationwide service of emotional support, counselling and information to anyone bereaved by death, regardless of age, race or belief. Local groups.

Foundation for the Study of Infant Deaths (Cot Death Research and Support)
Artillery House
11-19 Artillery Row
London SW1P 1RT
0870 787 0885 (admin)
0870 787 0554 (24-hour helpline)
www.sids.org.uk/fsid/

In Northern Ireland:
Friends of the Foundation for the Study of Infant Deaths
(028) 3833 2985

In Wales:
North Wales Scheme
01663 762388
Support and information for parents bereaved by a sudden infant death and gives new parents advice on reducing risk of cot death.

Stillbirth and Neonatal Death Society (SANDS)
28 Portland Place
London W1B 1LY
(020) 7436 7940
(020) 7436 5881 (helpline Mon-Fri 10am-3pm)
Run by and for parents whose baby has died either at birth or shortly afterwards.

Widwods
c/o 60 Rocks Park
Uckfield
East Sussex TN22 2AX
(01825) 765 084 (evenings)
Small support group of young widows aiming to provide practical and emotional support for those who experience the loss of partners. Please include an SAE for written replies to any query.

NAPPIES

The National Association of Nappy Services
To find a nappy laundry service in your area call (0121) 693 4949 or visit www.changeanappy.co.uk

The Real Nappy Association
PO Box 3704
London SE26 4RX
(020) 8299 4519
www.realnappy.com
For a free information pack including a full list of nappy suppliers, send a large SAE with two stamps on it.

The Real Nappy Project at the Women's Environment Network
PO Box 30626
London E1 1TZ
(020) 7481 9004 (Mon-Fri 10am-6pm)
www.wen.or.uk
Nappy line 01983 401959 (Mon, Wed 9am-12pm)
Gives information on the availability of modern shaped and fitted cloth nappies. Runs the Nappy Exchange Service, which provides a source of second-hand real nappies.

RELATIONSHIPS

RELATE: National Marriage Guidance
Herbert Gray College
Little Church Street
Rugby CV21 3AP
0845 456 1310
0845 130 4010 (helpline Mon-Fri 9.30am-4.30pm)
www.relate.org.uk
In Northern Ireland:
76 Dublin Road
Belfast BT2 7HP
(028) 9032 3454
www.relateni.org
In Wales:
Ty Merthyr
Little Water Street
Camarthen SA31 1ER
(01267) 236737
Confidential counselling on relationship problems of any kind. To find your local branch look under RELATE or Marriage Guidance in the phone book or contact the above addresses.

RIGHTS AND BENEFITS/ACCESS TO SERVICES

Child Poverty Action Group
94 White Lion Street
London N1 9PF
(020) 7837 7979
www.cpag.org.uk
Campaigns on behalf of low-income families. Provides advisers with information and advice for parents on benefits, housing, welfare rights, etc.

Child Support Agency
PO Box 55
Brierley Hill
West Midlands DY5 1YL
(08457) 133 133 (enquiry line)
08457 138924 (text phone)
(Both lines open Mon-Fri 8am-8pm, Sat 8.30am-5pm)
www.csa.gov.uk
In Northern Ireland:
(08457) 139 896
(08457) 132 243 704 (voice/minicom)
www.dsdni.gov.uk/csa
In Wales:
(08457) 138 000
(08457) 138 091 (Welsh language)
(08457) 138 099 (minicom)
The Government agency that assesses maintenance levels for parents who no longer live with their children. The agency will claim maintenance on behalf of the parent with care of the children, but if you are on benefits the money claimed will be deducted from your benefit.

Citizens Advice Bureaux
National Association of Citizens Advice Bureaux
Myddleton House
115-123 Pentonville Road
London N1 9LZ
(020) 7833 2181 (call for the telephone number of your local office)
www.nacab.org.uk
For advice on all benefits, housing, your rights generally, and many other problems. To find your local CAB look in the phone book or ask at your local library.

Patient Advice and Liaison Service (PALS)
Provide help and information about health services and, if you have a complaint can put you in touch with independent complaints services. To find your local PALS contact your local NHS Trust or PCT.

Commission for Racial Equality
St Dunstan's House
201-211 Borough High Street
London SE1 1GZ
(020) 7939 0000
www.cre.gov.uk
In Wales:
CRE Wales
3rd Floor
Capital Towers
Greyfriars Road
Cardiff CF10 3AG
(029) 2072 9200
Encourages good relations between people from different racial and ethnic backgrounds, the elimination of racial discrimination and promotion of equal opportunities

Community Relations Council (CRC) (NI)
Glendinning House
6 Murray Street
Belfast BT1 6DN
(028) 9022 7500
www.community-relations.org.uk
Provides advice and support in NI for those working to develop a society free from sectarianism.

Disability Alliance
Universal House
88-94 Wentworth Street
London E1 7SA
(020) 7247 8776
www.disabilityalliance.org
Information and advice on benefits for all people with disabilities. Publishes the Disability Rights Handbook – an annual guide to rights, benefits and services for those with disabilities and their families.

Equal Opportunities Commission
Arndale House
Arndale Centre
Manchester M4 3EQ
0845 601 5901
www.eoc.org.uk
In Northern Ireland:
Equality Commission for Northern Ireland
Equality House
7-9 Shaftesbury Square
Belfast BT2 7DP
(028) 9050 0600
(028) 9050 0589 (text phone)
www.equalityni.org
In Wales:
Windsor House
Windsor Lane
Cardiff CF10 3GE
(029) 2064 3552
Information and advice on issues of discrimination and equal opportunities.

Family Welfare Association
501-505 Kingsland Road
London E8 4AU
(020) 7254 6251
www.fwa.org.uk
National charity providing free social work services and support for children and families. Provides financial support for families in need throughout the UK.

Health and Social Services Councils
HSSCs exist to help users of the NHS. They advise on where and how to get the service you need, and can help if you've got a complaint. For your local HSSC, look in your phone book under the name of your local Health and Social Services Council.

Jobcentre Plus/Social Security Office (Jobs & Benefits office)
For advice on all social security benefits, pensions and National Insurance, including maternity benefits and Income Support and income-based Jobseeker's Allowance, telephone, write or call in to your local Jobcentre Plus/Social Security Office (Jobs & Benefits office). The address will be in the phone book under 'Jobcentre Plus' or in Northern Ireland, 'Social Security Office'. Hours are usually 9.30am-3.30pm. In busy offices there may be a very long wait if you call in.

Labour Relations Agency (NI)
2-8 Gordon Street
Belfast BT1 2LG
(028) 9032 1442
www.lra.org.uk
Advice on maternity rights.

Maternity Alliance
3rd Floor West
2-6 Northburgh Street
London EC1V 0AY
(020) 7490 7639
(020) 7490 7638 (advice line)
www.maternityalliance.org.uk
Information on all aspects of maternity care and rights. Advice on benefits, maternity rights at work.

Race Equality First
Friary Centre, The Friary
Cardiff CF10 3FA
(029) 2022 4097
race.equality@enablis.co.uk
Councils are concerned with race and community relations in their area and often know of local minority ethnic organisations and support groups.

Social Security Offices: see Jobcentre Plus

Social Services
A social worker at your local social services office will give you information on benefits, housing, financial difficulties, employment, relationship problems, childcare and useful organisations. Look up social services in the phone book under the name of your local authority or, in Northern Ireland, your local Health and Social Services Board/Trust or ask at your local library. Phone, write or call in. There may also be a social worker based at the hospital to whom you could talk either during your antenatal care or when you or your baby are in hospital. Ask your midwife or other hospital staff to put you in contact.

SAFETY AND FIRST AID

Child Accident Prevention Trust (CAPT)
18-20 Farringdon Lane
London EC1R 3HA
(020) 7608 3828
www.capt.org.uk
In Northern Ireland:
Child Safety Centre
23a/b Mullacreevie Park
Killylea Road
Armagh BT60 4BA
(028) 3752 6521
In Wales:
Child Safe Wales
Gerry Hales Safety Centre
Llandough Hospital
Penlan Road
Penarth
Cardiff CF64 2XX
(029) 2071 6933
Provides information on safety products and sources of literature.

The Royal Society for the Prevention of Accidents (RoSPA)
Edgbaston Park
353 Bristol Road
Birmingham B5 7ST
(0121) 248 2000
www.rospa.com
In Northern Ireland:
Nella House
Dargan Crescent
Belfast BT3 9JP
(028) 9050 1160
www.rospa.com
In Wales:
7 Cleeve House
Lambourne Crescent
Cardiff CF14 5GP
(029) 2025 0600
Advice on the prevention of accidents of all kinds.

St John Ambulance
27 St John's Lane
London EC1M 4BU
0870 0104950
www.sja.org.uk
In Northern Ireland:
Erne
Knockbracken Healthcare Park
Saintfield Road
Belfast BT8 8RA
(028) 9079 9393
In Wales:
Priory House
Meridian Court
North Road
Cardiff CF4 3BL
(029) 2062 7627
www.stjohnwales.co.uk
Runs local first aid courses. Look for your nearest branch in the phone book, or contact the above addresses.

SMOKING

ASH
102 Clifton Street
London EC2A 4HW
(020) 7739 5902
www.ash.org.uk
In Wales:
374 Cowbridge Road East
Cardiff CF5 1GY
(029) 2064 1101
Provides information for the public and health professionals on the dangers of smoking.

NHS Asian Tobacco Helpline
0800 169 0 881 (Urdu)
0800 169 0 882 (Punjabi)
0800 169 0 883 (Hindi)
0800 169 0 884 (Gujarati)
0800 169 0 885 (Bengali)
www.givingupsmoking.co.uk
Counsellors offer confidential help and advice about every stage of quitting.

NHS Smoking Helpline
0800 169 0 169
Open daily 7am-11pm

NHS Pregnancy Smoking Helpline 0800 169 9 169
Textphone 0800 169 0 171
Open daily 12am-9pm

Quit
Ground Floor
211 Old Street
London EC1V 9NR
0800 00 22 00 (Quitline)
www.quit.org.uk
Advice on stopping smoking and details of local stop-smoking support services.

Smokers Helpline (NI)
0800 85 85 85
A freephone service which provides advice and support to smokers about quitting. The helpline staff will also be able to explain about specialist services available locally.

Ulster Cancer Foundation (NI)
(Temporary contact details)
Block 24, Pavilion 2
Belvoir Park Hospital
Hospital Road
Belfast BT8 8JR
(028) 9049 2007
0800 783 3339 (helpline)
www.ulstercancer.org
Carries out cancer research and education programmes in Northern Ireland. Also provides information on the dangers of smoking, and advice and support to smokers who want to quit.

SUPPORT AND INFORMATION

Home-Start UK
2 Salisbury Road
Leicester LE1 7QR
(0116) 233 9955
0800 068 6368 (infoline)
www.home-start.org.uk

In Northern Ireland:
133 Bloomfield Avenue
Belfast BT5 5AB
(028) 9046 0772

In Wales:
Titan House
Cardiff Bay Business Centre
Lewis Road, Ocean Park
Cardiff CF24 5BS
(029) 2049 1181
A voluntary home-visiting scheme. Volunteers visit families with children under five and offer friendship, practical help, and emotional support. Write for a list of local schemes.

Institute for Complementary Medicine
PO Box 194
London SE16 7QZ
(020) 7237 5165
www.icmedicine.co.uk
Charity providing information on complementary medicine and referrals to qualified practitioners or helpful organisations.

Minority Ethnic Community Health and Social Wellbeing Project (NI)
Multi-Cultural Resource Centre (MCRC)
7 Lower Crescent
Belfast BT7 1NR
(028) 9024 4639
www.mcrc-ni.org.uk
As part of MCRC, promotes two-way communication between minority ethnic groups and health service providers. Provides translation and interpreting services, multilingual materials and a reference library.

NHS Direct
0845 46 47
www.nhsdirect.nhs.uk
24-hour nurse led helpline giving health information and advice.

Parentline Plus
520 Highgate Studios
53-57 Highgate Road
London NW5 1TL
0808 800 2222 (helpline Mon- Fri 8am-10pm, Sat 9.30am-5pm, Sun 10am-3pm)
0800 783 6783 (text phone)
www.parentlineplus.org.uk
Free confidential helpline to anyone parenting a child. Runs parenting classes and has a range of leaflets and publications.

Patients' Association
PO Box 935
Harrow
Middlesex HA1 3YJ
(020) 8423 9111
0845 608 4455 (helpline)
Advice service for patients who have problems relating to health and health care.

Time for Mums (NI)
www.timeformums.fsnet.co.uk
A post-natal depression support group.

Twins and Multiple Births Association (TAMBA)
2 The Willows
Gardner Road
Guildford
Surrey GU1 4PG
0870 770 3305 (admin Mon- Fri 9.30am-5pm)
(01732) 868000 (helpline Mon-Fri 10am-1pm and 7pm-10pm, Sat, Sun 10am-10pm)
www.tamba.org.uk

In Northern Ireland:
216 Belmont Road
Belfast BT4 2AT
Also helpline (see above)
Information and support for parents of multiples. Network of local Twins Clubs.

Women's Health
52 Featherstone Street
London EC1Y 8RT
0845 125 5254 (helpline Mon-Fri 9.30am-1.30pm)
(020) 7490 5489 (minicom)
www.womenshealthlondon.org.uk
Information and support on many aspects of women's health. Provides a network of individual women who support others with similar health problems.

INDEX

EMERGENCY HELP

If your child is ill or has an accident and you need help quickly:

- **Phone your GP.** You can call at any time of the day or night. If you haven't been given a special number for calls outside surgery hours, phone the usual number and wait for an answer.
- **If your GP doesn't answer or can't get there quickly enough, take your child to the accident and emergency department of the nearest hospital with a children's unit.** Find out in advance where this is. Your health visitor will be able to help you.
- **If you think your child's life is in danger,** call an ambulance. Dial 999 and ask for the ambulance service. Say it's for a baby or a child. You don't need a coin or phonecard to dial 999 from a public phone box.

If you don't have a phone:

- Keep a couple of coins and/or a phonecard always ready in a special place.
- Find out in advance whether neighbours have a phone you could use in an emergency.